John S. Strauss, Wolfgang Böker and Hans D. Brenner (Editors)
Psychosocial Treatment of Schizophrenia

John S. Strauss
Wolfgang Böker
and Hans D. Brenner
(Editors)

Psychosocial Treatment of Schizophrenia

Multidimensional Concepts, Psychological, Family, and Self-Help Perspectives

Hans Huber Publishers
Toronto · Lewiston N.Y. · Bern · Stuttgart

Library of Congress Cataloging-in-Publication Data

Psychosocial treatment of schizophrenia.

Includes bibliographies and indexes.
1. Schizophrenia – Treatment.   2. Schizophrenics –
Rehabilitation.   3. Schizophrenics – Family relationships.
4. Psychiatric social work. I. Strauss, John S.
II. Böker, W., Dr. med.   III. Brenner, H. D. (Hans D.)
[DNLM: 1. Family Therapy.   2. Schizophrenia – therapy.
3. Socioenvironmental Therapy.   WM 203 P9739]
RC514.P71895   1986   616.89'82   86-15278

Canadian Cataloguing in Publication Data

Main entry under title:

Psychosocial treatment of schizophrenia

Bibliography: p.
Includes index.
ISBN 0-920887-10-4

1. Schizophrenia – Treatment.   2. Schizophrenics –
Rehabilitation.   I. Strauss, John S.   II. Böker, W.
III. Brenner, H. D.

RC514.P77   1986   616.89'8206   C86-094195-7

ISBN 0-920887-10-4
Hans Huber Publishers
Toronto · Lewiston N.Y. · Bern · Stuttgart

ISBN 3-456-81529-8
Hans Huber Publishers
Bern · Stuttgart · Toronto · Lewiston N.Y.

Copyright © 1987 by Hans Huber Publishers

12 Bruce Park Ave.
Toronto, Ontario M4P 2S3

P.O. Box 51
Lewiston, N.Y. 14092

Printed in Switzerland
by Lang Druck AG, Liebefeld/Bern

Preface

This period in the history of understanding mental illness is marked by two phenomena. The first is the ascendance of interest in biological processes that might relate to mental disorders. The second is the beginnings of recovery in psychosocial research from the disillusion following the peak years of focus on psychoanalysis.

In the psychosocial domain, many people in the mental health field, and many outside of it, became disillusioned when psychoanalysis as a treatment and theory fell short of what had been hoped. Psychoanalysis seemed to cure fewer people than had been expected; psychoanalytic "explanations" for individual behavior were difficult to prove, and they had very limited predictive power – the ultimate test of their utility. And the psychosocial emphasis generated by psychoanalysis, with its hopes for restructuring society from family processes all the way to urban planning, did not fulfill expectations. Perseveration of efforts to succeed – by out-Freuding Freud or by ever-expanding social engineering – fell rapidly and of their own weight, leaving much disillusion.

As these events were spreading disaffection in and with the mental health field, the advent of psychotropic medications, advances in biochemistry, and, more recently, progress in brain imaging shot forth, almost as in a game of "crack the whip." A focus on biologic aspects of mental illness emerged together with a hope for finding the answers perhaps through a new medical "magic bullet" or other biological cure. With the high hopes for progress in biological research, it seemed to some as though psychological and social concerns in mental illness could only be secondary.

In the course of these events, psychosocial efforts – especially those focused on severe mental illness – have been struggling. But perhaps as under the mythical bung bung tree, in whose shade nothing grows, it was necessary to spend several years in such struggles to get beyond the shadow cast by the previous psychosocial approaches, and to find new concepts and new methods.

As very positive evidence of the emergence from these struggles, the group of reports in this volume is particularly exciting. These reports reflect not one, but many new directions in understanding psychological and social aspects of schizophrenia and in developing improved treatments. The directions are new and they are not trivial. Methodology has improved considerably over that of the "old days" of psychosocial research – both in the attention to the building blocks of reliability and validity, and in the recognition of both the strengths and limitations of hypothesis-generating efforts. The new directions combine the advantages of being "basic" in their attention to fundamental processes of mental illness and recovery, while at the same time being of direct clinical relevance and validity – not always a characteristic of other areas of mental illness related research. Thus, these reports reflect the confluence of elements

5

constituting a new surge in research on psychological and social factors in severe mental illness – a surge that is developing new knowledge and perspectives while avoiding many of the major pitfalls of the past.

John S. STRAUSS

Foreword of the German Edition

The tremendous change that has taken place in psychiatry during the past decades – from a hospital-centered, essentially custodial form of care to an open approach, oriented toward therapy and rehabilitation without isolation from the surrounding community – has altered schizophrenic life to an extent that would have been inconceivable in the past. Today, many schizophrenics live outside the hospital, with their families, in residential communities, and sometimes in productive independence. This process also had a lasting influence on our understanding of the nature of schizophrenia and the possibilities of coping with the disease.

Up to now, psychiatric research has been slow to take note of this transformation. Still largely limited by a traditional linear conception of causality, it mainly studied individual causes and specific forms of treatment, hardly considering systemic approaches. However, we are convinced that the multi-dimensional theories of schizophrenia now emerging with ever more distinct outlines conclusively demand a new research paradigm and more complex treatment strategies. Clinical crisis intervention, acute and long-term medication, psychotherapy, cognitive and social training, as well as advising relatives represent several essential elements of therapeutic practice. Yet they are not a reflection of helpless eclecticism, but the consequence of our present knowledge.

Furthermore, we seem to have reached a point where it has become necessary for us to reconsider our role as psychiatric experts and our way of dealing with the patient. What can we learn from our patients? Which autonomous processes of recovery take their course without our interfering? Could it be that our treatment sometimes even does more harm than good? Is unconditional compliance of the patient more important than a cooperative alliance with him, even if this occasionally results in a crisis? Are relatives annoying trouble-makers or potential allies? Would it not be advisable to start a new and constructive dialogue with them? Our practical treatment habits often lag far behind our theoretical knowledge.

This situation formed the background of the meeting that took place in the Psychiatric University Clinic in Berne, Switzerland, at the beginning of May 1985. The meeting was initiated by the editors of this volume and involved outstanding scientists and clinicians from the United States and Europe. The focus of the discussion was on recent theoretical progress and its therapeutic consequences, which offer promising methods of coping with schizophrenia not only to the expert, but also to the patients and their relatives. Focusing on "The psycho-social management of schizophrenia," this international symposium – which was received with great interest – included topics as varied as systemic theoretical models, new psycho-social, cognitive, behavioral, and

7

pharmacological concepts of treatment, therapeutic work with relatives, and the possibilities and forms of self-help and active ways of coping.

We would like to take this opportunity to thank the members of the organizing committee and all the employees of our clinic, who accomplished the remarkable feat of turning a fully occupied hospital into a perfectly functioning convention center – just like that. We also thank our wives for seeing to it, both on stage and backstage, that everything ran smoothly and everybody felt welcome.

In our opinion, this volume conveys a vivid picture of the change our understanding of schizophrenia is currently undergoing in both research and practice. It collects selected and revised papers from the symposium in Berne, concluding with a newly written "outlook" on the prospective questions and objectives that may arise in future research. We thank all authors for their collaboration in considering our wishes and suggestions while adapting their papers.

The Department of Theoretical and Evaluative Psychiatry effectively assisted us in preparing the publication of this volume. For their editorial help and particularly for the critical inspection and correction of the manuscripts we would like to thank Dr. H. Wyss, cand. phil. D. Waldvogel and cand. phil. S. Wuergler, as well as Dr. M. Maurer for her careful preparation of the indexes of authors and subjects. Our special thanks are due to Dr. P. Stehlin of Hans Huber Publications, Berne, Dr. F. Kulhanek of the Division of Psychiatry and Psychopharmacology of Heyden/Squibb Inc., Munich, and Ms. M. Feuz and her colleagues from Translation Service USG, Berne, for their advice and support. And finally, Ms. F. Perret and Ms. R. Krebs deserve our gratitude for their arduous work and commitment in turning the manuscripts into final copy.

We hope that this collection of papers will stimulate further research and practical development of the foundations for an improved method of dealing with schizophrenia. Patients, relatives, colleagues, clinicians – they may all learn to improve their ways of coping with psychosis and its consequences, and to meet its many manifestations more effectively on the basis of a profounder knowledge.

Berne, Switzerland, September 1985   W. Böker and H. D. Brenner

Table of Contents

Contributors

ANDERSON, C., Ph. D., Associate Professor of Psychiatry, Western Psychiatric Institute and Clinic, University of Pittsburgh, 3811 O'Hara Street, USA – Pittsburgh, Pennsylvania 15213

BELLACK, A. S., Ph. D., Professor of Psychiatry, The Medical College of Pennsylvania, Department of Psychiatry, 3200 Henry Avenue, USA – Philadelphia, Pennsylvania 19129

BLACKWELL, G., R. N., M. S. W., Nurse Clinician Specialist, Rehabilitation Medicine Service, Brentwood Division of the West, Los Angeles VA Medical Center, Wilshire & Sawtelle Blvds., USA – Los Angeles, California 90073

BÖKER, W., Prof. Dr. med., Psychiatrische Universitätsklinik Bern, Bolligenstraße 111, CH-3072 Bern/ Ostermundigen

BOONE, S. E., Ph. D., University of California Los Angeles. Wilshire & Sawtelle Blvds., USA – Los Angeles, California 90073

BRENNER, H. D., PD Dr. med. et phil., Psychiatrische Universitätsklinik Bern, Bolligenstraße 111, CH-3072 Bern/Ostermundigen

BUCHKREMER, G., PD Dr. med., Psychiatrische und Nervenklinik der Westfälischen Wilhelms-Universität, Albert-Schweitzer-Straße 11, D-44 Münster/Westfalen

CIOMPI, L., Prof. Dr. med., Sozialpsychiatrische Universitätsklinik Bern, Murtenstraße 21, CH-3010 Bern

DONAHOE, C. P., Ph. D., University of California Los Angeles, Wilshire & Sawtelle Blvds., USA – Los Angeles, California 90073

FALLOON, I. R. H., M. D., Associate Professor of Psychiatry and Behavioral Sciences, University of Southern California, School of Medicine, 1934 Hospital Pl., USA – Los Angeles, California 90033

FOY, D. W., Ph. D., Adjunct Associate Professor of Medical Psychology, University of California Los Angeles, Wilshire & Sawtelle Blvds., USA – Los Angeles, California 90073

GROSS, G., Prof. Dr. med., Universitäts-Nervenklinik und Poliklinik, Venusberg, Sigmund-Freud-Straße 25, D-5300 Bonn 1

HAFEZ, H., M. D., Assistant Professor of Psychiatry, Yale University, Department of Psychiatry, School of Medicine, 25 Park Street, USA – New Haven, Connecticut 06519

HARDING, C. M., Ph. D., Yale University, Department of Psychiatry, School of Medicine, 25 Park Street, USA – New Haven, Connecticut 06519

HIRSCH, S. R., M. D., M. Phil., Professor of Psychiatry, University of London, Charing Cross Hospital Medical School, Department of Psychiatry, Fulham Palace Road, GB – London W6 8RF

HOGARTY, G. E., M. S. W., Associate Professor of Psychiatry, Western Psychiatric Institute and Clinic, University of Pittsburgh, 3811 O'Hara Street, USA – Pittsburgh, Pennsylvania 15213

JACOBS, H. E., Ph. D., University of California Los Angeles, Wilshire and Sawtelle Blvds., USA – Los Angeles, California 90073

JOLLEY, A. G., M. D., University of London, Charing Cross Hospital Medical School, Department of Psychiatry, Fulham Palace Road, GB – London W6 8RF

KATSCHNIG, H., Prof. Dr. med., Psychiatrische Universitätsklinik Wien, Währingergürtel 18–20, A-1090 Wien

KONIECZNA, T., Dr. phil., Ludwig Boltzmann Institut für Sozialpsychiatrie, Spitalgasse 11, A-1090 Wien

LEFF, J., M. D., Professor of Psychiatry, Medical Research Council, Social Psychiatry Unit, Friern Hospital, Friern Barnet Road, GB – London N11 3BP

LIBERMAN, R. P., M. D., Professor of Psychiatry, University of California Los Angeles, Wilshire & Sawtelle Blvds., USA – Los Angeles, California 90073

LIEBERMAN, P., M. D., Associate Professor of Psychiatry, Yale University, Department of Psychiatry, School of Medicine, 25 Park Street, USA – New Haven, Connecticut 06519

MANCHANDA, R., M. D., University of London, Charing Cross Hospital Medical School, Department of Psychiatry, Fulham Palace Road, GB – London W6 8RF

McRINK, A., S. R. N., R. M. N., University of London, Charing Cross Hospital Medical School, Department of Psychiatry, Fulham Palace Road, GB – London W6 8RF

SCHULZE-MOENKING, H., Dr. med., Psychiatrische und Nervenklinik der Westfälischen Wilhelms-Universität, Albert-Schweitzer-Straße 11, D-44 Münster/ Westfalen

STRAUSS, J. S., M. D., Professor of Psychiatry, Yale University, Department of Psychiatry, Yale University School of Medicine, Grace Education Building, 25 Park Street, USA – New Haven, Connecticut 06519

SUELLWOLD, L., Prof. Dr. phil., J.-W.-Goethe-Universität, Abteilung für Klinische Psychiatrie II, Heinrich-Hoffmann-Straße 10, D-6 Frankfurt am Main 71

TURNER, R. M., Ph. D., Associate Professor of Psychiatry, Temple University, Department of Psychiatry, 3401 North Broad Street, USA – Philadelphia, Pennsylvania 19140

WALLACE, C. J., Ph. D., Associate Clinical Professor of Medical Psychology, University of California Los Angeles, Wilshire & Sawtelle Blvds., USA – Los Angeles, California 90073

WING, J. K., M. D., Professor of Psychiatry, Medical Research Council, Social Psychiatry Unit, Institute of Psychiatry, De Crespigny Park, GB – London SE5 8AF

ZUBIN, J., Ph. D., Distinguished Research Professor of Psychiatry, University of Pittsburgh, School of Medicine, Veterans Administration Medical Center, Highland Drive, USA – Pittsburgh, Pennsylvania 15206

12

Psychosocial Factors Affecting the Long-Term Course of Schizophrenia

J. K. WING

A Theoretical Approach to Management

The theme of this meeting is timely. Two of the major advances in the care of people afflicted by schizophrenia likely to be made during the remaining years of this century are an improvement in the effectiveness and acceptability of pharmacological treatments and the application of recently acquired knowledge concerning environmental influences to help sufferers, their families and society more generally to 'live with schizophrenia'. The two sets of factors interact with and potentiate each other, both to exacerbate and to ameliorate the clinical and social course. It is not permissible, therefore, to talk about the *natural* course of schizophrenia (WING, 1978a).

Three recent long-term follow-up studies have demonstrated that some 20–25% of schizophrenic disorders clear up relatively quickly leaving little deficit, although the short-term course can be stormy, while a similar proportion lead to severe long-term social disablement (BLEULER, 1978; CIOMPI, 1980; CIOMPI & MUELLER, 1976; HUBER et al., 1979). These *proportions* may not have changed very much since the introduction of modern methods of treatment, though this does not mean that treatment has no beneficial effect. On the other hand, 50–60% run a fluctuating long-term course that might well be influenced substantially by medication and by factors in the physical and psychosocial environment. Since the quality of life even of the most severely and continuously disabled is also dependent, in part, on the quality of care available, it follows that devising new methods of achieving, and maintaining throughout a lifetime, the highest level of functioning possible given irreducible impairments ought to form a substantial part of our scientific endeavour. We are, at last, making some progress in this direction, as witnessed by the theme and content of this Symposium.

The term 'clinical management' has unwanted bureaucratic and autocratic undertones, but no other term conveys so well the complex and dynamic nature of the concept of care involved. It includes varied combinations of treatment, rehabilitation, behavioural programmes, training, family intervention, counsel, support, shelter, security, and welfare arrangements as indicated by repeated assessments of need. The aim is to make all parties – sufferers, family and other carers – aware of (a) the factors that are currently responsible for social disablement, (b) which of these factors can be modified and how, and (c) what can be done to cope if some factors seem, at least for the moment, immutable.

The following review of the theories that underlie this concept of management, and of the research undertaken to test their practical implications, provides only the barest of outlines. Details are available elsewhere (WING, 1975a, 1977, 1985a). Other papers in this symposium fill in many of the gaps. Only 'functional' schizophrenic disorders will be considered.

The overall strategy involves three levels of investigation (WING & HAILEY, 1972) (see Table 1). The first, and most fundamental, level concerns the causes of social disablement: (a) the nature of specific schizophrenic impairments and the factors that precipitate or amplify them, (b) the causes of social disadvantage, whether dependent on or independent of these impairments, and (c) the personal response – in terms of self-attitudes, self-esteem and self-confidence – of afflicted individuals.

Table 1: Three conceptual levels underlying long-term management

---

1. *Factors interacting to cause social disablement*
   1.1 Psychological and physical impairments
   1.2 Social disadvantages
   1.3 Adverse self attitudes, demoralisation

2. *Methods of preventing or minimising factors causing disablement*
   (specific, effective, acceptable and economic)
   2.1 Primary prevention
   2.2 Medical treatment
   2.3 Psychological methods – programmes, counselling, family intervention
   2.4 Training, education, provision of range of options for choice
   2.5 Support, shelter, security
   2.6 Welfare, ensure decent standard of living

3. *Services to identify social disablement, assess causes, and deliver the forms of treatment and care needed*

The more that is known at this first level, the more precise can be the construction of tests of hypotheses, at the second level of investigation; which is concerned with the effectiveness and acceptability of methods of ameliorating the individual's problems within an overall plan of management. It is important to test the various level 1 factors separately because the most effective action is not necessarily the same for each of the components.

Similarly, the more that is known at the first two levels, the easier it is to plan and prescribe services that will most efficiently and acceptably 'deliver' the particular pattern of methods of care that each individual needs. The best 'health services research' is carried out at this level 3 but is founded upon knowledge derived from levels 1 and 2.

14

The following section is based on a consideration of three types of theory concerning the relationship between schizophrenia and the environment. The first theory states that at least two schizophrenic syndromes can be distinguished, each with its own characteristics and implications for the course and outcome. The second states that these two syndromes are precipitated or made worse by different kinds of environmental factors and clarifies their relationship to social disadvantage. The third states that 'secondary' handicaps (adverse personal reactions to disability and the circumstances associated with it) can be as important in determining social outcome as 'primary' or 'intrinsic' impairment. All three theories are relevant to level 1 of the overall strategy.

Level 1: Disease, Disability, Disadvantage, Distress, Disablement

Positive and negative syndromes

The two major types of schizophrenic syndrome are commonly designated 'positive', 'florid' or 'productive' and 'negative', 'defect' or 'deficit' (WING, 1985b). Symptoms of the florid syndrome include the mood-incongruent first rank phenomena of Kurt SCHNEIDER and hallucinations and explanatory delusions based upon them. Auditory hallucinations that do not come within SCHNEIDER's group, and are not affectively based, are usually regarded as part of the central syndrome nevertheless.

Conditions characterised by delusions that are not affectively based but are not part of the 'first rank' syndrome are often diagnosed clinically as schizophrenic although there is much to be said for adding an extra identity-tag in order to discover whether they have separate concomitants. According to the International Pilot Study of Schizophrenia (WHO, 1973), such paranoid states are relatively uncommon among 'non-organic' psychoses. Much depends, of course, on whether there is full information on the previous clinical course, since first rank symptoms tend to be most clear-cut during the early stages of the psychosis.

Because positive symptoms are usually most obvious during acute episodes of schizophrenia they are often used as criteria for dating episodes, including first onset. They can, however, persist over very long periods of time, albeit in modified and attenuated form. Moreover, many patients who experience one episode of florid schizophrenia are likely to experience another (WHO, 1979). The liability to relapse, even after a period with no apparent symptoms, is an 'invisible' impairment (part of what ZUBIN calls 'vulnerability') which, in its way, can have as profound an impact on social performance as the acute episode itself.

It should be emphasized that hallucinations and delusions can vary in severity. At one extreme they are overwhelming in their impact and dominate behaviour. At the other, the individual can choose how far to attend to them or elaborate them or act upon them. The extent to which an individual can acquire a degree of 'insight' is therefore crucial in management.

The negative syndrome includes blunting of affect, slowness, underactivity, poverty of speech and inability to use non-verbal means of communication. (Catatonia is best considered separately.) This group of symptoms is highly intercorrelated and, in protected environments, stable over long periods of time. Social withdrawal is the most obvious behavioural correlate (WING, 1961; WING & BROWN, 1970). There have been numerous attempts to define the nature of the cognitive deficit, from the time of BABCOCK (1933) onwards, but its essence has remained elusive. Moreover, the negative symptoms have not been defined so precisely as to be unambiguously 'schizophrenic'. On the contrary, as usually defined, they can occur in conditions that few psychiatrists would regard as having a close relationship with schizophrenia. Chronic retarded depression, Kanner's and Asperger's syndromes, dementia, other organic psychoses, encephalitis and severe physical disabilities are all frequently accompanied by such symptoms. If positive symptoms are not known to have occurred at some point in the course, a diagnosis of schizophrenia must be regarded as dubious, even if some other condition is not evidently responsible.

The relationship between the two syndromes, which occur together in a large proportion of cases diagnosed by clinicians, is not well understood. An analogy could be drawn with the damage and release symptoms that were interpreted by Hughlings JACKSON in terms of a hierarchy of levels of the nervous system. Several attempts have been made to apply these ideas to schizophrenia (e.g. EY, 1975) without stimulating many productive empirical investigations.

Each syndrome can appear, at any particular time, by itself or together with the other, and each can be more or less severe. However, the florid syndrome tends to be more dramatic in its appearance and disappearance while it is more difficult to define a particular point at which the negative syndrome should be regarded as present.

In a large series investigated by OWENS & JOHNSTONE (1980), 80% of 510 hospital residents with a diagnosis of chronic schizophrenia were classified as CATEGO S+, with further proportions in classes S?, P+ and P?, based on symptoms occurring at the worst period of the disorder. Since most will have had negative symptoms at the time of the study, it is clear that most schizophrenic disorders tend to be characterised, though not necessarily at the same time, by both types of syndrome.

The negative syndrome is more important for prognosis of the social outcome, since it tends to antedate and to follow the more acute florid symptoms; i.e. the negative syndrome is associated with an insidious onset and a chronic course (WHO, 1979).

If the positive syndrome occurs alone, without much evidence of negative symptoms except during acute attacks, the prognosis tends to be relatively

16

good. There is some evidence that such attacks are particularly likely to be precipitated by toxic substances or cerebral pathology (DAVISON & BAGLEY, 1969; CONNELL, 1958; SLATER et al., 1963).

The fact that onset is earlier and the course more severe in men than in women explains why relatively fewer men with schizophrenia marry and why their fertility is lower (STEVENS, 1969; ZUBIN, 1978). A later onset, commoner in women, is associated with a predominance of florid and affective symptoms and occurs in people who have already had time to develop their personal and social potential.

Environmental influences on schizophrenic syndromes

Reactivity of the schizophrenic syndromes

Evidence that the severity of the negative syndrome is dependent, to some extent and in some cases, on the quality of the social environment, was presented in a series of investigations carried out during the late 1950s and 1960s (WING & BROWN, 1970; WING & FREUDENBERG, 1961). The theory was put forward that 'poverty of the social environment' tended to increase slowness, underactivity, flatness of affect, poverty of speech and social withdrawal and that a socially rich environment tended to decrease these symptoms. No claim was made for complete restitution – rehabilitation and follow-up studies suggested that patients varied in the level of functioning attained but that most did continue to show some apparently irreducible impairment (BROWN et al., 1966; WING, 1960; WING et al., 1964). Moreover, the principle was thought to hold for all types of social setting, not just for long-stay hospital wards (BROWN et al., 1966).

In one of the rehabilitation studies it was observed that too vigorous attempts at social stimulation, in patients who had not been sufficiently prepared for rehabilitation, could lead to relapse of florid symptoms that had not been apparent for years previously (WING et al., 1964). Other studies suggested that 'life events' which most people take in their stride appeared to precipitate an acute onset of florid symptoms, including a first onset (BROWN & BIRLEY, 1968). Finally a series of investigations showed that some schizophrenic patients, particularly those whose relatives were critical of aspects of behaviour that were not recognised as part of an 'illness', were at high risk of relapse following discharge from hospital. The risk was highest in patients who did not take the medication prescribed, and who were constantly in 'face-to-face' contact with the relative concerned (BROWN et al., 1962; BROWN et al., 1972; VAUGHN & LEFF, 1976). A controlled study of intervention, based on these principles, has demonstrated that the relapse rate can be significantly reduced (LEFF et al., 1982).

The original sketch of a theory linking these two sets of observations was based on the hypothesis that 'thought disorder' was a key intermediary (WING

17

& BROWN, 1970, p. 22 and p. 181). Subsequent results have led to refinements but no essential change (WING, 1977; WING et al., 1972). Schizophrenic patients find it difficult, even painful, to communicate, because of the 'thought disorder' that lies behind poverty of speech and 'derailment' and because of their impaired use of non-verbal means of communication. This, together with slowness and underactivity (which must have a non-social component), makes social withdrawal a natural means of protection but the process can go too far, particularly in understimulating surroundings. A socially intrusive environment, on the other hand, whether at home or in an over-optimistic rehabilitation unit, means that the patient cannot withdraw into a protective shell but is forced to interact and try to communicate. Florid symptoms then manifest themselves more openly and the resulting speech and behaviour abnormalities often lead to a crisis.

Somewhere between the two extremes lies the optimum social environment, in which the expectations of others are clearly evident, predictable and consonant with the patient's actual abilities. However, in schizophrenia, as in any chronically disabling condition, much depends on other factors that affect the ability to cope. One such is over-medication. Another is physical fitness. People with chronic schizophrenia, in our current study of day and residential settings that provide an alternative to the large psychiatric hospital, tend to smoke too much, to be overweight, to take a high salt, high fat, low fibre diet, and to avoid exercise. Their dental, eyesight and hearing problems may not be remedied, nor the various physical ailments that afflict them.

Social disadvantages

A long experience of poverty, prejudice, low-grade work or unemployment, and lack of friends or social supporters, are handicapping in themselves, independently of whether an individual becomes diagnosed as afflicted by schizophrenia. There is, nevertheless, an interaction, since a degree of impairment and deterioration in cognitive and affective skills often predates the overt onset and may itself have led to social disadvantage. Work on marital and occupational status, on family support, on social isolation and on emigration suggests that some people who will later be recognised as schizophrenic have already become socially disadvantaged because of 'invisible impairments', before the diagnosis is made.

An unfavourable social environment is likely to amplify this process further.

Equally important for the long-term course is what kind of reception the sufferer receives once the disorder is recognised. The expectation during most of this century that a diagnosis of schizophrenia meant that the individual would usually need to live permanently in an institution, to say nothing of the poverty of the social environment often provided there (WING & BROWN, 1970), illustrates the fact that social disadvantage may become augmented by disability as well as augmenting it. A spiral of harmful interaction then ensues.

18

But much the same may be true in these supposedly more enlightened days when a proper reaction against the overuse of institutions has sometimes resulted in disabled people receiving no care at all, since 'being in the community' is regarded as itself 'therapeutic'. Social disadvantage is then actually greater than it was in former times (LEACH & WING, 1980) and stigma actually increased.

It is therefore essential at this first level of assessment of problems to determine the deficits in social, educational, vocational and recreational skills that may be due to a lack of opportunity to acquire them rather than to incapacity. Similarly, more obviously disadvantageous circumstances such as poverty, poor housing, unemployment and isolation should be examined in order to discover how they have arisen. The assessment should be dynamic rather than purely descriptive.

Self-attitudes

Disease, disability and disadvantage must cumulatively affect self-attitudes, although some people cope better than others. LEMERT's theory of 'secondary deviation' is closer to my formulation than GRUENBERG's 'social breakdown syndrome' or DOHRENWEND's 'demoralisation', though there are elements in common (DOHRENWEND & DOHRENWEND, 1969; LEMERT, 1951; WING, 1978b, pp. 140–166; WING & BROWN, 1970, pp. 22–24; ZUSMAN, 1967).

'Institutionalism', the gradual acceptance by an inmate of the values and routines of the institution so that he or she eventually no longer wishes to live any other sort of life, is an extreme example of the development of handicapping attitudes. We found that the longer schizophrenic patients had been resident the less likely they were to say they wanted to leave hospital, and that this remained true even when age at admission was taken into account (WING, 1961; WING & BROWN, 1970).

Subsequent experiments showed that certain adverse attitudes could be changed by training in specific environments but that there was no 'transfer of training'. For example, a change in attitudes to work, following experience in an industrial rehabilitation unit, did not carry with it a change in attitudes to discharge (WING, 1960; WING et al., 1964).

The more severe the clinical impairments the less room there is for improvement due to a reduction in secondary reactions. An attitude of indifference may be a negative symptom that can only be reduced to a limited extent by environmental procedures. Similarly, unrealistic attitudes may be part of a delusional system which is unresponsive to social measures. I would not accept LEMERT's 'primary deviation' theory of schizophrenia, later generalised to become 'labelling theory' (GOFFMAN, 1961; SCHEFF, 1966; WING, 1978b).

Although the theory of adverse secondary reactions was first worked out using institutionalism as an example, this is an extreme and probably limiting case of a much more general rule. Attitudes to discharge from day centres, hostels and group homes tend to follow the same pattern. People with schizophrenic impairments tend to become defeated. Their low motivation may then be regarded as a manifestation of a purely 'primary' deficit even when it has been amplified, and could be partially overcome, by environmental influences.

Social disablement

The three types of factor – impairment, disadvantage and adverse self-attitudes – interact with each other and with all the other circumstances that make each individual's life unique. Someone with schizophrenia who comes into Manfred BLEULER's large intermediate group, where the course depends a good deal on the social environment, has to walk a tightrope with different kinds of danger on each side. Too much and too little social stimulation carry different kinds of risk. The extraordinary thing is that many patients do learn to cope; usually through trial and error and after a long period of suffering. They do not necessarily express this in so many words or even recognise how they are coping. The most articulate have to speak for the rest (WING, 1975b). The same is true of many relatives, who learn to understand that social withdrawal is not necessarily unfriendliness, nor slowness or laziness. Very few patients or relatives are given much long-term help by professionals, although some basic principles can now be formulated (WING, 1975a, 1977).

In considering the course of schizophrenia from this point of view, it appears that most families experience an early turbulent phase. Some patients and some relatives learn, eventually, how to deal with the various problems they encounter and work out how to 'live with schizophrenia'. Others do not. Family ties may be broken and the patient becomes institutionalised or vagrant, or family life continues in an atmosphere of tension and pain. Even in the latter case, however, many families do 'settle down'. This may not occur for many years and until the patient is middle-aged, siblings have long left home, and the parents (or, more likely, the widowed mother) have become elderly. The florid symptoms become less evident and, although the negative ones tend to persist, they are often less severe than they would be in a completely unstimulating social environment such as an old-fashioned 'back ward'. With help, this process could become more usual and less painful.

Such a change could be due to coming to terms, over a period of years, with a set of chronic disabilities. If so, it is particularly difficult in schizophrenia but it is not essentially different from the process that occurs in physical handicaps. All of us have to try to learn to live with ourselves as we grow older.

Level 2: Needs for Care: The Components of 'Management'

The concept of need

Underlying the concept of need there are three kinds of social assumptions about what is 'normal' and what constitutes a reasonable quality of life.

a) Any severe symptom or disability, and any physical condition resulting in lowered social functioning (social disablement), is likely to be regarded as indicating a potential need for some effective and acceptable form of 'care' (treatment, rehabilitation, support, behavioural programmes, training, family intervention, counselling, shelter, security, welfare arrangements, etc.). These will be considered in detail by contributors to this conference. Whether the potential need becomes actual depends on the attitudes of all those involved in offering or accepting services. We have considered, at level 1, some of the factors that can exacerbate or ameliorate the various manifestations of schizophrenia. In a systematic assessment, these can be translated into hypotheses about methods of care which can then be tested. The same approach can be applied to behavioural abnormalities.

b) A second assumption is that the individuals affected should have reached average levels of self-care, domestic, social and occupational skills, education and self-direction. Any disadvantage in these respects indicates a potential need for help.

c) The third assumption is that the individuals affected should not be living in poverty, and that standards of housing and material welfare should at least not fall below specified minimum standards. Any disadvantage in these respects indicates a potential need for the relevant benefits and discretionary awards.

A systematic assessment of the presence of problems in each of these areas of functioning leads to a consideration, for each problem, of a hierarchical list of methods of care that are regarded, in the light of current professional knowledge, as most likely to solve it or to reduce its severity to the lowest level possible and maintain it there. If the selected method of care is actually being provided for the given problem, the need is met. If not, it is unmet.

Allowance can be made, in such a scheme, for methods of care that have been offered and refused, or that have been tried and have failed. In these cases, the next most appropriate method in the list is chosen. There is also a place in the scheme for the situation in which a method of care is being provided, although the problem for which it would be appropriate is not actually present (overprovision). A preliminary survey using the needs assessment system has already been published (WYKES et al., 1982) and a more detailed and systematic version is now under test. A further advantage is that it would be easy to add a technique for assessing the effectiveness of providing those aspects of care that are determined to be necessary, and of continuing to monitor progress at regular intervals over many years. The system would also lend itself to use by a clinical team with a microcomputer.

The actual techniques of helping people with schizophrenia and those around them to 'live with schizophrenia' if all known methods of help have been tried but problems still remain have been described elsewhere (WATTS & BENNETT, 1983; WING, 1977; WING & MORRIS, 1981). As soon as the analytic approach so far discussed is completed, the resulting profile of problems and needs for care has to be synthesised into a management programme. This involves consideration of the attitudes of all the three parties involved: the sufferer, the relatives and others in the immediate social environment, and the professional people who control access to services. Each of the three groups sees a different set of problems and often fails to appreciate the difficulties faced by the others. It may therefore be useful to look through the eyes of each group separately.

Self-help

Those people who are severely impaired in their ability to communicate have much greater difficulty in coming to terms with their disability than those who are handicapped in other ways. If the impairment is severe there is very little chance to achieve a satisfactory solution unless others help them. The central problem is one of insight. The positive symptoms of schizophrenia carry a peculiar conviction to most of those who experience them, which cancels out the scepticism of relatives or professional helpers. Given that many have always been somewhat detached from social opinion and that the first onset often occurs during the rebellious teens anyway, it is not surprising that sufferers find themselves at odds with their relatives and unwilling to take advice from them. Sometimes it is only after prolonged experience and suffering that patients then begin to understand some of the factors that make matters better or worse.

A list of factors that are at least partially under the control of afflicted individuals, shown in Table 2, contains some of the major keys to self-help. Examples have been given elsewhere of each of these techniques of self-management (WING, 1977). The degree of insight required to use the techniques sensibly is uncommon and many never attain this degree of control. Severity of impairment is an important factor and it can vary independently of the quality of the social environment. Many meet with difficulties that are outside their competence to deal with: for example, an over-involved relative who uses the emotional relationship to intrude upon the sufferer and force him or her into unwanted interaction; a lack of protected environments such as day centres, sheltered workshops or group homes; a critical attitude from friends or employers; an unrealistic professional helper who does not understand the impairments; accidental stresses such as can occur to anyone.

Table 2: Factors partially under the control of afflicted people

---

- Whether and how to take medication
- Recognition and avoidance of triggering situations
- Specific and restricted social withdrawal
- Methods of dealing with primordial symptoms
- Using all one's talents
- Finding work within competence; keeping active
- Finding companions who are trustworthy and not intrusive
- Helping others to understand the condition

Many afflicted people are not highly intelligent, competent and articulate. The less capacity an individual has to recognize and cope with intrinsic impairments, extrinsic disadvantages, and personal reactions, the more important become the sympathy and the help of those with whom he or she has to live.

The problems of relatives

A study of schizophrenic patients admitted to three English mental hospitals in 1956 showed that, on discharge, 40% went to live with parents, 37% (mostly women) with a spouse, 8% with some other relative or friend, and 15% went to lodgings, rooming houses or residential jobs. By the time of follow-up five years later, only 29% were living with parents; there was less change in the other groups. Few separations from parental homes were due to disturbed behaviour, which parents tolerated with remarkable fortitude. A third were due to the death or ill-health of a parent and a third to positive reasons for leaving. Parents often made very little complaint even when they felt great distress and some developed very skilful methods of managing disturbed behaviour. Three-quarters of the parents were over the age of 60 and 40% over the age of 70. There was a high divorce and separation rate, probably three times that in the general population. It was particularly high among male patients (BROWN et al., 1966).

Since relatives are almost as much in the front line as patients, so far as living with schizophrenia is concerned, it is surprising that there have been so few informed surveys of their views on the subject. Much work appears to have been carried out with the major object of selecting quotations that fit the author's preconceptions of the pathogenesis of schizophrenia. Relatives do, of course, acquire considerable experience of coping with difficult behaviour but their methods are inevitably trial and error. Some learn not to argue with a deluded patient; others never learn. Some discover just how far they can go in trying to stimulate a rather slow and apathetic individual without arousing resentment. Others push too hard, find their efforts rejected or that they make matters worse, and then retreat into inactivity themselves. Some never give up intruding until the patient is driven away from home.

23

One of the major complaints by relatives is that when they ask for advice from professional people as to the best way to react to positive or negative symptoms, they receive no answer at all or the question is simply turned back on them: 'What do *you* do?' Nevertheless, many relatives do find a way to live with schizophrenia that provides the whole family with a supportive and comfortable home. Some of the factors that are partly under relatives' control are shown in Table 3.

Table 3: Factors partially under the control of relatives

- Creating a non-critical, accepting environment
- Behaving, as a family, with reasonable consistency
- Providing an optimal degree of social stimulation
- Keeping aims realistic
- Learning how to cope with fluctuating insight and unpredictability
- Learning how to respond to delusions or disturbed behaviour
- Learning how to cope with underactivity and low motivation
- Making best use of the professional help available
- Learning to use welfare arrangements
- Obtaining rewards from the patient's presence
- Helping the afflicted person

A new development during the past decade has been the establishment of effective charitable organisations in many countries whose aim is to promote the welfare of people afflicted by schizophrenia, improve the services provided, educate the public about the nature of the disorder and the professionals about the real problems of living with it and, above all, provide mutual comfort and support. The National Schizophrenia Fellowship in the U. K. (ROLLIN, 1980) was probably the first of these. There are thriving organisations in Australia, Canada, Eire, New Zealand, the USA and elsewhere. The movement has become worldwide with the initiation this year, of the World Schizophrenia Fellowship. Single-topic pressure groups have certain problems but when the topic is as misunderstood, neglected and unprovided for as schizophrenia the advantages far outweigh the disadvantages. Professional carers should welcome this development, which will profoundly affect the nature of their work during the next decade.

The role of professionals

The papers to be read at this conference demonstrate how far professional opinion has changed during the past twenty-five years. Among the leaders of opinion, the professional role is becoming one of partnership with afflicted people, their families and supporters, each learning from the other how better to live with schizophrenia. The influence of this concept is likely to be one of the most important factors determining the way psychiatry develops during the rest of this century.

Some of the factors that are partly under the control of professional carers are shown in Table 4.

Table 4: Factors partially under the control of professional carers

- Keeping up to date with theoretical and technical advances in one's own discipline
- Not claiming too much
- Recognising the 'primary care' role of relatives
- Accepting a partnership role with affected people and families
- Overcoming artificial professional and administrative boundaries
- Adopting a standard needs assessment procedure with regular evaluation and updating
- Taking proper note of physical as well as mental health
- Providing a 'care coordinator' (key worker) for each person/family needing long-term care
- Operating an efficient multidisciplinary team system that can delegate responsibility to act in whatever professional or administrative capacity is required.
- Taking a serious interest in the planning, organisation and coordination of district services

Level 3: Needs for Services. The Delivery of Care

To go into detail about the way that services should be planned, organised and administered would take us too far from the theme of this meeting (see WING, 1985a, b; WING & HAEFNER, 1973; WING & HAILEY, 1972). However, it is essential for professional carers to recognise that methods of delivery of care are important determinants of therapeutic outcome. This is most obvious in the extreme case, when people in need of care are not in touch with services at all. Services should be geographically responsible, so that efforts are made to identify all those likely to be in need. An epidemiological approach is basic here, because the local socio-economic structure, physical characteristics, population dynamics and traditions of service provision give clear indications of the size and nature of the psychiatric problems that can be expected in a particular district, and therefore of the likely extent of need. Services should also be comprehensive and integrated, i.e. many different types of care should be available but there should be continuity of responsibility throughout.

If these three requirements are not satisfied, the best efforts of expert professional carers will often be frustrated, because their help will not be made available to many who could benefit from it. The long-term management of schizophrenia, in particular, cannot successfully be carried out unless all three conditions are fulfilled.

The types of service needed can be visualised in terms of three ladders or staircases with landings (see Table 5). Each covers the needs of part of an ordinary day's activity – a residence at night, a place for occupation during the day, and recreational opportunities in the evenings and at weekends. Disabled people need help in each of these spheres of life, though not necessarily all at the same time or to a uniform degree. Great flexibility is therefore required. There may be movement up or down any of the staircases and periods for short or long-term rest at each landing. The bannisters or handrails represent the efforts of therapists, carers and supporters to help afflicted people move up the staircases and to maintain their position.

Finally, it is necessary to say a word about concepts of 'institutional' and 'community care'. Table 6 sets out some of the characteristics that have led to the development of stereotyped attitudes towards each, so much so that the

Table 5: Ladders and resting places. (Staircases and landings.)

	Working hours	Nighttime	Leisure hours
	(Occupational functions)	(Domestic functions)	(Recreational and social functions)
Independent			
———	Can occupy self	Maintains home	Plenty of interests
———	Sheltered paid work	Supervised flat or lodging	Restaurant or club
———	IT day unit	Group home	Reserved hours in leisure activity
———	OT day unit	Staffed hostel Hospital-hostel (Haven)	Home OT or accompanied
———	High dependency day unit	Secure unit	Special recreational provisions
Highly dependent			

N.B. (a) There are, of course, many more steps than are shown
   (b) One individual may be at different levels on the three staircases; hence the need for highly flexible and coordinated use of services.
   (c) If living with a relative, a disabled person may be at almost any level, including the lowest, on each staircase. Relatives often make up for deficiencies in services and thus disguise the gaps.

Psychosocial bannisters:
Handrails are necessary for most disabled people. They represent, in this analogy, the function carried out by staff and supporters – assessment, monitoring, shelter, security, welfare, treatment, programmes, continuity, counsel, allocation of services.

terms are now often used as mere slogans. In fact, sheltered communities can have all the characteristics of open care while a terraced house in an ordinary street can be like a small and isolated prison. Plans for services must be based on epidemiological knowledge of needs, not on slogans.

Table 6: "The Total Institution" and "Open Care"

Characteristic	Total institution	Open care
Power	Oligarchic, bureaucratic, restrictive, monolithic, custodial	Clear line of management, open access, representative authority, based in units
Staff organisation	Hierarchical, authoritarian, no initiative allowed	Autonomy within clear guidelines, team working, continuity of caring
Physical boundaries	Walls, gatehouses	None visible
Psychological boundaries	Graded parole impermeable barriers	Permeable both ways, flexible security
Buildings	Large blocks, dormitories	Human scale, «invisible» locally
Stigma	Concentrated	Diluted
Outside controls	Easily evaded, occasional scandals	Broad mgt. committees, independent inspectorate, in public view
Staff attitudes	Stereotypes of inmates, officer status, sole authority	Individuality and dignity respected, part of wider support network
Social milieu	Social poverty	Socially rich
Daily routine	Block movement, rigid timetable, doing nothing	Many options according to need
Welfare	Pauperism, neglect, low standards	Standards of local community

Bibliography

BABCOCK, H.: Dementia praecox: A psychological study. New York: Science Press, 1933.
BLEULER, M.: Die schizophrenen Geistesstörungen im Lichte langjähriger Kranken- und Familiengeschichten. Stuttgart: Thieme, 1972. The schizophrenic disorders: Longterm patient and family studies. Translated by S. M. Clemens. New Haven: Yale University Press, 1978.
BROWN, G. W.; BIRLEY, J. L. T.: Crisis and life changes and the onset of schizophrenia. J. Hlth. Hum. Behav. *9,* 203–214, 1968.
BROWN, G. W.; BIRLEY, J. L. T.; WING, J. K.: Influence of family life on the course of schizophrenic disorders: A replication. Brit. J. Psychiat. *121,* 241–258, 1972.
BROWN, G. W.; BONE, M.; DALISON, B.; WING, J. K.: Schizophrenia and social care. Maudsley Monograph No. 17. London: Oxford University Press, 1966.

BROWN, G. W.; MONCK, E.; CARSTAIRS, G. M.; WING, J. K.: Influence of family life on the course of schizophrenic illness. Brit. J. Prev. Soc. Med. *16,* 55–68, 1962.

CIOMPI, L.: The natural history of schizophrenia in the long term. Brit. J. Psychiat. *136,* 413–420, 1980.

CIOMPI, L.; MUELLER, Ch.: Lebenslauf und Alter der Schizophrenen: Eine katamnestische Langzeitstudie bis ins Senium. Heidelberg: Springer, 1976.

CONNELL, P.: Amphetamine psychosis. London: Chapman and Hall, 1958.

DAVISON, K.; BAGLEY, C. R.: Schizophrenia-like psychoses associated with organic disorders of the central nervous system. In: HERRINGTON, R. N. (ed.): Current problems in neuropsychiatry. London: R.M.P.A., 1969.

DOHRENWEND, B. P.; DOHRENWEND, B. S.: Social status and psychological disorder. A causal inquiry. New York: Wiley, 1969.

EY, H.: Des idées de Jackson à un modèle organodynamique en psychiatrie. Toulouse: Privat, 1975.

GOFFMAN; E.: Asylums: Essays on the social situation of mental patient and other inmates. Harmondsworth: Penguin, 1961.

HUBER, G.; GROSS, G.; SCHUETTLER, R.: Schizophrenie: Eine verlaufs- und sozial-psychiatrische Langzeitstudie. Heidelberg: Springer, 1979.

LEACH, J.; WING, J. K.: Helping destitute men. London: Tavistock, 1980.

LEFF, J.; KUIPERS, L.; BERKOWITZ, R.; EBERLEIN-FRIES, R.; STURGEON, D.: A controlled trial of social intervention in the families of schizophrenic patients. Brit. J. Psychiat. *141,* 121–134, 1982.

LEMERT, E.: Social pathology. New York: McGraw-Hill, 1951.

OWENS, D. G. C.; JOHNSTONE, E. C.: The disabilities of chronic schizophrenia – their nature and the factors contributing to their development. Brit. J. Psychiat. *136,* 384–395, 1980.

ROLLIN, H. (ed.): Coping with schizophrenia: The National Schizophrenia Fellowship. London: Burnett Books, 1980.

SCHEFF, T. J.: Being mentally ill. Chicago: Aldine, 1966.

SLATER, E.; BEARD, A. W.; GLITHERO, E.: The schizophrenic-like psychoses of epilepsy. Brit. J. Psychiat. *109,* 95–150, 1963.

STEVENS, B. C.: Marriage and fertility of women suffering from schizophrenia or affective disorders. Maudsley Monograph No. 19. London: Oxford University Press, 1969.

VAUGHN, C. E.; LEFF, J. P.: The influence of family and social factors on the course of psychiatric illness. Brit. J. Psychiat. *129,* 125–137, 1976.

WATTS, F. N.; BENNETT, D. H. (eds.): Theory and practice of psychiatric rehabilitation. London: Wiley, 1983.

WING, J. K.: A pilot experiment on the rehabilitation of long-hospitalised male schizophrenic patients. Brit. J. Prev. Soc. Med. *14,* 173–180, 1960.

WING, J. K.: A simple and reliable sub-classification of chronic schizophrenia. J. Ment. Sci. *107,* 862, 1961.

WING, J. K.: Impairments in schizophrenia: A rational basis for social treatment. In: WIRT, R. D.; WINOKUR, G.; ROFF, M. (eds.): Life history research in psychopathology, Vol. 4. Minneapolis: University of Minnesota Press, 1975a.

WING, J. K. (ed.): Schizophrenia from within. London: National Schizophrenia Fellowship, 78, Victoria Road, Surbiton, KT6 4NS, 1975b.

WING, J. K.: The management of schizophrenia in the community. In: USDIN, G. (ed.): Psychiatric medicine. New York: Brunner-Mazel, 1977.

WING, J. K.: Social influences on the course of schizophrenia. In: WYNNE, L. C.; CROMWELL, R. L.; MATTHYSSE, S. (eds.): The nature of schizophrenia. New York: Wiley, 1978a.

WING, J. K.: Reasoning about madness. London: Oxford University Press, 1978b.

WING, J. K.: Long-term care in schizophrenia: Contributions from epidemiologic studies in the U. K. In: BARRATT, G. (ed.): Mental disorders in the community: Progress and challenge. New York: Guildford Press. (To be published in 1986), 1985a.

WING, J. K.: Positive and negative symptoms and the diagnosis of schizophrenia. Paper read at the meeting of the Royal College of Psychiatrists, July, 1985b. (To be published.)

WING, J. K.; BENNETT, D. H.; DENHAM, J.: The industrial rehabilitation of long-stay schizophrenic patients. Med. Res. Council memo. No. 42. London: H.M.S.O., 1964.

WING, J. K.; BROWN, G. W.: Institutionalism and schizophrenia. London: Cambridge University Press, 1970.

WING, J. K.; FREUDENBERG, R. K.: The response of severely ill chronic schizophrenic patients to social stimulation. Amer. J. Psychiat. *118*, 311–322, 1961.

WING, J. K.; HAEFNER, H. (eds.): Roots of evaluation: The epidemiological basis for planning psychiatric services. London: Oxford University Press, 1973.

WING, J. K.; HAILEY, A. M. (eds.): Evaluating a community psychiatric service: The Camberwell register, 1964–1971. London: Oxford University Press, 1972.

WING, J. K.; LEFF, J. P.; HIRSCH, S.: Preventive treatment of schizophrenia: Some theoretical and methodological issues. In: COLE, J.; FREEDMAN, A.; FRIEDHOFF, A. (eds.): Psychopathology and psychopharmacology. 1972.

WING, J. K.; MORRIS, B. (eds.): Handbook of psychiatric rehabilitation practice. London: Oxford University Press, 1981.

WORLD HEALTH ORGANIZATION: The international pilot study of schizophrenia. Geneva, WHO, 1973.

WORLD HEALTH ORGANIZATION: Schizophrenia: An international follow-up study. New York: Wiley, 1979.

WYKES, T.; CREER, C.; STURT, E.: Needs and the deployment of services. In: WING, J. K. (ed.): Long-term community care. Psychol. Med. Suppl. No. 2, 41–55, 1982.

ZUBIN, J.: Introduction to section XII, onset and course. In: WYNNE, L. C.; CROMWELL, R. L.; MATTHYSSE, S. (eds.): The nature of schizophrenia. New York: Wiley, 1978.

ZUSMAN, J.: Changing appearance of psychotic patients. Int. J. Psychiat. *3*, 216–237, 1967.

Possible Implications of the Vulnerability Hypothesis for the Psychosocial Management of Schizophrenia[1]

J. ZUBIN

The term "management" has been defined as "the whole system of care and treatment of a disease or a sick individual" (WEBSTER, 1976). In the case of chronic schizophrenia, "management is basically a matter of helping affected individuals, their relatives and the community at large to live with schizophrenia" (WING, 1978, p. 254). Thus, the term "management" might lead one to infer that schizophrenia is a disease that is life-long, has no cure, and the only option open to the therapist is to try to manage the patient to cope as well as possible with his/her predetermined fate, as is the case with Huntington's Chorea or Parkinsonism.

I was, therefore, glad to note that Professor WING has worded his title to refer to "long-term" course rather than "life-long" course. I would, however, go even further and state that even long-term course may not be a necessary outcome of schizophrenia. The long-term course may be largely an artifact and not a natural part of the course of the disorder, but due to the impact of iatrogenic, nosocomial and ecogenic forces. These sometimes stand in the way of the natural healing process that applies to schizophrenia as it does to other mental disorders, as well as to some physical disorders.

The assumption that schizophrenia is necessarily a long-term disorder leading to deterioration or to severe reduction in quality of life may be a relic of a previous era which persists despite the evidence to the contrary. The generally benign outcome of schizophrenia that has been demonstrated by three outstanding long-term European studies, i.e., the studies of Manfred BLEULER (1972), Luc CIOMPI (1980a), and Gerd HUBER et al. (1980), has not yet been fully appreciated. Manfred BLEULER has pointed out that the reason why Eugen BLEULER, Emil KRAEPELIN, Kurt SCHNEIDER and their colleagues endowed schizophrenia with such a jaundiced outlook was the biased sample of patients they saw. These patients were drawn largely from those whose families had given them over to institutionalization and who were already on a chronic course. KRAEPELIN saw the task of the clinician as consisting mainly of diagnosing, providing a prognosis, and leaving the disorder to take its natural

1 Supported by the Medical Research Service of the Veterans Administration. The author wishes to acknowledge the help of Dr. Richard DAY in developing several sections of this paper.

course (ZUBIN et al., in preparation). In the USA too, the average practitioner is exposed continuously to the recidivists in his practice and forgets about those who had only one episode and were never readmitted! (Apparently from 23 to 39% of schizophrenic patients have only one episode and the proportion having an episodic course with final remission is from 35% to 78% [ZUBIN et al., 1985b].)

The reason for this cultural lag in the acceptance of the more benign character of schizophrenia is perplexing. It may lie in the cultural persistence of the "Degeneration Theory," which was very prominent during the 19th century. It suggested the presence of a familial degenerative strain that became increasingly more severe over successive generations, eventually causing extinction of the line (ZUBIN et al., in preparation). Although science has long ago disproved this theory, the folklore may still retain it, and it may influence patients, family members, the general public, and even some clinicians to regard schizophrenia as a degenerative disease. This hypothesis may have had some influence on KRAEPELIN's thinking about the etiology of mental disorders including dementia praecox, manic depressive psychosis, hysteria, and even some physical disorder, since, as ACKERKNECHT (1968) points out, KRAEPELIN was much influenced by the "Degeneration Theory" even though he expressed numerous reservations.

We all recognize that the model we adopt for the etiology of schizophrenia is bound to determine our approach to its management. There are at least seven scientific classes of models for the etiology of schizophrenia (ecological, developmental, learning theory, genetic, internal environment, neurophysiological and neuroanatomical) (ZUBIN et al., 1985b). These can be classified into two major divisions: biological and environmental. I have selected three representative subsets of the seven etiological models and one superordinate model – the vulnerability model –, and will limit our discussion to the management policies of each of them. In order to focus the discussion, I will target primarily the management of negative and positive symptoms (PNS) by each of them and contrast their approaches. Briefly stated, positive symptoms are behaviors that schizophrenics engage in but normals do not. Negative symptoms, when inverted to their opposites (e.g., "withdrawal" to "sociability"), are behaviors normals engage in but schizophrenics do not, or only in a diminished manner.

First, let us give a brief description of the three chosen models. The first is the biological or disease model inherited from KRAEPELIN's days and combines the four biologically based etiological models (genetic, internal environment, neurophysiological and neuroanatomical). The disease model, simply stated, postulates that schizophrenia is a disease similar to diabetes in so far as the disease is a permanent characteristic of the patient to which he has to adjust with the help of his physician in order to minimize the hazard to health and happiness which the disease presents. At best, the patient is a permanently sick person who once in a while may undergo an episode of health. In addition, the prevalent attitude towards the disease model inherited from KRAEPE-

LIN is that it is a degenerative disease leading to deterioration or severe reduction of efficient living.

The etiology of the disease is presumed to be genetic or at least organic, and the treatment is aimed at reducing the symptoms by means of suitable neuroleptic or other biochemical means, since no cure is available at this time. In other words, the goal of therapy is to reduce the impact of the symptoms, but the disease itself persists even if it goes into remission, presumably affecting behavior through residual symptoms. The disease model is represented here by one of the most vigorous proponents of the biological model – Crow (1980). He postulates two distinct subtypes of schizophrenia based on PNS. Type I is largely characterized by positive symptoms with biochemical dysregulation probably due to dopaminergic activity. Type II is largely characterized by negative symptoms that are associated with gross structural abnormality (cerebral atrophy, enlarged ventricles). MacKay (1980) adds further that the negative symptoms may reflect chronic dopaminergic underactivity while positive symptoms emerge when there is a burst of dopaminergic overactivity. He postulates further that the negative symptoms are chronically present but that positive symptoms are periodically superimposed on them. According to this disease model PNS forms a permanent feature of schizophrenic behavior.

The second is the environmental model inherited from Sir Aubrey Lewis, represented by John Wing. It is essentially the ecological model described earlier. Professor Wing's is a hard act to follow, but I am fortunate in so far as he has already laid down the basis for the model. It is firmly rooted in Anglo-European traditions of descriptive psychopathology and more recent thought about the role of social factors in psychiatric disorders. It is primarily concerned with socioenvironmental factors affecting the onset, phenomenology, course and outcome.

The third model is the behavioral model emerging from and encompassing the developmental and learning theory models and represented here by Kurt Salzinger's (1981, 1984) and Wallace and Boone's (1983) approach. It postulates that there is no schizophrenic disorder except that which is seen in the behavior of the patient and that these behaviors, PNS, can be targeted individually for elimination by means of behavior modification techniques.

The superordinate model which attempts to provide living space for all the models is the vulnerability model. It stipulates that regardless of which of the seven etiological models may be operative in a given case, the patient is essentially a vulnerable individual. This vulnerability may exist only as a risk or may be elicited, if sufficient stress and strain impinge on the patient. In order to identify vulnerable individuals, regardless of whether they suffer an episode, a series of studies to find markers of vulnerability are in progress (Zubin, in press a). Beginning with patients who have demonstrated vulnerability by developing an episode, a characteristic is found that differentiates them from the general population and from non-schizophrenic patients. They are then followed up to determine whether the marker persists after the episode terminates and whether it is also found in unaffected first degree relatives with a risk

32

higher than in the general population. Those markers that meet these criteria are regarded as vulnerability markers. If they vanish with the end of the episode and are absent in unaffected first-degree relatives, they are regarded as episode markers. Since the advent of the drug era and of the new psychosocial therapies, the focus of attention is no longer the episode itself, because remission of acute symptoms is usually so readily attained. Now the focus has been shifted to the attempt to prevent future episodes or recidivism. This has become the goal of a study of recidivism in schizophrenia conducted by our Biometric Research Unit.

The vulnerability hypothesis, in contrast with the biological models, does not imply a chronic disorder but a permanent vulnerability to develop the disorder. Episodes are postulated as time limited. When the episode terminates, the individual usually returns to his premorbid level of adjustment to every day living. Thus, schizophrenia is postulated to be an episodic illness in the same sense as depression, epilepsy, or allergy. However, even a vulnerable individual who has undergone a sufficiently stressful life event to elicit an episode need not necessarily develop an episode. There are at least three protective factors which may abort the episode if they are favorable, and aid and abett the episode if they are unfavorable. These are (1) the social network, (2) the ecological niche which the patient occupies, and (3) the premorbid personality including his/her intelligence, personal competence, and learned coping skiils. One way of epitomizing the difference between the vulnerability model and the disease model is to indicate that while the disease model regards the patient as essentially ill, but may have intermittent periods of wellness, the vulnerability model regards the patient as essentially well, but may have one or more intermittent episodes of illness.

We can now turn to the therapeutic strategies which each of these models dictates.

In a recent review of a symposium on PNS, after surveying the contributions of the seven outstanding contributors to this field, I found that there was a consensus on the following results (ZUBIN, in press a):

1. Positive symptoms generally respond to neuroleptic treatment while negative symptoms generally do not, though GOLDBERG (in press) makes out a case for the responsiveness of even negative symptoms to neuroleptics.
2. Positive symptoms tend to be independent of intelligence while negative symptoms show an inverse correlation with intelligence, especially in patients who show structural brain impairment and have a poor premorbid personality.
3. Negative symptoms seem to persist and thus become more apparent in long-enduring episodes or multiple episodes, while positive symptoms have shorter durations and seem generally to wax and wane with the episodes.
4. Positive symptoms are aggravated by amphetamine injections presumably because dopamine transmission is facilitated. The effect on negative symptoms is either absent or non-spectacular.

33

5. Negative symptoms correlate with deviations in brain structure, especially in poor premorbids.
6. There is general agreement that both negative as well as positive individual items are not specific to schizophrenia. Whether combination of items into syndromes will show greater specificity remains to be seen.
7. There is some agreement that positive symptoms are associated more with neurochemical rather than structural anomalies in the brain.
8. It is generally agreed that there is difficulty in distinguishing between negative symptoms and depressive symptoms and criteria for schizoid personality.
9. There is general agreement that positive and negative symptoms are independent and that there may be four categories of schizophrenia with regard to the presence and absence of both types of symptoms: (1) both present, (2) both absent (remitted), (3) negative present but not positive, and (4) positive present but not negative. The majority of patients seem to fall in the first category.

It was not possible to find a model for integrating these findings which would cast light on the etiology of PNS, but the following conjectures regarding their etiology were made by the authors (ZUBIN, in press a):

1. Negative symptoms are the result of the impact of the psychosis, leading to reduction of normal behavior because the individual has been overwhelmed by the disruption produced by the psychosis.
2. They are the effect of antipsychotic drugs, e.g., akinesia and sedation.
3. The effect of institutionalization.
4. Residual effect of the psychosis after the episode ends.
5. Effect of depressive episodes accompanying schizophrenia.
6. The effect of the reemergence of the premorbid negative personality traits at the termination of the acute episode.

The disease model is geared to deal with the acute positive symptoms by means of psychopharmacological intervention, lending some credence to the biological sources of the episode. One management strategy suggested by CROWS's model for Type I patients with positive symptoms could be to utilize monitored changes in dosage treatment as a means of lessening dangers of relapse and tardive dyskinesia. Presumably, the danger of relapse under no medication and even under medication must also be studied so as to prevent it. Similarly, the danger of continuing in the episode or even exacerbating it must be carefully monitored. Challenging techniques such as the amphetamine or ritalin type of biochemical challenge can be used to probe for the presence of the episode or its termination. Similarly, certain behavioral techniques (ZUBIN & STEINHAUER, 1981; ZUBIN, in press b) can serve the same purpose. As far as the negative symptoms go, since they are regarded as invariant, and especially resistant to drug treatment, there seems to be no other option except perhaps psychosocial intervention.

34

The behavioral model seems tailor-made to deal with PNS since it regards the disorder as consisting primarily of the presenting symptoms without any underlying general disorder. The behavior modifiers can train their guns on each symptom in turn and devise methods for eliminating it. According to this approach, the title of this symposium should be "Remedying Schizophrenic Behavior" rather than "Management of Schizophrenia." SALZINGER (personal communication) describes the behavior modification approach as follows:

Negative symptoms, or as I prefer to call them, behavioral deficits, in schizophrenia are taken care of by behavior modification, in the main, by shaping behavior and by imitation learning. Shaping means that one reinforces ever closer approximations to the desired response. For example, if you wish to produce social behavior in a person who has none, you would first reinforce looking at other people, then listening to them, then saying something brief like "hello" and then a short conversation, and then have them speak to other people for longer periods of time, eventually getting them to telephone people or approaching strangers at a party to socialize with them. Imitation learning could be introduced by reinforcing the patients to first observe the model and then to imitate rather simple responses of short duration, and eventually more complex behavior of longer and longer duration; finally, one can then reinforce the spontaneous occurrence of the behavior that was originally emitted only as an imitation.

Positive symptoms would have to be dealt with by the following means, according to behavior modification: Punishment plus reinforcement of other, usually incompatible responses, that is, responses whose appearance would make the occurrence of the undesirable response impossible. Extinction is of course another method and can be used if a patient is emitting deluded speech, with positive reinforcement used when the speech is nondelusional. One can also employ a discriminative stimulus for other behavior when a patient emits undesirable behavior, as for example, by starting a conversation about the next meal, or about last nights baseball game, or about an election coming up, etc., whenever the patient becomes delusional or hallucinated.

WALLACE and BOONE (1983) have given several examples of how behavioral treatment may be applied to improving social skills by eliminating some of the negative symptoms. Thus, the problem of lack of conversation skills was dealt with by reinforcing continuous speech with an interlocutor. Eye contact and voice volume were improved by an assertion-training format in which improved behavior was reinforced. Training in recognizing possible options for responding in challenging situations was improved by a modified assertion-training format. Community-living skills and problem-solving skills were taught by a specially devised training program. Thus, by targeting the various negative symptoms, considerable progress can be made in their elimination.

With regard to the psychosocial model, Professor WING has already covered it amply. The only thing left for me to do is to contrast its approach with that of the vulnerability model. WING and BROWN (1970) divide up the handicaps that the schizophrenic suffers from (among which are included the negative symptoms) into three distinct types: (1) premorbid (low IQ, difficult personality, social withdrawal), which they regard not so much as premorbid as possibly prodromal, although the considerable evidence for low IQ being premorbid, contradicts it; (2) primary disabilities, consisting of negative and of positive symptoms; (3) secondary disabilities – these stem not from the illness itself but from the social and medical consequences of having been ill. These include handicaps due to institutionalization, social stigma, loss of self-confidence and self-esteem, induced dependence and other inadvertant difficulties resulting from the patient's social interaction with members of the medical profession, relatives, and the general public. One of the basic tenets of WING's model is that schizophrenic patients are biologically vulnerable to both under- and overstimulating environments. The psychosocial model has given rise to a variety of interventions which have proved to be of considerable value in the management of schizophrenia. Among those that can be traced to the psychosocial approach are (1) training in social skills, (2) education of family attitudes especially with regard to high emotional expression, (3) education for communication in families suffering from communication deviance and a variety of similar techniques that are covered by the specialists in these areas who are present at this symposium.

The major points of difference between this model and the vulnerability model lie in the interpretation of premorbid handicaps, negative symptoms, and chronicity.

Regarding premorbid personality, WING regards deviant traits that are present before the episode erupts as prodromal while the vulnerability model regards them as independent of the episode. Though there is an association between premorbid personality and the development of an episode, this association is rather mild (ZUBIN et al., 1983). Thus, while the risk of schizophrenia for extremely deviant premorbid personalities is 9.36, and the risk for mildly deviant personalities is 0.69, the risk for normal premorbid personalities is only 0.67. However, 90% of even the severely deviant personalities do not develop episodes, presumably because they are not vulnerable to schizophrenia. Hence, to regard extremely deviant personalities as prodromal runs the risk of being wrong 90% of the time.[2]

The vulnerability model is presented with two dilemmas by PNS. First, the vulnerability hypothesis does not allow any room for sustained chronicity, since every patient is supposed to emerge from the episode sooner or later. How to explain the frequency of chronicity in our daily practice is one dilemma. Secondly, since negative symptoms are associated with chronic states, how can they be explained? There is no problem with positive symptoms, since the vulnerability hypothesis accepts them as characteristic of the

2 The figures quoted here are based on the combination of two studies – M. BLEULER's study of premorbid personality in his probands and ESSEN-MOLLER's study of the general population in his Lundby study. The assumption that the two samples are drawn from similar populations may not be tenable, and the equivalence of the personality determinations by the two investigators not entirely acceptable, but it is the best data I can find for relating premorbid personality to the occurrence of an episode of schizophrenia.

episode and they wax and wane with it.[3] But negative symptoms and chronicity present a problem.

While WING regards some of the negative symptoms as intrinsic, the vulnerability hypothesis assimilates this syndrome completely into WING's "secondary" or "external" disabilities. Thus, vulnerability theory regards negative symptoms as neither inevitable (KRAEPELIN) nor intrinsic (WING). Instead, it regards them as essentially due to an artifact, developing as a social consequence of being labelled and treated as a schizophrenic by medical specialists, relatives, close friends, and other members of the patient's social network.

The chronicity issue

Another point of difference between the vulnerability and behavioral model on the one hand, and the disease and WING's psychosocial model on the other hand, is their negative attitude toward the episodic nature of schizophrenia which the vulnerability model stresses. If it be episodic, how explain chronicity? I was glad to find that Professor Luc CIOMPI has also struggled with this problem (CIOMPI, 1980a). Our combined arguments pro and con the assumption that chronicity is an indigenous component of schizophrenia are as follows:

Arguments Against Chronicity as an Indigenous Component of Schizophrenia

1. *Not Universal:* Not all schizophrenics develop chronic states. In his follow-up study, M. BLEULER found no more than 10% continuously hospitalized after first admission.
2. *Prevalence is Exaggerated:* The apparent prevalence of chronicity is due to the accumulation of a small proportion of chronics, but even of these, in M. BLEULER's follow-up, 30% remain in the hospital for lack of any other home.
3. *General Trend in Outcome is Remission Rather than Chronicity:* Long-term follow-up studies (BLEULER, 1972; CIOMPI, 1980b; HUBER et al., 1980) indicate that the general trend is toward improvement rather than deterioration. Sporadic recovery can occur even after a lifetime of chronicity.
4. *Environment Rather than Heredity May be Associated with Chronicity:* Long-term outcome is often independent of family history of schizophrenia. Consequently, environment rather than heredity may influence the appearance of chronicity. Such moderating variables as social networks, eco-

---

3 It is true that some proportion of chronic patients also cling to their positive symptoms. This occurs during an exacerbation or as a new episode of the illness is superimposed on the continuing negative symptoms. When positive symptoms arise, they often lend themselves to amelioration through neuroleptic treatment. Why positive symptoms persist in some patients is a perplexing question. They sometimes persist even after the episode is terminated as a result of incidental "gains" which they bring in the form of increased attention.

logical niches, and premorbid personality, if favorable, may mitigate the impact of stressors, but if unfavorable, may exacerbate the impact leading to chronicity.

5. *Chronicity is Associated with Psychosocial Factors:* (a) Life events play a triggering role in recidivism and in maintenance of chronic episodes. (b) Labelling impact prevents readjustment, especially occupationally. (c) Highly critical families play a role in the prolongation and resumption of schizophrenia episodes.

6. *Negative Symptoms Sometimes do Improve with Neuroleptic and Other Treatments and Do Respond to Amphetamines.* (BORONOW & VAN KAMMEN, 1982.)

Other arguments that appear to favor the indigenous nature of chronicity are, to my mind, flawed:

1. *Irreversibility of Negative Symptoms:* (a) It has been claimed that the presence of irreversible negative symptoms characterizes chronic schizophrenia, but negative symptoms may be associated with chronicity because they may have been premorbidly present, and when the episode ends, the patients return to their premorbid level including their negative symptoms. As evidence for this possibility, 70% of BLEULER's probands had deviant premorbid personalities including negative symptoms, and about 58% of these poor premorbids were regarded as attaining a moderately severe, or severe, end state (chronic) (ZUBIN et al., 1983). Furthermore, deviant behavior can develop due to institutionalization and isolation and may be mistakenly regarded as a natural consequence of schizophrenia. For example, negative symptoms are also seen in long-term prisoners, neglected residents of old age homes, nursing homes, etc. (b) It is often difficult to distinguish chronic schizophrenics from other chronic patients in the back wards of institutions, but these symptoms often disappear under social stimulation (PAUL, 1977; WING & BROWN, 1970).

2. *Biochemical or Organic Basis:* No general accepted evidence is available for any specific somatic, biochemical or other organic basis for chronic schizophrenia. Chemical intervention, though effective in the acute phase against positive symptoms, is not generally effective in the chronic phase against negative symptoms; the latter may be more amenable to psychosocial intervention.

3. *Ubiquity of Chronicity:* It has been claimed that chronicity is ubiquitous, and that it transcends differences in environments. However, cross-cultural studies indicate that developing countries have better outcomes and hence less chronicity than developed countries (WHO 1974, 1978).

Thus, it may be concluded that the proposition that chronicity is not an indigenous part of the course of schizophrenia (except in a small proportion of cases) is quite tenable in view of currently available evidence (CIOMPI, 1980a; CUTTING, 1983; ZUBIN, in press b; ZUBIN et al., 1985b).

It is clear that the vulnerability and the behavioral models differ from the others on one major issue, whether chronicity and negative symptoms are part of the natural history of schizophrenia or are they artifacts of iatrogenic, nosocomial and ecogenic factors.

The question of the intrinsic or indigenous character of chronicity and negative symptoms cannot be resolved until we find the basic cause of schizophrenia, discover the vulnerability markers and follow up patients sufficiently long to note whether negative symptoms and chronicity are natural parts of the progress of the disorder. Meantime, we can adopt several strategies to determine the indigenous character of PNS and chronicity.

With regards to positive symptoms, it is assumed that they largely wax and wane with the episode. With regard to the negative symptoms, a quandary exists. They usually are associated with so-called chronic states. It is clear that some of these negative traits may have existed premorbidly, and their persistence postmorbidly is due to the return to the premorbid status. But what about the traits that did not exist premorbidly? Are they part of the schizophrenic process?

One way of answering this question is to determine whether the negative symptoms are mutable. If they are not, perhaps we can accept them as part of the schizophrenic process and not as an incidental effect produced by iatrogenic, nosocomial and other ecogenic influences. If they are mutable, the likelihood is that they may have been produced as side effects. But the question remains whether the intervention that eliminated them represents an efficacious way of treating the disorder rather than only eliminating a side effect. Only the presence of these side effects in non-schizophrenic patients, who are subjected to the noxious niche which post-episode schizophrenics occupy in life, can finally resolve this issue.

Depending upon the presumed source of the negative symptoms, the following strategies, based in part on CARPENTER et al. (in press), are proposed:

1. If the negative symptoms are a response to the psychosis resulting from self-preoccupation or from a defense maneuver to dampen its impact, they should generally disappear with the recovery from the episode provided they have not been stamped in by nosocomial and/or iatrogenic influences.
2. If they are induced by drug treatment (akinesia, sedation), a change in the treatment regime should eliminate them.
3. If they reflect the understimulation WING and BROWN (1970) found to be the case in many instances, they can be eliminated by environmental manipulation.
4. If they are induced by the acute psychotic episode or occur post episodically, proper therapeutic intervention should be found by clinical trial and error, leading to their elimination.
5. If these strategies fail to eliminate the negative symptoms, they could be regarded as genuine aspects of the schizophrenic process which gives schizophrenia its chronic characteristics. However, before accepting this

conclusion it would be of interest to determine whether these negative symptoms are not a reflection of the premorbid personality characteristics.
6. Another question that needs to be tackled is whether negative symptoms are specific to schizophrenia and not found in depression and other psychiatric or non-psychiatric statuses. For example, are they characteristic of individuals who are neglected or isolated through incarceration in prisons or in poorly managed nursing homes. Only comparative studies can answer this question.

All these strategies require in addition a long-term follow-up to determine the permanency of the negative symptoms and whether they return after being eliminated.

As a final point in the discussion of negative symptoms, it must be remembered that though psychosocial variables have not been demonstrated to be as important as biological variables in the etiology of schizophrenia, they have been shown to play a most important role in the triggering of an episode and in outcome. If we adopt the vulnerability hypothesis, good outcome as opposed to poor outcome may be determined not so much by biology as by the type of social network, by the ecological niche to which the patient is returned when the episode ends and by the premorbid personality resumed when the episode terminates. In investigations of outcome, it becomes necessary that control groups or comparison groups of other patients or normals must be equated on these psychosocial variables before sufficient conclusions can be drawn. Even on such biological factors as mortality, comparisons that do not include psychosocial variables such as social networks would be unacceptable, since the evidence that social networks are important factors in survival is now well established. For this reason the current data on the higher mortality rates for schizophrenia compared to other mental disorders and to normal controls are highly suspect if no suitable controls are introduced. The same holds true for the other psychosocial variables. Hence, in the investigations for the elimination of negative symptoms, the same principal must be followed and controls for psychosocial variables must be introduced when the efficacy of treatment outcome is being investigated.

Bibliography

ACKERKNECHT, E. H.: The theory of degeneration. Chapter VII. In: ACKERKNECHT, E. H.: Short history of psychiatry. New York, London: Hafner Publishing Company, 1968. [Based on Georges Genil-Perrin: "Histoire des origines et de l'évolution de l'idée de dégénérescence en médecine mentale". Paris 1913].
BLEULER, M.: The schizophrenic disorders: Long-term patient and family studies. New Haven, CT: Yale University Press, 1978. [Die schizophrenen Geistesstörungen im Lichte langjähriger Kranken- und Familiengeschichten. Stuttgart: Thieme, 1972].
BORONOW, J. D.; VAN KAMMEN, D. P.: Amphetamine lowers negative schizophrenic symptoms. Presented at the American Psychiatric Association Meeting – New Research Section, May, 1982.

CARPENTER, W. T., Jr.; HEINRICKS, D. W.; ALPHS, L. D.: Treatment of negative symptoms. Schizophr. bull. (in press).

CIOMPI, L.: Ist die chronische Schizophrenie ein Artefakt? - Argumente und Gegenargumente. Fortschr. Neurol. Psychiat. *48,* 237–248, 1980a.

CIOMPI, L.: The natural history of schizophrenia in the long term. Brit. J. Psychiat. *136,* 413–420, 1980b.

CROW, T. J.: Molecular pathology of schizophrenia: More than one disease process? Brit. Med. J. *280,* 66–68, 1980.

CUTTING, J.: Schizophrenic deterioration. Brit. J. Psychiat. *143,* 77–84, 1983.

GOLDBERG, S. C.: Negative and deficit symptoms in schizophrenia do respond to neuroleptics. Schizophr. Bull. (in press).

HUBER, G.; GROSS, G.; SCHUETTLER, R.; LINZ, M.: Longitudinal studies of schizophrenic patients. Schizophr. Bull. *6,* 592–605, 1980.

MACKAY, A.: Positive and negative schizophrenic symptoms and the role of dopamine. Brit. J. Psychiat. *137,* 379–383, 1980.

PAUL, G. L.: Psychosocial treatment of chronic mental patients: Milieu versus social-learning programs. Cambridge, MA: Harvard University Press, 1977.

SALZINGER, K.: Remedying schizophrenic behavior. In: TURNER, S. M.; CALHOUN, K. S.; ADAMS, H. E. (eds.): Handbook of clinical behavior therapy. New York: Wiley, 1981.

SALZINGER, K.: The immediacy hypothesis in a theory of schizophrenia. In: SPAULDING, W. D.; COLE, J. K. (eds.): Nebraska Symposium on Motivation: Theories of schizophrenia and psychosis. Lincoln: University of Nebraska Press, 1984.

WALLACE, C. J.; BOONE, S. E.: Cognitive factors in the social skills of schizophrenic patients: Implications for treatment. In: SPAULDING, W. D.; COLE, J. K. (eds.): Nebraska Symposium on Motivation, 1983. Theories of schizophrenia and psychosis. Lincoln: University of Nebraska Press, 1984.

WEBSTER: Third New International Dictionary. G. C. Merriam Co., Publishers, 1976.

WING, J. K.: The management of schizophrenia. In: WING, J. K. (ed.): Schizophrenia. Towards a new synthesis. London: Academic Press, 1978.

WING, J. K.; BROWN, G. W.: Institutionalism and schizophrenia. London: Cambridge University Press, 1970.

WORLD HEALTH ORGANIZATION: International pilot study of schizophrenia. Geneva: Wiley, 1974.

WORLD HEALTH ORGANIZATION: Schizophrenia: An international follow-up study. London: Wiley, 1978.

ZUBIN, J.: Negative symptoms: Are they indigenous to schizophrenia? Schizophr. Bull. (in press a).

ZUBIN, J.: Implications of the vulnerability model for DSM-IV. In: MILLON, T.; KLERMAN, G. (eds.): Contemporary issues in psychopathology. Guilford Press (in press b).

ZUBIN, J.; KIETZMAN, M. L.; STEINHAUER, S. R.: General clinical psychology in relation to psychiatry. In: SHEPHERD, M. (ed.): Handbook of psychiatry (Vol. 5). London, New York: Cambridge University Press, 1985a.

ZUBIN, J.; MAGAZINER, J.; STEINHAUER, S. R.: The metamorphosis of schizophrenia: From chronicity to vulnerability. Psychological Medicine *13,* 551–571, 1983.

ZUBIN, J.; OPPENHEIMER, G.; NEUGEBAUER, R.: Degeneration hypothesis and the stigma of schizophrenia (in preparation).

ZUBIN, J.; STEINHAUER, S. R.: How to break the logjam in schizophrenia: A look beyond genetics. J. Nerv. Ment. Dis. *169,* 477–492, 1981.

ZUBIN, J.; STEINHAUER, S. R.; DAY, R.; VAN KAMMEN, D. P.: Schizophrenia at the crossroads: A blueprint for the 80's. Comprehensive Psychiatry *26,* 217–240, 1985b.

Basic Disorders:
Instability of Cerebral Functions

L. SUELLWOLD

Process studies have established the importance of "psychological deficits" in schizophrenics. Compared to acute symptoms, these less conspicuous handicaps are usually of a longer duration and thus exert great influence on the patients' lives (HUBER et al., 1979).

The concept of "specific vulnerability" (ZUBIN & SPRING, 1977), which can be based on the results of experimental schizophrenia research and high-risk studies, implies that the deviations of a "schizophrenic mind" persist throughout the whole life-span.

Does our present knowledge permit us to characterize these deviations? As many studies succeeded in proving, we may assume that the intellectual capability of schizophrenics is not constantly diminished, but varies strongly. These variations are independent of motivational factors; it was possible to identify specific types of tasks that were more likely than others to lead to the appearance of a certain deficit. The error rate in sort-and-selection tests, for instance, increases more in schizophrenics than in healthy subjects when confused by distractors similar to the correct solution. Likewise, an increasing number of irrelevant surrounding stimuli in perception experiments leads to an increasing number of mistakes. Generally speaking, the number of inadequate reactions multiplies when several differing responses to a particular stimulus are possible (COHEN, 1971).

OLTMANNS and NEALE (1978) consider distractibility a central characteristic of the schizophrenic illness, since it interferes not only with attentiveness, but also with thought processes and, e.g., the act of selecting a reaction, as required in speech. Thus, distractibility by peripheral elements has far-reaching effects.

Attempts to isolate a schizophrenic speech disorder remained unsuccessful. Speech anomalies can be ascribed to the same deficits that were identified in the analysis of cognitive processes (MAHER, 1972). Every spoken word co-activates an associative surrounding field. This process, however, can be inhibited in the normal course of events and thus does not enter into consciousness. Word selection – normally governed by context – is not constant in schizophrenic patients, causing subsidiary associations to break into the flow of speech. Language becomes inadequate, even incoherent in severe cases. The comprehension of language, too, is impaired because context cannot be put to sufficient use. This does not facilitate the analysis of meaning, as the quantity of information overtaxes the patient's capacity (SCHWARTZ, 1978).

Distraction from the correct reaction or from the relevant stimulation are characteristics that can be found throughout the results of experimental investigations. The analysis of disorders of attentiveness had already shown that these were not simply due to deficient filter mechanisms (BROADBENT, 1971). Instead, the disorders affect a purposeful, category-selecting form of attentiveness that is necessary for the classification of acquired information. On the basis of reaction-time experiments, SHAKOW (1962) concludes that the general concept of schizophrenic deficits consists in a handicapped ability to maintain a comprehensive attitude. Focus cannot be maintained, the schizophrenic does not make use of expectations the way a healthy person would do, and the selection of the appropriate reaction is not facilitated by selective attitudes. Speech and thought are impaired by the lack of effective determinative tendencies. Behavior virtually disintegrates into small fragments. The interference theory (BROEN, 1968) had already corrected the one-sided notion that the basal deficits present in schizophrenia were confined to impairments of selective attentiveness. According to this theory, the inadequate effectiveness of reaction hierarchies established through experience is the explanatory hypothesis for the schizophrenic's fluctuating between appropriate and inappropriate reactions.

The variety of individual findings produces a common feature allowing certain conclusions to be drawn concerning the nature of breakdown susceptibility. This applies not only to specifiable functions, but to all mental processes. Crucial points of the disturbance can therefore not be localized. The central role of memory in the evaluative analysis of current stimuli makes it clear that information assimilation is not an isolated or purely passive process. The assimilated material is already classified in the short-term memory, which in turn is a necessary prerequisite for organizing material to be stored on a long-term basis. It is precisely this process that is particularly prone to disturbances in schizophrenics; interferences lead to the disintegration of information. Difficulties in making use of the context in selecting reactions and analyzing meanings, a common finding, can be understood as a consequence of the breakdown susceptibility in the short-term memory: the relevant context is not simultaneously available to the working memory (KUKLA, 1980; JOST, 1983; MAIER & PLAUM, 1983; BRENNER, 1983). At the same time, the utilization of stored experience is impaired, the organized access to information has been handicapped and rendered imprecise by interferences (POLJAKOV, 1973; KUKLA, 1980; BRENNER, 1979). Many patients subjectively notice that they are no longer able to make purposeful use of their memory (SUELLWOLD, 1977; SUELLWOLD & HUBER, 1986). The breakdown susceptibility of memory processes explains the changes in perceptions which do not occur without expectations nor without the influence of stored knowledge.

All disorders are necessarily interrelated. The impairments found in schizophrenic patients are not inabilities which can be localized in particular functions but disorders affecting the effective performance of mental processes (KUKLA, 1980). How can they be integrated into a model of mental functions?

In order to underline the importance of "central mediating processes" for complex performances, i.e., mental activities situated between the reception of stimuli and the ensuing reactions, HEBB (1967) took up a hypothesis of the neurophysiologist CUNNINGHAM: Complex performances can only be explained by assuming that arousal can be stored in developing arousal circuits. Neuron systems temporarily forming closed circuits permit such conservation. Neuron systems that remain closed for a certain time could take on a more stable form as "functional cerebral organs" rapidly allowing repeated adaptive performances and relieving higher control centers because of their automatic character.

The breakdown susceptibility of mental processes, which – by their nature of purposeful activities – presuppose the formation of such functional circuits in groups of cells that remain stable for a shorter or longer period of time, must be seen as a comprehensive typification of a schizophrenic basic disorder. Neuron groups interfere with one another; the tendency to disintegration is at least greater than the temporary stability required for adaptation. The schizophrenia-specific dissociation, which affects thought processes and affectivity (BERNER, 1983), represents the clinically observable side of increased breakdown susceptibility.

Therefore, we can characterize the nature of breakdown susceptibility with a model, enabling us to approach the paroxysmal nature of the schizophrenic illness. Moreover, we can describe the type of deficient reactions which occur as a consequence of interruptions in mental processes: slowing down, blocking, distracted and inadequate reactions (PLAUM, 1978). The increased expenditure of time is probably an attempt at compensation. Blocking phenomena occur in various areas of behavior (SUELLWOLD, 1983), the disconnection of thought being just *one* incisive manifestation. If the patient fails to produce a reaction, he/she is usually unable to continue the behavioral sequence; the current program becomes dispersed and is obviously no longer present in the short-term memory. Incorrect reactions are more or less in the associative proximity of the correct reaction. The sources of irrelevant associations can be coincidentally distracting stimuli originating from the patient's surroundings or from the past (SHAKOW, 1962). The interruptions can be of affective or non-affective nature. This brings us to the question of emotionality in the concept of basic disorders.

Cognitive performances are more accessible to experimental studies. Furthermore, attentiveness is a fundamental function in interacting with the environment. For this reason, our present understanding of schizophrenic basic disorders displays a distinctive and presumably one-sided orientation toward disturbances in information assimilation – a state of affairs that has been critically examined by CIOMPI (1982), for example. Current research in the field of emotions (IZARD, 1981; MANDL & HUBER, 1983) has led to the hypothesis that emotions constitute a phylogenetically old sub-system providing primary environmental orientation, a hypothesis supported, e.g., by experimental data from ethology and developmental psychology. Hence, emotional reactions do not exclusively occur succeeding or accompanying cognitive processes. "Anhedonia" (MEEHL, 1962), the deep incapacity to enjoy, is always an independent factor in the assessment of subjective deficits (SUELLWOLD, 1983; SUELLWOLD & HUBER, 1986). The loss of the capacity to experience positive emotional reactions is probably a primary disorder. On the one hand, this influences the patient's whole behavior: since reinforcing consequences fail to occur, the level of activity is reduced. On the other hand, the patient attempts to avoid emotional arousal on account of its disorganizing effect, as many studies have demonstrated (BOEKER & BRENNER, 1983).

The exact nature of disorders in the area of emotionality is even harder to establish than that of disorders of perceptual processes and thought processes. At this point, the concept displays a gap that cannot be filled in as yet. Corresponding to our fundamental assumption that basic disorders are of a comprehensive nature, schizophrenia may not be considered a sole disturbance of emotionality explaining all other aspects, nor a sole disturbance of information assimilation. This leads us to the next and final question, which was discussed by HEMSLEY in 1977: How do basic disorders relate to the psychopathology of schizophrenia?

With reference to MILLER (1960), HEMSLEY classifies prominent clinical phenomena in differing levels of adaptation to an information overload. In our opinion, however, this model of disorders in information processing and corresponding strategies of adaptation does not do justice to the complexity of schizophrenic processes. Returning to our starting point, the tendency of temporarily stable functional systems (neuron groups) to disintegrate appears to be a form of dysfunctional influencing by other mental processes, which – provided a focus can be established – normally remain submental. Common consequences are retardation of the respective performances, blocking, and inappropriate reactions. If breakdown susceptibility is intensified by interference, further effects and symptoms of such an instability are probable. Certain psychopathological phenomena support this assumption, e.g., when imagination interferes with perceptual processes, as is the case in hallucinatory experiencing; or when certain notions dysfunctionally influence motor activity, as in catatonic occurrences. Further examples could be given.

The concept of basic disorders makes it clear that the schizophrenic individual is endowed with a particular type of breakdown susceptibility deviating only gradually from a healthy condition, but nevertheless requiring psychotherapeutical strategies to be developed, strategies that do justice to this peculiarity. At the same time, it is becoming increasingly obvious that further research is necessary for the concept of basic disorders to generate more adequate therapeutic measures.

Bibliography

BERNER, P.: Die Unterteilung der endogenen Psychosen. Differentialdiagnostik oder Differentialtypologie? In: GROSS, G.; SCHUETTLER, R., (Hrsg.): Empirische Forschung in der Psychiatrie. Stuttgart: Schattauer, 1983.

BOEKER, W.; BRENNER, H. D.: Selbstheilungsversuche Schizophrener. Psychopathologische Befunde und Folgerungen für Forschung und Therapie. Nervenarzt *54*, 578–589, 1983.

BRENNER, H. D.: Experimentalpsychologische Untersuchung zur Verwertung früherer Erfahrungen bei chronisch Schizophrenen. In: ECKENSBERGER, L. (Hrsg.): Bericht über den 31. Kongress der Deutschen Gesellschaft für Psychologie. Göttingen: Hogrefe, 1979.

BRENNER, H. D.: Störungen der Selektion und Analyse von akustischem Reizmaterial bei Schizophrenen: Eine experimentelle Untersuchung zur Informationsverarbeitung. In: BRENNER, H. D.; REY, E.-R.; STRAMKE, W. G. (Hrsg.): Empirische Schizophrenieforschung. Bern: Huber, 1983.

BROADBENT, D. E.: Decision and stress. New York: Academic Press, 1971.

BROEN, W.: Schizophrenia: Research and theory. New York: Academic Press, 1968.

CIOMPI, L.: Affektlogik. Über die Struktur der Psyche und ihre Entwicklung. Stuttgart: Klett-Cotta, 1982.

COHEN, R.: Beiträge experimentalpsychologischer Untersuchungen zur Frage der Situationsabhängigkeit schizophrener Störungen. In: KRANZ, H.; HEINRICH, K. (Hrsg.): Schizophrenie und Umwelt. Stuttgart: Thieme, 1971.

HEBB, D. O.: Einführung in die moderne Psychologie. Weinheim: Beltz, 1967.

HEMSLEY, D. R.: What have cognitive deficits to do with schizophrenic symptoms? Brit. J. Psychiat. *130*, 167–173, 1977.

HUBER, G.; GROSS, G.; SCHUETTLER, R.: Schizophrenie. Eine verlaufs- und sozialpsychiatrische Langzeitstudie. Heidelberg: Springer, 1979.

IZARD, C. E.: Die Emotionen des Menschen. Weinheim: Beltz, 1981.

JOST, K.: Störungen des unmittelbaren Behaltens bei Schizophrenen. In: BRENNER, H. D.; REY, E.-R.; STRAMKE, W. G. (Hrsg.): Empirische Schizophrenieforschung. Bern: Huber, 1983.

KUKLA, F.: Zum Konzept der Informationsverarbeitung bei der Untersuchung und Erklärung kognitiver Störungen – Ein Überblick unter besonderer Berücksichtigung der Schizophrenie. Prob. u. Ergebn. d. Psychol. *73*, 75–94, 1980.

MAHER, B.: The language of schizophrenia: A review and interpretation. Brit. J. Psychiat. *120*, 3–17, 1972.

MAIER, Th.; PLAUM, E.: Untersuchungen zum Problem schizophrener Denkstörungen im Zusammenhang mit spezifischen Gedächtnisdefiziten. In: BRENNER, H. D.; REY, E.-R.; STRAMKE, W. G. (Hrsg.): Empirische Schizophrenieforschung. Bern: Huber, 1983.

MANDL, H.; HUBER, G. L. (Hrsg.): Emotion und Kognition. München: Urban & Schwarzenberg, 1983.

MEEHL, P. E.: Schizotaxia, schizotyp, schizophrenia. Am. Psychologist *17*, 827–838, 1962.

MILLER, J. G.: Information input overload and psychopathology. Am. J. Psychiat. *116*, 695–704, 1960.

OLTMANNS, Th. F.; NEALE, J. M.: Distractability in relation to other aspects of schizophrenia disorder. In: SCHWARTZ, St. (ed.): Language and cognition in schizophrenia. Hillsdale, NJ: Lawrence Erlbaum, 1978.

PLAUM, E.: Hypothesen zu möglichen Basis-Störungen der geistigen Leistungen Schizophrener. Psychiat. Neurol. med. Psychol. *30*, 74–84, 1978.

POLJAKOV, J.: Schizophrenie und Erkenntnistätigkeit. Stuttgart: Hippokrates, 1973.

SCHWARTZ, St. (ed.): Language and cognition in schizophrenia. Hillsdale, NJ: Lawrence Erlbaum, 1978.

SHAKOW, D.: Segmental-set: A theory of formal psychological deficit in schizophrenia. Arch. Gen. Psychiat. *6*, 1–17, 1962.

SUELLWOLD, L.: Symptome schizophrener Erkrankungen. Heidelberg: Springer, 1977.

SUELLWOLD, L.: Schizophrenie. Stuttgart: Kohlhammer, 1983.

SUELLWOLD, L.: Subjektive defizitäre Störungen bei schizophren Erkrankten. In: BRENNER, H. D.; REY, E.-R.; STRAMKE, W. G. (Hrsg.): Empirische Schizophrenieforschung. Bern: Huber, 1983.

SUELLWOLD, L.; HUBER, G.: Schizophrene Basisstörungen. Heidelberg: Springer, 1986.

ZUBIN, J.; SPRING, B.: Vulnerability – a new view of schizophrenia. J. Abnorm. Psychol. *86,* 103–126, 1977.

Toward a Coherent Multidimensional Understanding and Therapy of Schizophrenia: Converging New Concepts

L. Ciompi

Unlike other papers focusing on individual areas, my contribution to this volume remains on a metalevel, aiming at integrating several fields of schizophrenia research into a coherent, economic, and plausible global concept relevant for therapy. Over the last few years, this difficult but necessary attempt has occupied my main interest. It arose from my earlier investigations concerning long-term evolution, chronification, and rehabilitation of schizophrenics (cf. Ciompi & Mueller, 1976; Ciompi et al., 1979; Ciompi, 1980a and b; Dauwalder et al., 1984) as well as from detailed studies of general biological and psychological concepts, above all the general systems theory, Piaget's genetic epistemology, and psychoanalysis.

I would like to start the discussion with two contradictory and provocative statements about the present state of knowledge concerning the nature and treatment of schizophrenia:

- On the one hand, the "scientific scandal" – as Manfred Bleuler put it – continues: after more than 80 years of intensive research, we still have not reached a true understanding of the connections between the many facets this condition displays, a condition that is as frequent as it is enigmatic.
- On the other hand, it is my conviction that the period of guessing how to put the pieces of the schizophrenic jigsaw puzzle together is gradually coming to an end. To quite an extent, this is due to researchers who feature among the authors of this volume.

My paper is subdivided into three parts. I will discuss:

- *first,* some of the gaps I consider to be decisive in obstructing our understanding of schizophrenia;
- *second,* several conceptual models attempting to fill in these gaps;
- *third,* the therapeutic consequences of these new integrative concepts.

However, it will not be possible to treat so wide a topic in detail on so limited a scale; many facts must be – and in this context certainly can be – taken for granted. My own contribution to a more coherent view, i.e., the integrative psycho-biological concept of "affective logic," will only be presented in an extremely sketchy manner. For more details, I must refer the reader to other publications (Ciompi, 1982, 1984b, 1985).

48

Gaps in our Understanding of Schizophrenia

During the last decade, schizophrenia research has made significant progress in several respects. I am particularly thinking of

- the diagnostic improvements achieved through the introduction of standardized instruments such as DSM III;
- the proof of genetic as well as environmental influences, gained by recent studies of twins and adoptees;
- the evidence – provided by recent course studies covering several decades – of long-term courses that are considerably better and more varied than hitherto realized;
- the discovery of ventricular and functional cerebral anomalies thanks to computer tomography, PET-Scan, and other modern methods of examination;
- the more recent insights into the importance of disturbances in information processing, including the so-called "basic disorders";
- the increasingly successful prospective and retrospective search for risk factors and predictors (cf. particularly the recently published study by HART-MANN et al., 1984);
- the successful identification of unfavorable psychological influences such as under- and overstimulation, life-events, family atmosphere and dynamics, disturbed communication patterns, institutional and socio-cultural conditions;
- the success of increasingly refined biological and psychosocial combination therapies such as those conceptualized by HOGARTY et al. (1973, 1974), GOLDSTEIN et al. (1978), BRENNER et al. (1980), ANDERSON et al. (1980, 1983), LEFF et al. (1982), FALLOON et al. (1982), and by myself (CIOMPI, 1981).

Taking all those advances into account, why are we still unable to define the nature of schizophrenic disorders in a comprehensive manner? I believe because we still lack insight into the logical relations between all these aspects, especially into the interactions between the following partly overlapping polarities:

- biological/somatic factors
- inborn factors
- intrapsychic processes
- cognitive processes (thinking)
- structural aspects ("trait")
- acute productive conditions

- psychosocial factors
- acquired factors
- interpersonal and family processes
- affective processes (feeling)
- dynamic aspects ("state")
- chronic unproductive conditions

Only concepts explaining the interplay between such polarities are capable of filling in the existing gaps. In other words, we need models focusing on the *interactions* between the different aspects of schizophrenia, whether biological and psychosocial, intrapsychic and interpersonal, cognitive and affective, or productive and unproductive. The optimism expressed in my second initial statement is based on the fact that several such models have recently emerged in schizophrenia research.

Integrative Concepts

According to my opinion, the following integrative models most deserve our interest:

- The *stress-diathesis model:* schizophrenic disorders appear under stress on the basis of an inherited disposition or «diathesis» (FALCONER, 1965; ROSENTHAL, 1970; GOTTESMAN & SHIELDS, 1976).
- The *stimulus-window model:* schizophrenics pathologically respond to both overstimulation and understimulation; in an atmosphere of optimal stimulation, however, they can function quite well (WING & BROWN, 1970; WING, 1975).
- The *vulnerability hypothesis:* the central disorder of schizophrenia is a vulnerability to stress that is partially inherited and partially acquired; thus, schizophrenia is essentially an episodic condition (ZUBIN & SPRING, 1977; ZUBIN et al., 1983).
- The *information-processing model:* schizophrenics mainly suffer from disorders in information processing (VENABLES, 1963; CHAPMAN & CHAPMAN, 1973; and other authors, cf. NUECHTERLEIN & DAWSON, 1984).
- The concept of the so-called *basic disorders:* before, between, and after acute episodes, many schizophrenics display minor disorders of thinking, feeling, and physical well-being; manifest psychotic symptoms are generated on the basis of these pre-existing minor disorders (HUBER et al., 1979; SUELLWOLD, 1981, 1983).
- The *interactive developmental model:* schizophrenic (and other) disorders develop in a constant process of interaction with favorable and unfavorable environmental influences (STRAUSS & CARPENTER, 1981).
- The *neural plasticity hypothesis:* as a consequence of the phenomenon of neural plasticity, interactions between non-specific genetic and environmental influences can lead to cerebral structural changes constituting the basis of schizophrenic vulnerability (HARACZ, 1984).
- The *integrative psycho-biological model* (CIOMPI, 1981, 1982, 1984b, see below).

Other important integrative elements must be derived from modern cybernetics, communication and systems theory (VON BERTALANFFY, 1950; MILLER, 1975; MATURANA, 1982), and from stress and crisis theory (cf., e.g., CAPLAN, 1964; JACOBSON, 1974). I will not discuss all these models here, partly for lack of space and partly because this is done by the authors themselves. Never-

50

theless, they obviously overlap in many areas, pointing to a common denominator that forms the basis for my own concept.

Mainly, the above-mentioned models all share the characteristic of being typically multiconditional and tending to combine both biological and psychosocial aspects. Furthermore, all of them – but especially the stress-diathesis, the vulnerability, the basic disorders, and the information-processing model – more or less explicitly postulate that genetic impairments, and possibly also acquired impairments, generate a vulnerable premorbid "terrain" that may eventually be decompensated by certain stressors, particularly psychosocial ones. According to this view, psychotic episodes are generally agreed to be reactions to overtaxation of disposed individuals. This interpretation is supported by the research on life-events (BROWN & BIRLEY, 1970; DOHRENWENDT & EGRI, 1981) and on the decompensating effects of psychosocial overstimulation (WING & BROWN, 1970). The term "overstimulation" certainly also applies to an upset family atmosphere in the sense of ambiguous and contradictory communications (SINGER et al., 1978), of "high expressed emotions" (BROWN et al., 1972; VAUGHN & LEFF, 1976 a and b), or of "negative affective style" (DOANE et al., 1981, 1985). In this context, special mention should be made of the contribution of DAY (1985) concerning the unfavorable influences of a permanently "toxic" (i.e., confusing, overdemanding, invading) environment, as opposed to critical single "life-events." The continuous interactions between vulnerability and destabilizing as well as stabilizing environmental influences are very well differentiated in the interactive developmental model of STRAUSS and CARPENTER (1981). The same authors (1974, 1977) also demonstrated that various developmental aspects or "axes," such as psychopathology and social or professional behavior, function with certain inherent dynamics as so-called "linked open systems."

Nevertheless, certain important gaps still persist. Most of the aforementioned models contribute more to the understanding of acute productive episodes than to the – clinically far more important – chronic unproductive states and their interrelations. As we all know, several European and American long-term studies, among them our own (BLEULER, 1972; CIOMPI & MUELLER, 1976; HUBER et al., 1979; TSUANG et al., 1979; HARDING et al., 1985), have decisivly unhinged the classical concept of an inevitably unfavorable and irreversible course of schizophrenia. Chronification seems to depend on unfavorable psychosocial influences rather than on genetic/biological factors; according to the stimulus-window model, it is favored by chronic understimulation; and according to the concept of basic disorders, by overcompensatory mechanisms of avoidance and defense against the underlying vulnerability to stress. ZUBIN's vulnerability model emphasizes the episodic nature of schizophrenia and radically questions whether chronic unproductive states really belong to the basic illness. CROW (1980) even speculates on two different illnesses, one possibly caused by a slow virus. Quite similar to my own hypothesis, which I formulated several years ago (CIOMPI, 1980a), HARDING, ZUBIN and STRAUSS (1985) recently suspected the chronic unproductive states to be predominantly a kind of "psychosocial artifact." The relations between acute and chronic states obviously still give rise to many questions. In my opinion, by far not enough attention is being paid to psychological, social, and neural habituation effects. Furthermore, the afore-mentioned models do not provide a satisfactory explanation for the interactions between structure and dynamics, nor for those between cognitive and affective or intrapsychic and interpersonal processes.

To me, this seems to be the point where my own integrative psychobiological concept entails some real progress. It is based on a system-theoretic model of the psychic apparatus, in which PIAGET's finding about the genesis of cognitive structures as well as the results of modern psychoanalysis concerning the formation of affective/cognitive intrapsychic representations occupy a pivotal position. Recent research on family- and communication-specific dynamics also play an important role.

According to PIAGET (1972, 1976, 1981), the psychic apparatus essentially consists of a complex hierarchy of internalized cognitive "schemata" or reference systems. From birth on, based on processes of assimilation and accommodation, these systems are continuously formed by concrete action, eventually functioning as "programs" for future patterns of thought and behavior, i.e., for information processing in a given context. Moreover, they also determine perception and communication.

However, since actions are always connected with pleasure/unpleasure experiences, these reference systems always include cognitive structures combined with affective components, as also supported by recent research on emotions.

Therefore, a hierarchy of cognitive/*affective* (and not only cognitive) systems of reference is generated (cf. Fig. 1), leading to a "thinking/feeling" or "feeling/thinking," which I call "affective logic" (CIOMPI 1982, 1985).

There is little doubt that the key phenomenon of neural plasticity simultaneously causes action to form an analogous network of limbo-thalamico-cortical neural systems with integrated cognitive and affective components, representing a condensation of all concrete experiences. In other words, external dynamic transactions are transformed into internal structure. Thus, clear and unambiguous social conditions, interpersonal relationships, communication processes, etc., must be reflected in equally clear and unambiguous intrapsychic reference systems, whereas ambiguous and contradictory external conditions must find their counterpart in ambiguous internal structures. The pathogenic effect of confusing communication patterns therefore becomes more understandable. Another important fact is that, according to PIAGET, all these reference systems, as well as the psyche as a whole, are typical equilibrated systems in the sense of modern systems theory. Through multiple negative or positive, i.e., stabilizing or destabilizing feedback loops, they continuously interact with the body, the nervous system, and the whole physical and social environment. *It is thus in these systems that information processing really takes place,* the notion of "information" being used here in a very

Arrows represent feedback loops with the environment. Black lines symbolize cognitive structures; warm and cold colors (missing in this representation) affective components.

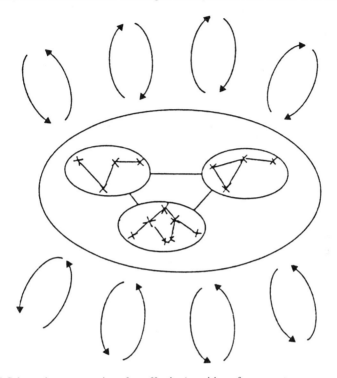

Figure 1: Schematic representation of an affective/cognitive reference system

general sense: It includes everything an individual has to cope with, cognitive stimuli as well as affective stimuli.

These basic notions, presented here in an extremely condensed and simplified but hopefully still understandable manner, lead to a *model of schizophrenia in three phases,* based on the vulnerability and the information-processing hypothesis. Rather than a clearly delimitable "disease entity" with a predetermined course, this model considers acute schizophrenic episodes and chronic states to be an open life process in vulnerable individuals under the continuous influence of a multitude of factors, as illustrated in Figure 2 (cf. CIOMPI, 1984a).

1. During the **premorbid phase,** lasting from birth until the outbreak of the psychosis, partly disturbed affective/cognitive reference or information-processing systems develop through interactions and vicious circles between genetic/biological and psychosocial factors. These defective systems

53

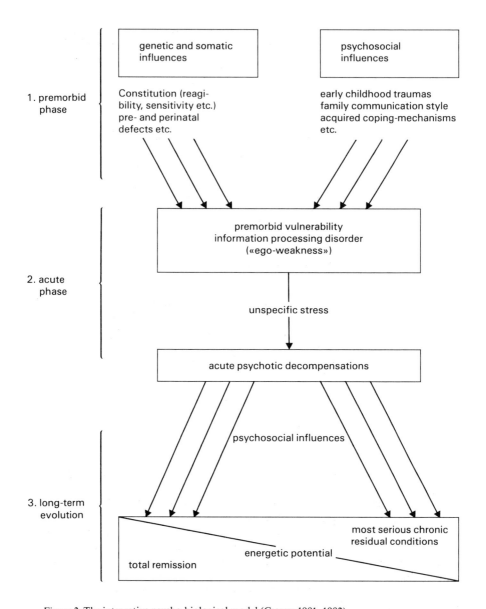

Figure 2: The integrative psycho-biological model (CIOMPI 1981, 1982)

constitute the actual carriers of schizophrenic vulnerability. Pathogenic defects are particularly likely to be situated in the crucial self- and object-representation systems (KERNBERG, 1976), which regulate not only inter-personal relations, but also the fundamental distinctions between inner and outer world. Such vulnerability can, but *need not,* lead to psychotic states.

2. During the phase of **acute productive psychotic decompensations,** these vulnerable coping systems are critically overtaxed by unfavorable psychosocial influences, especially by stressful interpersonal situations and life-events. Such episodes are reversible. Again, they can, but *need not,* lead to chronic states.

3. **Chronic states** with predominantly unproductive negative symptoms appear predominantly under unfavorable psychosocial circumstances in interaction with persisting productive symptoms and underlying vulnerability. They represent a mixture of unfavorable milieu influences, stereotypes, and overcompensatory attitudes of avoidance and defense against the persisting sensitivity to stress. Psychosocial and neural habituation effects, too, doubtlessly play an important role: The longer both productive and unproductive states last, the more they are consolidated.

This integrative psycho-biological model – also presented here in an extremely condensed way – is obviously based on all the preceding ones. To what extent, however, does it offer new insights?

1. The concept of disturbed affective/cognitive reference systems (or cerebral association pathways) as carriers of schizophrenic vulnerability is especially economic, i.e., it considerably reduces the number of necessary hypotheses. It establishes a logical connection between vulnerability and information processing while integrating many possible partial causes, whether biological or psychosocial, inborn or acquired, affective or cognitive, or structural or dynamic. It could therefore be the missing link filling in some of the important gaps we were talking about.

2. Since the affective/cognitive reference systems are to be considered typical systems in the modern sense, general cybernetic and system-theoretic concepts (e.g., concerning feedback effects, homoeostatic regulations, morphogenetic processes, etc.) now become applicable to intrapsychic structures and processes as well.

3. The concept of internalized reference systems as condensation of concrete experience also establishes a logical link between intrapsychic and interpersonal (e.g., family) processes, thus deepening our understanding of both.

4. Moreover, the model sheds light on several other correlations, even though detailed reasons for this fact cannot be given here. For instance, it fully corresponds with the recently formulated hypothesis of the central importance of neural plasticity in schizophrenia by HARACZ (1984). It also opens up possibilities for a new understanding of psychopathology in the light of modern crisis theory and of the systemic concepts of MATURANA (1982)

concerning autopoiesis as fundamental characteristic of biological systems (cf. CIOMPI, 1985; CIOMPI & HUBSCHMID, 1985).

5. Most of all, this "integrative psycho-biological model" is also relevant for therapy. On the one hand, it provides better understanding of several well-known therapeutic effects, and on the other hand, it leads to new therapeutic approaches.

Therapeutic Consequences

The interpretation of schizophrenic phenomena as information-processing disorders in the afore-mentioned broad sense logically leads to the general therapeutic (and preventive) postulate of improving information processing. In principle, this can be achieved in two ways which are closely connected by numerous interactions, namely:

1. by simplifying the incoming information
2. by functionally strengthening the internal information-processing systems

Both methods have successfully been applied for a long time, the first rather in acute productive, the second rather in chronic unproductive states. A simplifying effect on information, for instance, is certainly realized by neuroleptic medication, both by reducing and filtering incoming cognitive stimuli and by dampening the related affective reactions. Quite similarly, however, the milieu and sociotherapeutic protection from all kinds of overstimulation, too, corresponds to a simplification of the incoming "information" in a braod sense. The same is true for the therapeutic clarification of family structures and communications, the reduction of face-to-face contacts with so-called "high-EE families," or the transformation of "high" into "low-EE families" (cf. VAUGHN & LEFF, 1976 a and b; LEFF et al., 1982). Finally, a simplification obviously also occurs through the clarification and unification of the available information for patients and relatives concerning the illness, its treatment, and its prognosis, as successfully introduced in the so-called "educational approach" (ANDERSON et al., 1980, 1983; BERKOWITZ et al., 1984).

On the other hand, all the training and rehabilitation methods, especially those focusing on social and professional skills, contribute to the strengthening of information-processing systems, i.e., the above-mentioned internalized cognitive/affective behavioral "programs." This particularly applies to as carefully conceptualized a training program as those introduced in the United States by PAUL and LENTZ (1977), FALLOON et al. (1982), and others, or in Europe by BRENNER et al. (1980). They all not only improve specific social or vocational skills, but also the – presumably more important – superordinate self and object representations, e.g., by intensifying the weak feelings of one's own value and identity and, consequently, the capability for interpersonal

56

relationships. Quite in the sense of our concept, so-called "cognitive" training programs are therefore by no means limited to intellectual components, they also encompass important affective aspects.

In addition to explaining known therapeutic effects, the proposed integrative concept also gives rise to several therapeutic approaches that have either been neglected or never been used up to now. They can be summarized in the following nine general therapeutic principles for a purposeful "psychosocial management of schizophrenia":

1. Simplification of the therapeutic setting

Particularly in treating acute patients, the need for simplifying information leads to the demand for as relaxing a therapeutic setting as possible, i.e., a small, transparent, low stimulating and as "normal" as possible milieu, run by consistent and specially selected personnel. This demand is in sharp contrast to the usual atmosphere of hectic admission wards in psychiatric hospitals. As early as the 1970s, the Soteria experiment of MOSHER et al. (1975) and MATTHEWS et al. (1979) showed that such a milieu can distinctly improve acute psychotic symptoms within days, and without medication. We are currently observing the same kind of phenomenon in a similar project.

2. Optimal continuity of personnel and concept; consistent central reference person

Including aftercare and relapse prevention, the treatment of schizophrenics invariably takes *years*. During this time, patients and relatives usually are confronted with a confusing multitude of therapeutic teams and concepts inside and outside the hospital. To simplify information, however, we need optimal (not total) continuity, which is best achieved in the form of a central, consistent, and reliable reference person who functions as an "ombudsman," i.e., supervises and coordinates the whole treatment on a long-term basis (cf. also the studies of FRIIS et al., 1982).

3. Clear, unambiguous communications, affectively and cognitively congruent

It is well known that schizophrenics and their relatives are particularly prone to using complicated, confused, and affective/cognitively contradictory forms of communication (cf. BATESON et al., 1956). Dealings with them should therefore be as clear, unambiguous, and affective/cognitively congruent as possible. (As the Bible says: "Your speech be yes, yes, no, no!")

4. Harmonization of available information

All relevant people concerned, i.e., patient, therapists, relatives, etc., should have the same clear and simple information about the nature of the illness, its treatment, prognosis, chances, and risks. Positive experiences in this sense are related by HOGARTY et al. (1973, 1974), ANDERSON et al. (1980, 1983), CARPENTER and HEINRICKS (1983), and BERKOWITZ et al. (1984).

5. Induction of joint, realistically positive expectations

According to our own investigations (CIOMPI et al., 1979; DAUWALDER et al., 1984), the expectations of patients, therapists, and relatives are among the most important factors determining the course of the illness. Thus, the induction of joint, realistically positive expectations including a clear awareness of existing risks, as justified by the afore-mentioned new long-term course studies, gains particular significance.

6. Elaboration of clear, concrete, and joint therapeutic goals and priorities

Clear, concrete, and attainable goals or partial goals (e.g., concerning the patient's housing or professional situation) should be *negotiated* (not dictated) between therapists, patient, and relatives in a therapeutically important process setting definite priorities. To avoid overtaxation, there is a general rule to be followed: one change at a time.

7. Affective/cognitive polarization of the relevant therapeutic field

This postulate virtually summarizes all the preceding ones. Within and around schizophrenics, i.e., in patients, relatives, therapists, etc., we mostly find a highly confusing chaos of contradictory concepts, opinions, hopes, and fears. Through the above-mentioned measures, this counterproductive environment is meant to be relaxed, settled, and – similarly to a magnetic force field – "polarized" toward joint expectations and goals, affectively as well as cognitively. This generates a unified therapeutic "gradient" in the desired direction, resulting in a regulating and explaining effect both on the environmental and the intrapsychic level (cf. Fig. 3).

8. Avoidance of over- and understimulation; principle of "optimal stimulation"

This postulate, too – formulated already 15 years ago by WING and BROWN (1970) – summarizes several of the preceding ones. As we know, it leads to a flexible technique of "optimal psychosocial stimulation" between the Scylla of overstimulation and the Charybdis of understimulation, leading either to intensification of acute productive or to chronic unproductive symptoms.

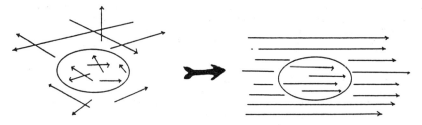

Figure 3: Diagram of the "polarization" of the external and internal therapeutic field

9. "Synergistic combination" of socio- and pharmacotherapy

According to our hypothesis, neuroleptics have a similarly simplifying effect on information as some of the proposed psychosocial measures. For therapy *and* prevention, this parallelism opens the way to a "synergistic combination" of both, i.e., to using one as an alternative for the other depending on circumstances and therapeutic possibilities. Instead of obligatory long-term medication with its biologically and socially toxic side effects, we can now explore new selective strategies such as the time-limited pharmacotherapy successfully tested by HERZ et al. (1982) and CARPENTER and HEINRICKS (1983), or the low-dosage medication reported by KANE et al. (1983) (cf. also FALLOON et al., 1983).

These nine therapeutic principles are currently being tested in one of our research programs taking place in a Soteria-like setting (cf. CIOMPI & BERNASCONI, in press). This program is based on the attempt to comb the best current proceedings for items of interest in the sense of our model of schizophrenia and to integrate those items into a coherent therapeutic concept that is relevant for psychiatric practice. I would like to thank all those whose work has contributed to this integration tentative which I now submit to their criticism.

Bibliography

ANDERSON, C.: A psycho-educational model of family treatment for schizophrenia. In: STIERLIN, H.; WYNNE, L. C.; WIRSCHING, M. (eds.): Psychosocial intervention in schizophrenia. Berlin, Heidelberg, New York, Tokyo: Springer, 1983.
ANDERSON, C.; HOGARTY, G.; REISS, D.: Family treatment of adult schizophrenic patients. A psycho-educational approach. Schizophr. Bull. *6*, 490–505, 1980.
BATESON, G.; JACKSON, D. D.; HALEY, J.; WEAKLAND, J. W.: Towards a theory of schizophrenia. Behav. Science *1*, 251–264, 1956.
BERKOWITZ, R.; EBERLEIN-FRIES, R.; KUIPERS, L.; LEFF, J.: Educating relatives about schizophrenia. Schizophr. Bull. *10*, 418–429, 1984.
BERTALANFFY VON, L.: An outline of general systems theory. Brit. J. Phil. Sci. *1*, 134–165, 1950.
BLEULER, M.: Die schizophrenen Geistesstörungen im Lichte langjähriger Kranken- und Familiengeschichten. Stuttgart: Thieme, 1972.

BRENNER, H. D.; STRAMKE, W. G.; MEWES, J.; LIESE, F.; SEEGER, G.: Erfahrungen mit einem spezifischen Therapieprogramm zum Training kognitiver und kommunikativer Fähigkeiten in der Rehabilitation chronisch schizophrener Patienten. Nervenarzt 51, 106–112, 1980.

BROWN, G. W.; BIRLEY, L. T.: Crisis and life changes and the onset of schizophrenia. London: Cambridge Univ. Press, 1970.

BROWN, G. W.; BIRLEY, L. T.; WING, J. K.: Influence of family life on the course of schizophrenic disorders: A replication. Brit. J. Psychiat. 121, 241–258, 1972.

CAPLAN, G.: Principles of preventive psychiatry. New York: Basic Books, 1964.

CARPENTER, W. T.; HEINRICKS, D. W.: Early intervention time limited, targeted pharmacotherapy in schizophrenia. Schizophr. Bull. 9, 533–542, 1983.

CHAPMAN, L. J.; CHAPMAN, J. P.: Disordered thought in schizophrenia. New York: Appleton-Century-Crofts, 1973.

CIOMPI, L.: Ist die chronische Schizophrenie ein Artefakt? Argumente und Gegenargumente. Fortschr. Neurol. Psychiat. 48, 237–248, 1980a.

CIOMPI, L.: The natural history of schizophrenia in the long term. Brit. J. Psychiat. 136, 413–420, 1980b.

CIOMPI, L.: Wie können wir die Schizophrenen besser behandeln? Ein neues Krankheits- und Therapiekonzept. Nervenarzt 52, 506–515, 1981.

CIOMPI, L.: Affektlogik. Über die Struktur der Psyche und ihre Entwicklung. Ein Beitrag zur Schizophrenieforschung. Stuttgart: Klett-Cotta, 1982.

CIOMPI, L.: Is there really a schizophrenia? The long-term course of psychotic phenomena. Brit. J. Psychiat. 145, 636–640, 1984a.

CIOMPI, L.: Modellvorstellungen zum Zusammenwirken biologischer und psychosozialer Faktoren in der Schizophrenie. Fortschr. Neurol. Psychiat. 52, 200–206, 1984b.

CIOMPI, L.: Zur Integration von Fühlen und Denken im Licht der «Affektlogik». Die Psyche als Teil eines autopoietischen Systems. Psychiatrie der Gegenwart, Bd. I, 3. Aufl. Berlin, Heidelberg, New York: Springer, 1985 (im Druck).

CIOMPI, L.; BERNASCONI, R.: Soteria Berne: First experiences with a new milieu therapeutic concept for acute schizophrenics (in press).

CIOMPI, L.; DAUWALDER, H. P.; AGUE, C.: Ein Forschungsprogramm zur Rehabilitation psychisch Kranker. III. Langschnittuntersuchungen zum Rehabilitätserfolg und zur Prognostik. Nervenarzt 50, 366–378, 1979.

CIOMPI, L.; HUBSCHMID, T.: Psychopathologie aus der Sicht der Affektlogik. Ein neues Konzept und seine praktischen Konsequenzen. Vortrag am Symposium "Psychopathologie und Praxis", Heidelberg, 1984 (im Druck).

CIOMPI, L.; MUELLER, C.: Lebenslauf und Alter der Schizophrenen. Eine katamnestische Langzeitstudie bis ins Senium. Berlin, Heidelberg, New York: Springer, 1976.

CROW, T. J.: Molecular pathology of schizophrenia: More than one disease process? Brit. Med. J. 280, 66–68, 1980.

DAUWALDER, H. P.; CIOMPI, L.; AEBI, E.; HUBSCHMID, T.: Ein Forschungsprogramm zur Rehabilitation psychisch Kranker. IV. Untersuchung zur Rolle von Zukunftserwartungen bei chronisch Schizophrenen. Nervenarzt 55, 257–264, 1984.

DAY, R.: Social stress and schizophrenia. From the concept of recent life events to the notion of toxic environments, 1985 (to be published).

DOANE, J. A.; FALLOON, I. R. H.; GOLDSTEIN, M. J.; MINTZ, J.: Parental affective style and the treatment of schizophrenia. Predicting course of illness and social functioning. Arch. Gen. Psychiat. 42, 34–42, 1985.

DOANE, J. A.; WEST, K. L.; GOLDSTEIN, M. J.; RODNICK, E. H.; JONES, J. E.: Parental communication deviance and affective style: Predictors of subsequent schizophrenia spectrum disorders in vulnerable adolescents. Arch. Gen. Psychiat. 38, 679–685, 1981.

DOHRENWENDT, W. P.; EGRI, G.: Recent stressful life events and episodes of schizophrenia. Schizophr. Bull. 7, 12–23, 1981.

FALCONER, D. S.: The inheritance of lability to certain diseases estimated from the incidence among relatives. Annals of Human Genetics 29, 51–76, 1965.

FALLOON, I. R. H.; BOYD, J. L.; McGILL, C. W.; RAZANI, J.; MOSS, H. B.; GILDERMAN, A. M.: Family management in the prevention of exacerbations of schizophrenia. A controlled study. J. Med. *306*, 1437-1441, 1982.

FALLOON, I. R. H.; LIBERMAN, R. P.: Interactions between drug and psychosocial therapy in schizophrenia. Schizophr. Bull. *9*, 543-554, 1983.

FRIIS, S.; KARTERND, H.; KLEPPE, S.; LORENTZEN, S.; LYSTRUP, S.; VAGLUN, P.: Reconsidering some limiting factors of therapeutic communities. A summary of six Norvegian studies. In: PINES, M.; RAFAELSEN, L. (eds.): The individual and the group. New York: Plenum Publishing Corp. 573-581, 1982.

GOLDSTEIN, M. J.; RODNICK, E. H.; EVANS, J. R.; MAY, P. R. A.; STEINBERG, M. R.: Drug and family treatment in the aftercare of acute schizophrenics. Arch. Gen. Psychiat. *35*, 1169-1177, 1978.

GOTTESMAN, I. I.; SHIELDS, J.: A critical review of recent adoption, twin and genetic perspectives. Schizophr. Bull. *2*, 360-398, 1976.

HARACZ, J. L.: A neural plasticity hypothesis of schizophrenia. Neurosci. Biobeh. Rev. *8*, 59-71, 1984.

HARDING, C. M.; BROOKS, G. W.; ASHIKAGA, T. et al.: Aging and social functioning in once-chronic schizophrenic patients 21-58 years after first admission: The Vermont story. In: HUDGINS, G.; MILLER, N. (eds.): Schizophrenia, paranoia and schizophreniaform disorders in later life. New York: Guilford Press, 1985 (to be published).

HARDING, C.; ZUBIN, J.; STRAUSS, J. S.: Chronicity in schizophrenia: Fact, partial fact or artifact? 1985 (to be published).

HARTMANN, E.; MILOFSKY, E.; VAILLANT, G.; OLDFIELD, M.; FALKE, R.; DUCEY, C.: Vulnerability to schizophrenia. Prediction of adult schizophrenia using childhood information. Arch. Gen. Psychiat. *41*, 1050-1056, 1984.

HERZ, M. I.; STYMANSKI, H. V.; SIMON, J. C.: Intermitted medication for stable schizophrenic outpatients: An alternative to maintenance medication. Am. J. Psychiat. *139*, 918-922, 1982.

HOGARTY, G. E.; GOLDBERG, S. C.; SCHOOLER, N. R. and the collaborative study group: Drug and socio-therapy in the aftercare of schizophrenic patients. Arch. Gen. Psychiat. *28*, 54-64, 1973 and *31*, 603-608, 1974.

HUBER, G.; GROSS, G.; SCHUETTLER, R.: Schizophrenie: Eine verlaufs- und sozialpsychiatrische Langzeitstudie. Berlin, Heidelberg, New York: Springer, 1979.

JACOBSON, G. F.: Programs and technics of crisis intervention. In: ARIETI, S. (ed.): American handbook of psychiatry. New York: Basic Books, 1974.

KAHNEMANN, D.: Attention and effort. Englewood, NJ: Prentice-Hall Inc., 1973.

KANE, J. M.; RIFKIN, A.; WOERNER, M.; REARDON, G.; SARANTAKOS, S.; SCHIEBEL, D.; LORENZI, J. R.: Low-dose, neuroleptic treatment of outpatient schizophrenics. Arch. Gen. Psychiat. *40*, 893-896, 1983.

KERNBERG, O.: Object relations theory and clinical psychoanalysis. New York: Jason Aronson, 1976. [Dt.: Objektbeziehungen und Praxis der Psychoanalyse. Stuttgart: Klett-Cotta, 1981.]

LEFF, J. P.; KUIPERS, L.; BERKOWITZ, R.; EBERLEIN-FRIES, R.; STURGEON, D.: A controlled trial of social intervention in the families of schizophrenic patients. Brit. J. Psychiat. *141*, 121-134, 1982.

MATTHEWS, S. M.; ROPER, M. T.; MOSHER, L. R.; MENN, A. Z.: A non-neuroleptic treatment for schizophrenia. Analysis of the two-year postdischarge risk of relapse. Schizophr. Bull. *5*, 322-333, 1979.

MATURANA, H. R.: Erkennen: Die Organisation und Verkörperung von Wirklichkeit. Braunschweig: Vieweg, 1982.

MILLER, J. G.: General systems theory. In: FREEDMAN, A. M.; KAPLAN, H. J.; SADOCK, B. J. (eds.): Comprehensive textbook of psychiatry. Baltimore: William & Wilkins, 1975.

MOSHER, L. R.; MENN, A. Z.; MATTHEWS, S.: Soteria. Evaluation of a home-based treatment for schizophrenics. Am. J. Orthopsychiat. *45*, 455-467, 1975.

NUECHTERLEIN, K. H.; DAWSON, M. E.: A heuristic vulnerability/stress model of schizophrenic episodes. Schizophr. Bull. *10*, 300-312, 1984.

61

PAUL, G. L.; LENTZ, R. J.: Psychosocial treatment of chronic mental patients. Milieu versus learning programs. Cambridge, London: Harvard University Press, 1977.
PIAGET, J.: Die Psychologie der Intelligenz. Olten, Freiburg i.Br.: Walter, 1972.
PIAGET, J.: Die Äquilibration der kognitiven Strukturen. Stuttgart: Klett, 1976.
PIAGET, J.: Intelligence and affectivity. Their relationship during child development. In: BROWN, T. A.; KAEGI, C. E. (eds.): Annual reviews monograph. Palo Alto: University of California, 1981.
ROSENTHAL, D.: Genetic theory and abnormal behavior. New York: McGraw Hill, 1970.
STRAUSS, J. S.; CARPENTER, W. T.: The prediction of outcome in schizophrenia: I. Characteristics of outcome. Arch. Gen. Psychiat. 27, 739–746, 1972.
STRAUSS, J. S.; CARPENTER, W. T.: The prediction of outcome in schizophrenia: II. Relationship between predictor and outcome variables. Arch. Gen. Psychiat. 31, 37–42, 1974.
STRAUSS, J. S.; CARPENTER, W. T.: Prediction of outcome in schizophrenia: III. Five-year outcome and its predictors. Arch. Gen. Psychiat. 34, 159–163, 1977.
STRAUSS, J. S.; CARPENTER, W. T.: Schizophrenia. New York: Plenum, 1981.
SINGER, M. T.; WYNNE, L. C.; TOOHEY, B. A.: Communication disorders in the families of schizophrenics. In: WYNNE, L. C.; CROMWELL, R. L.; MATTHYSSE, S. (eds.): The nature of schizophrenia. New York, Chichester, Brisbane, Toronto: Wiley, 1978.
SUELLWOLD, L.: Basis-Störungen: Ergebnisse und offene Fragen. In: HUBER, G. (Hrsg.): Schizophrenie. Stand und Entwicklungstendenzen der Forschung. Stuttgart: Schattauer, 1981.
SUELLWOLD, L.: Schizophrenie. Stuttgart, Berlin, Köln, Mainz: Kohlhammer, 1983.
TSUANG, M.; WOOLSON, R.; FLEMING, J.: Long-term outcome of major psychoses: I. Schizophrenia and affective disorders compared with psychiatrically symptom-free surgical conditions. Arch. Gen. Psychiat. 36, 1295–1301, 1979.
VAUGHN, C.; LEFF, J.: The measurement of expressed emotion in the families of psychiatric patients. Brit. J. Soc. Clin. Psychol. 15, 157–165, 1976a.
VAUGHN, C.; LEFF, J.: The influence of family and social factors on the course of psychiatric illness. Brit. J. Psychiat. 129, 125–137, 1976b.
VENABLES, P. H.: Selectivity of attention, withdrawal and cortical activation. Arch. Gen. Psychiat. 9, 92–96, 1963.
WING, J.: Impairments in schizophrenia. In: WIRT, R.; WINOKUR, G.; ROFF, M. (eds.): Life history research in psychopathology, Vol. IV. University of Minnesota Press, 1975.
WING, J. K.; BROWN, G. W.: Institutionalism and schizophrenia. London: Cambridge University Press, 1970.
ZUBIN, J.; MAGAZINER, J.; STEINHAUER, S.: The metamorphosis of schizophrenia: From chronicity to vulnerability. Psycholoc. Med. 13, 551–571, 1983.
ZUBIN, J.; SPRING, B.: Vulnerability: A new view of schizophrenia. J. Abnorm. Psychol. 86, 103–123, 1977.

Early Intervention Medication as an Alternative to Continuous Depot Treatment in Schizophrenia: Preliminary Report

S. R. Hirsch, A. G. Jolley, R. Manchanda, A. McRink

Background

The initial findings of the prophylactic effect of neuroleptics in preventing relapse are well established now (Hirsch, 1982), and the continuous use of neuroleptics is virtually ubiquitous in the maintenance phase of schizophrenic illness. However, Hogarty and Ulrich (1977), using life table methods, have demonstrated that eventually 65% of patients on medication and 87% of patients on placebo will eventually relapse. Thus 13% of patients do not need treatment and in only 22% medication can indefinitely prevent relapse, while in the remaining 65% relapse is only postponed.

Interest in alternatives to neuroleptic medication has grown with a recognition of actual and potential risks associated with continuous drug exposure. Prominent among these is the risk of tardive dyskinesia, estimated to occur in 6–15% of chronic patients. Distressing extrapyramidal side effects also occur. Added to this is the possibility that neuroleptics may exacerbate the negative symptoms of the illness and possibly impair social functioning (Falloon et al., 1978).

Once such strategy which has become the focus of increasing interest aims at the identification of the earliest signs of relapse with prompt but time-limited treatment during such periods. This strategy involves patients being kept drug-free with a regular monitoring of their clinical state for such early signs. As such it offers the possibility of a considerable reduction in total neuroleptic exposure. The approach may be termed "early brief treatment" in contrast to the conventional "sustained treatment" in the maintenance phase of schizophrenia.

The possibility of recognizing early signs of relapse is suggested by a retrospective study of early signs of schizophrenic decompensation by Herz and colleagues (1980). It is well recognized that affective symptoms are a frequent accompaniment of schizophrenic illness (Johnson, 1981; Knights & Hirsch, 1981) and that their intensity parallels that of schizophrenic symptoms (Knights & Hirsch, 1981). Herz and colleagues (1980) found that such affective changes together with the emergence of neurotic symptoms bore a potentially valuable temporal relationship to the onset of relapse. In their study 87% of patients experienced mood changes and neurotic symptoms prior to the onset of psychotic symptoms according to both the patients and their relatives. The nature of symptoms reported is outlined in Table 1. These were mostly of a non-specific dysphoric type. In more than two thirds of the cases the duration of such symptoms, which they termed *prodromal symptoms*, was more than one week, after which the florid psychotic symptoms occurred. HERZ argued that such prodromal symptoms represented the early stages of schizophrenic decompensation and hypothesized that a prompt introduction of neuroleptics at such stages would ameliorate prodromal symptoms and prevent subsequent progression to relapse. In a later uncontrolled pilot study of early brief treatment HERZ demonstrated that *prodromal symptoms* disappeared within two weeks of the introduction of neuroleptics (HERZ et al., 1982).

Table 1: Frequency of Patients Reporting Prodromal Symptoms (HERZ & MELVILLE, 1980)

Prodromal symptom	Frequency
Nervous and tense	> 70%
Impaired concentration Sleep disturbance Restlessness Depression Reduced enjoyment Pre-occupation with one or two things	> 60%
Loss of interest Ideas of reference	> 50%

Such an "early brief treatment" approach we felt offered several benefits in comparison to conventional sustained drug exposure. These benefits we felt would be principally derived from reduced neuroleptic exposure and include a reduction in persistent side effects such as akathisia, akinesia and sedation and an overall "affective brightening" (CARPENTER et al., in press) manifesting itself in improved sense of well-being, self esteem and social performance. We hypothesized that such a strategy would probably lead to an increased frequency of relapse, but that by prompt recognition and treatment, such relapses could be attenuated to the point that their negative effects would be outweighed by the potential benefits of the new strategy. We also argued that if prodromal symptoms were related to the process of schizophrenic decompensation then their frequency should be greater in neuroleptic-free patients.

Aims

We designed a study therefore which aimed to identify early signs suggestive of impending relapse and to determine if prompt, time-limited intervention for early signs prevented serious decompensation. We also aimed to determine if the new strategy produced an increase in the frequency of prodromal episodes or any long-term increase in overall psychopathology. Finally we aimed to assess if there were any overall psycho-social dividends accruing from such a strategy in comparison to conventional sustained treatment.

Method

Sample

A total of 45 patients have been recruited into the study to date. All meet DSM-III criteria for a diagnosis of schizophrenia (APA, 1980). We felt that the early brief treatment strategy was most applicable to stable remitted patients. Accordingly to be included in the study patients were required to have been free of florid psychotic symptoms for a period of at least six months and to have been stabilized on a fixed dose of depot neuroleptic medication for at least two months prior to recruitment into the study. A research depot neuroleptic clinic was established and participating clinicians were requested to refer patients whom they felt might benefit from the alternative treatment strategy. Some 45% of patients referred to the clinic in this manner were included in the study.

Experimental design

The patients were randomised into two groups; the control group (N = 23) received fluphenazine decanoate in clinically optimal (i.e. pre-trial) doses while the experimental group (N = 22) received equivalent doses of placebo injections.

Prodromal symptoms were defined on a clinical basis as the *emergence* of neurotic or affective symptoms persisting for two or more days and causing noticeable distress to the patient. *Relapse* was defined as the re-emergence of florid psychotic symptoms such as delusions, hallucinations, bizarre behaviour or thought disorder.

Each patient and his or her nearest relative (where possible) was given a one-hour teaching session about schizophrenia and in particular about the early signs of relapse. These sessions were given in groups of 6-10 patients and covered material about the aetiology, symptoms, treatment and natural history of the illness. Patients were also instructed about prodromal symptoms and asked to identify any changes they had noted prior to previous relapses. The importance of contacting the research team at the earliest sign of prodromal developments was emphasized.

After commencement on the trial patients were seen every four weeks alternately by the psychiatrist and the community psychiatric nurse. It was necessary to be flexible for individual patients, depending on their clinical state so that additional visits were made to monitor patients who had relapsed, developed prodromal symptoms, failed to keep an appointment or missed an injection. Patients were seen weekly during the prodromal episodes. At all times the patients had a source of contact by telephone with the psychiatrist or community psychiatric nurse.

Additional neuroleptic medication was given to all patients who developed *prodromal symptoms* or *relapse*. This was usually haloperidol 10 mg per day together with procyclidine 10 mg per day although flexibility of dosage was allowed. All patients were given a starter pack of three days of oral medication if they were unable to make contact with a member of the research team at the earliest sign of decompensation.

A record of the number of interventions additional to those scheduled together with the dose frequency and reasons for giving additional medication was kept for each patient.

The treatment for prodromal symptoms continued for a period up to two weeks unless relapse had occurred. Treatment for relapse was continued for a period of four weeks after the remission of symptoms. Patients were dropped out of the trial and regarded as treatment failures if they (1) refused to comply with the treatment programme, (2) relapsed for a period of greater than eight weeks or (3) relapsed on two or more occasions within a six-month period.

Measures

For this preliminary analysis of our early results we used four measures.

1. *Symptom Check List 90 (SCL-90)* (DEROGATIS et al., 1973): This is a self-rating inventory consisting of 90 items relating to affective and neurotic symptoms and psychoses. The amount of distress engendered by each symptom is rated on a five-point scale (0–4). The scale was rated before entering the trial and every four weeks thereafter either at home during visits by the CPN or during attendance at the psychiatric clinic in hospital. The patients filled for episodes in the preceding four weeks.
2. *Manchester Scale* (KRAWIECKA et al., 1977): An eight-item scale for rating psychotic symptoms on five points (0–4). A subscale excluding depressive and anxiety items was used to rate the severity of psychotic symptoms. The subscale consists of both positive and negative symptoms of schizo-

phrenia. It was administered by the psychiatrist at baseline and at two monthly intervals.

3. *Global Assessment Scale* (ENDICOTT et al., 1976): Consists of ten grades of psychopathology and overall functioning on a 0–100 scale. It was administered together with the *Manchester Scale.*

4. *Bradburns Positive and Negative Affect Scales* (BRADBURN, 1969): A self-report inventory consisting of five items relating to positive and five items relating to negative affects, as experienced by the patient over the previous month. The *Affect Balance Scale,* constructed from these items is a measure of general well being used in population studies. Patients were rated on this scale at baseline and monthly thereafter.

Results

Table 2 outlines the baseline sociodemographic and clinical characteristics of the two treatment groups. There were no significant differences between the groups, although a trend towards longer duration of illness in the control group is identifiable. The age of onset of illness is higher than what one would expect in a unselected sample. It should be recalled that a requirement for inclusion in the study was that patients should be free of florid psychotic symptoms for a period of at least six months. A later age onset would be commensurate with the better prognostic group selected in this matter.

Table 2: Baseline Sociodemographic and Clinical Characteristics of Sample

Sample characteristic	Control group (N = 23)	Experimental group (N = 22)
Mean age	43	41
Sex	9/14	8/14
Living with relative/companion	74%	68%
Mean age of onset	28	29
Mean duration of illness	16	12
Mean no. previous hospitalisations	3.3	3.1
Mean total neuroleptic dose (fluphenazine decanoate, mg) in previous 2 months	77	65
> 6 months in hospital	42%	34%
Most recent illness > 1 year ago	91%	74%

All differences non-significant

Table 3 outlines the six-month outcome for the whole sample of 45 patients recruited in this study. A trend toward an increased rate of relapse may be identified in the placebo group. However relapse for the purpose of this study was defined merely as the re-emergence of psychotic symptoms. Such events were in most cases considerably less dramatic than relapse as generally conceived in clinical practice. It is notable in this respect that the trend towards increased relapse in the placebo group was not accompanied by any increase in the frequency of hospitalisation. This pattern would confirm our hypothesis that the early brief treatment strategy is not associated with any increase in the frequency of serious relapses.

The six-month outcome for all patients completing the trial is outlined in Table 4.

Table 3: Six Month Outcome for all Patients Entering the Study

Outcome variable	Control group (N = 23)	Experimental group (N = 22)
Dropouts:		
Refused to comply	3	2
Relapsed > 8 weeks	1	1
⩾ 2 relapses in 6 months	0	1
Total	4	4 ns
Relapses:		
Relapse with remission	0	3
Ill more than 8 weeks	1	1
Total	1	4 ns
Total admitted to hospital:	1	1 ns

Table 4: 6 Month Outcome of Patients Completing Trial

	Control group (N = 19)	Experimental group (N = 18)
No. patients with prodromal episodes	4	8
Total no. of unscheduled intervention	10	35
Mean depot fluphenazine per patient/month (mg)	38.3	0
Total oral haloperidol per group (mg)	515	1075
Total neuroleptic per patient over 6 months (halperidol, equivalents, mg)	2670*	60*

* $p < 0.01$, t-test

As predicted there is a significant reduction in total neuroleptic exposure in the experimental group. This reduction in drug exposure is accompanied by a slight trend towards improvement in general well being (Figure 1). Also to be noted is a trend toward an increased number of prodromal episodes in the experimental group. This would suggest that such episodes bear a relationship to neuroleptic withdrawal and offers some substance to the view underlying this study that such neurotic and affective symptoms form part of the process of schizophrenic decompensation.

Mean group scores on measures of symptom distress (Figure 2), psychosis (Figure 3) and global psychopathology (Figure 4) failed to reveal any significant differences throughout the trial period. This would confirm the hypothesis that the early brief treatment strategy is not associated with any overall long-term deterioration in psychopathology.

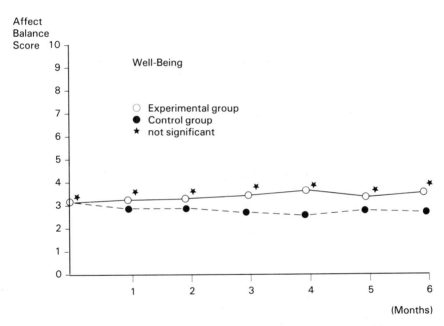

Figure 1: Affect Balance Scale Plotted Against Time for Experimental and Control Groups

69

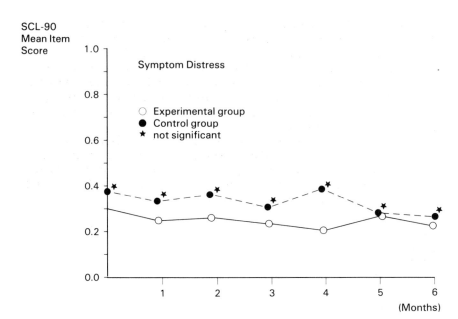

Figure 2: Mean Item Score of SCL-90 Plotted Against Time for Experimental and Control Groups

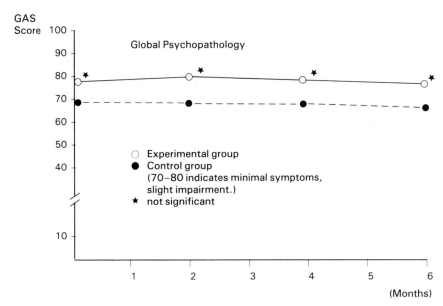

Figure 3: Global Assessment Scale (GAS) Score Plotted Against Time for Experimental and Control Groups

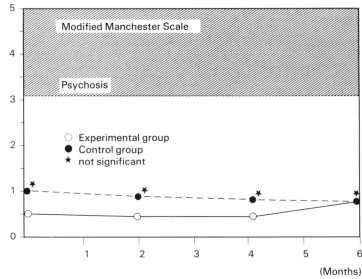

Figure 4: Mean Modified Manchester Item Score Plotted Against Time for Experimental and Control Groups

Conclusions

There are indications that the early brief treatment strategy enables a significant reduction in neuroleptic exposure which is not associated with any increase in the frequency of serious relapse. It would also appear that this treatment approach does not result in any overall long-term deterioration in clinical
status. Potential benefits of the strategy include reduced risk of irreversible
neuroleptic side effects and possible improvements in patients general well-
being. This latter change augers well for potential longer-term improvements
in social functioning. This is only a preliminary report of the first 45 patients
monitored for six months. A one- and hopefully two-year follow-up will give a
better indication of the success or failure of this approach. A longer period of
observation and larger numbers will enable us to use more sophisticated
measures of social function to see if social benefits outweigh the anticipated
increase rate of symptom recurrence in the experimental group. This will clarify the potential benefits and risk of this approach for the maintenance of
schizophrenic patients in the community.

Bibliography

AMERICAN PSYCHIATRIC ASSOCIATION: Diagnostic and statistical manual of mental disorders, 3rd. ed. Washington DC: APA, 1980.

BRADBURN, N. M.: The structure of psychological well being. Chicago: Aldine, 1969.

CARPENTER, W. T. Jr.; HEINRICKS, D. W.; ALPHS, L. D.: Treatment of negative symptoms. Schizophr. Bull. (in press).

DEROGATIS, L. R.; LIPMAN, R. S.; COVI, L.: An outpatient psychotic rating scale (SCL-90) – preliminary report. Psychopharmacol. Bull. 9, 13–28, 1973.

ENDICOTT, J.; SPITZER, R. L.; FLEISS, J. L.; COHEN, J.: The global assessment scale. Arch. Gen. Psychiat. 33, 766–771, 1976.

FALLOON, I.; WATT, D. C.; SHEPARD, M.: The social outcome of patients in a trial of long-term continuation therapy in schizophrenia: Pimozide versus Fluphenazine. Psychol. Med. 8, 265–274, 1978.

HERZ, M. I.; MELVILLE, C.: Relapse in Schizophrenia. Am. J. Psychiat. 137, 801–805, 1980.

HERZ, M. I.; SZYMANSKI, H. V.; SIMON, J.: Intermittent medication for stable schizophrenic outpatients. An alternative to maintenance medication. Am. J. Psychiat. 139, 918–922, 1982.

HIRSCH, S. R.: In: WING, J. K. (ed.): Handbook of Psychiatry. Cambridge University Press, Vol. 3, 74–87, 1982.

HOGARTY, G.; ULRICH, R.: Temporal effects of drug and placebo in delaying relapse in schizophrenic outpatients. Arch. Gen. Psychiat. 34, 297–301, 1977.

JOHNSON, D. A. W.: Studies of depressive symptoms in schizophrenia. – I. The prevalence of depression and its possible causes. II. A two year longitudinal study of symptoms. Brit. J. Psychiat. 139, 89–101, 1981.

KNIGHTS, A.; HIRSCH, S. R.: «Revealed» depression and drug treatment for schizophrenia. Arch. Gen. Psychiat. 38, 806–811, 1981.

KRAWIECKA, M.; GOLDBERG, D.; VAUGHAN, M.: A standardized psychiatric assessment scale for rating chronic psychotic patients. Acta Psychiat. Scand. 55, 299–308, 1977.

A Controlled Study of Family Therapy, Social Skills Training and Maintenance Chemotherapy in the Aftercare Treatment of Schizophrenic Patients: Preliminary Effects on Relapse and Expressed Emotion at one Year

G. E. HOGARTY, C. ANDERSON

In 1977, those concerned with the aftercare treatment of schizophrenia had reached something of an impasse in their efforts to forestall relapse. For years it had been believed that the traditionally high relapse rate observed among schizophrenic patients in the first year post-discharge was due in large part to the patient's failure to comply with antipsychotic medication. While drug noncompliance indeed remains a leading cause of schizophrenic relapse (68% in the first year post discharge) (HOGARTY, 1984), nevertheless a series of double-blind, prospective and well-controlled trials of oral neuroleptic and injectible fluphenazine decanoate had demonstrated that relapse rates not only remained high (35% to 40%) but also were not different between routes of administration (HOGARTY et al., 1979; SCHOOLER et al., 1980; FALLOON et al., 1978). As such, drug noncompliance was an insufficient explanation of schizophrenic relapse.

Why, then, were these drug-maintained patients relapsing?

Earlier studies of the *therapeutic environment* (ANDERSON et al., in press), including inpatient studies and our own outpatient trial had indicated that high stimulating forms of psychosocial intervention had either precipitated relapse in certain outpatients or evoked long dormant schizophrenic symptoms in chronically hospitalized patients. Similarly, other studies of the apparent expectations for performance contained in developed cultures, and the apparent stress contained in the "expressed emotion" of certain families, also suggested that stimulation from the *natural environment* could be a provocation of the psychotic process in vulnerable patients as well (ANDERSON et al., in press). These sources of environmental "press," together with a considerable literature on the pathophysiology of schizophrenia associated with cerebral dysfunctioning, led us, in 1977, to formulate an operational theory upon which the principles of family *and* patient treatment could be better established. (The theory, rationale and supporting literature are presented elsewhere [ANDERSON et al., in press].)

*   and the EPICS Schizophrenia Research Group

It seemed to us that there was a common denominator in the findings from the studies of culture, life events, family attitudes, and behavior, intensive psychotherapies and the incomplete prophylaxis of antipsychotic medication. The commonality appeared in the form of offending stressors, "triggers" or stimuli (associated with the characteristics of the therapeutic or natural environment), which required the schizophrenic patient to make an adaptive response to complex, vague, excessive, or emotionally charged expectations; a response which in turn seemed capable of precipitating a cognitive dysfunction in the context of affective or autonomic disregulation. If the demands of the environment or the underlying deficits were sufficiently severe, then these factors operating alone or more likely together might represent a sufficient cause for schizophrenic relapse, even when the receipt of antipsychotic medication was assured! On the other hand, antipsychotic drug regulation (of attention and arousal deficits at least) and/or the provision of a more benign, stimuli controlled external environment, operating alone or more likely together, might indeed account for a reduction in schizophrenic relapse! With this theory or a «model» as a basis, a program of family and individual treatment was proposed in the form of a grant application to the National Institute of Mental Health. Support was received in 1978 and the following study initiated in early 1979. Since that time, two independent studies of family therapy have been published (FALLOON et al., 1982; LEFF et al., 1982) containing many similarities both to our own underlying theory, to our principles of practice and to our results. (These will be discussed below.)

Definitions of Treatment

Family Therapy

Our family therapy component was a psychoeducational and management strategy designed to lower the emotional climate of the home, while at the same time maintaining finely calibrated expectations for the patient's performance in the hope of avoiding both the positive and negative symptoms of schizophrenia which might be associated with "over"- or "under"-stimulation. The treatment sought to increase the stability and predictability of family life by decreasing the family's anxiety and guilt, increasing their self-confidence and providing a sense of cognitive mastery through the provision of information concerning the nature and course of schizophrenia and specific management strategies thought to be helpful in coping with schizophrenic symptoms. Table 1 outlines the goals and treatment strategies embodied in the family approach; the first three phases were most often employed during year one. A volume describing, in detail, both the content, structure and process of this family psychoeducation and management approach is currently in press (ANDERSON et al., in press).

Table 1: Overview of the Process of Treatment: Family Therapy

Phases	Goals	Techniques
Phase I Connection	Connect with the family and enlist cooperation with program Decrease guilt, emotionality, negative reactions to the illness Reduction of family stress	Joining Establishing treatment contract Discussion of crisis history and feelings about the patient and the illness Empathy Specific practical suggestions which mobilize concerns into effective coping mechanisms
Phase II Survival skills workshop	Increased understanding of illness and patient's needs by family Continued reduction of family stress De-isolation – enhancement of social networks	Multiple family (education and discussion) Concrete data on schizophrenia Concrete management-suggestions Basic communication skills
Phase III Reentry and application	Patient maintenance in community Strengthening of marital/parental coalition Increased family tolerance for low level dysfunctional behaviors Decreased and gradual resumption of responsibility by the patient	Reinforcement of boundaries (generational and interpersonal) Task assignments Low key problem solving
Phase IV Maintenance	Reintegration into normal roles in community systems (work, school) Increased effectiveness of general family processes	Infrequent maintenance sessions Traditional or exploratory family therapy techniques

From Schizophrenia Bulletin 6, 495, 1980.

Social Skills Training

The model of social skills training developed was closely tied to the behavioral techniques elaborated earlier by WALLACE et al. (1980), LIBERMAN et al. (1975) and HERSEN & BELLACK (1976), but differed from established social skills training approaches in some regards. While highly "structured" (relative to family therapy), considerable time was initially devoted by therapists to establishing a therapeutic alliance and utilizing such psychotherapeutic techniques as support, empathy, and unconditional regard. Further, as much emphasis was placed on the development of social *perception* as social *performance* skills. The treatment process unfolded over a two-year period (rather than weeks or months) with training focused on individual, problematic behaviors manifest in the context of the family and, later, problem behaviors involved in resocialization and vocational settings beyond the family. The goal of social skills training was to develop the social competence of patients by enhancing social behaviors (verbal and nonverbal) as well as social perception and judgment. The expectation was that improved social competence would more likely facilitate positive interpersonal experiences and thereby decrease conflict. The focus of treatment was on patient behaviors believed to elicit high expressed emotion, particularly criticism, from significant others. As such, our social skills training was an *indirect* attempt at lowering the emotional climate of the household in contrast to the more direct approach embodied in family therapy. Table 2 describes the goals and techniques of social skills training. A more detailed description of the content structure and process is available elsewhere (GREENWALD et al., 1985). In the first year of treatment post-discharge, the emphasis was essentially on Phases I through IV.

Table 2: Overview of the Process of Treatment: Social Skills Training

Phases	Goals	Techniques
Phase I Stabilization and Assessment	Establish therapeutic alliance Assess social performance and perception skills Assess behaviors which provoke expressed emotion	Empathy and rapport Role play 14 scenes Self and family reports of social performance
Phase II Positive Statements (within family)	Provide alternate response to hostility: compliments, appreciation, interest in others	*I*nstruction *M*odeling *R*ole play *F*eedback *H*omework
Phase III Social Performance (within family)	Resolution of conflict via enhanced verbal and nonverbal behaviors	*I M R F H* Re: preferences, refusals, response to and expression of criticism: via: speech latency, voice tone, gaze, gestures, facial expression
Phase IV Social Perception (within family)	Correct identification of content, context and meaning of messages	*I M R F H* – therapists skills: message reading, labeling of idea, summarize intent and response, timing and setting of response
Phase V Extra Familial Relationship	Enhance socialization skills Enhance prevocational and vocational skills	Assessment of assets, needs and network. *I M R F H* – re: *Socialization:* conversation and listening skills, dating, recreational activities *Vocational:* attention, concentration, memory, career fixation, job interviewing, work habits, supervisor-employee relationship training

Study Design

Consecutive admissions to the inpatient service of our Institute were recruited for study between February 1979 and September 1983. Patients met Research Diagnostic Criteria (RDC) for schizophrenia or schizo-affective disorder and needed to have lived in for one of the three months prior to admission, and would likely return to, a household that was defined as "high" in Expressed Emotion. A significant other residing in the household was rated "high" if he/she expressed 6 or more critical comments toward the patient, had a rating of 4 or 5 on the judgment of emotional over-involvement, or had a positive rating of hostility following an audio taped interview in which the Camberwell Family Interview Schedule was administered. All raters were trained to reliabilities of .80 or greater on the essential components of expressed emotion. Training and experience in the use of the CFI traditionally took six months prior to a rater actually evaluating study relatives. Patients were excluded from study if they were outside the age range 17 to 55, presented evidence of organic brain syndrome, or had a recent history of alcohol or substance abuse that in any way could "explain" the presenting psychotic episode. Further, patients who suffered renal, hepatic, or cardiovascular disease precluding the use of the antipsychotic medication were also excluded. Patients were predominantly male (75%), young (mean age 25), multi-episode, and of middle to low social class. Whenever possible, patients were maintained on injectible fluphenazine decanoate in order to avoid the confound between drug noncompliance and other variables presumed to account for relapse.

Since the Family Therapy/Social Skills Study was one of a number of concurrent investigations, assignment to the various protocols was made on a calendar basis, i.e., on the basis of alternate weeks or months which were predetermined before patients were actually admitted to hospital. The study thus attempted to provide a "nested" drug-treated control group, i.e., one in which the therapists themselves would be "blind" to the control condition. This design was sought based on the past experience of the investigator, which often indicated that controls were inconsistently treated. Frequently, for example, it was not that experimental subjects had done particularly well, but that controls did significantly less well than expected in studies of the psychotherapies. As such, all high EE patients scheduled for treatment protocols were, at the point of hospital admission, first randomized on a calendar basis to the Family Therapy/Social Skills Study or to a concurrent Dosage Study, which investigated the potential interaction between expressed emotion, drug dose, and relapse. Within protocols, patients were further randomized to the Family Therapy alone, Social Skills alone, or a combination of Family Therapy and Social Skills. (*All* patients were maintained on medication and had available the supportive services of a nurse clinician.) Within the Dosage Study, high EE patients were further randomized at the point of hospital admission to a physician recommended aftercare dose of fluphenazine decanoate or a low dose.

Standard dose, high EE patients, thus served as *controls* for both the Family Therapy/Social Skills Study and the Dosage Study. These control and experimental patients were identified shortly following hospital admission and served as controls or experimentals throughout the two years of study, regardless of whether or not they ultimately entered into or complied with the aftercare protocols.

During the course of study intake, 132 patients were thus randomized to their potential treatment cells as soon after hospital admission as diagnosis and EE assessments could be completed (two days to two weeks). Thirty patients among the 132 were administratively terminated: 15 patients, evenly distributed across treatment cells, refused protocol and/or withdrew their signed consent prior to or immediately following discharge. (To our knowledge, these few refusals do not differ in background characteristics among treatment conditions.) The remaining 15 administrative terminations were also equally dispersed across treatment conditions: Nine patients were found *not* to have an RDC diagnosis of schizophrenia or schizo-affective disorder when the diagnostic process was ultimately completed following the EE assessment. (There was considerable pressure for diagnosticians to "move quickly" in order to enable the family therapist to engage with families as soon as possible.) Six additional patients (across treatments) were dropped from study when they were transferred to state facilities where they remained hospitalized for more than six months.

Among the 102 eligible subjects and their families thus available for study, we differentiated between subjects who met criteria for treatment exposure (N = 88), and those who either relapsed during the process of engagement or otherwise did not meet the criteria for treatment exposure (N = 14). Treatment exposure was defined as follows: Family Therapy equaled attendance by the family at the psychoeducational workshop (within a month of admission) plus one example of attempting to implement a management procedure at home; Social Skills Training equaled the completing of baseline assessments of skills deficits (Phase I) plus at least one session in skills rehearsal; Control treatment equaled at least two individual sessions of supportive therapy provided by the nurse clinician plus one month of continuous maintenance oral neuroleptic medication or three consecutive injections of fluphenazine decanoate. We distinguished between treatment "takers" and "partial takers," because the latter patients are rarely mentioned in the results of published studies. But their inclusion in the analysis does influence the interpretation of results.

Whenever possible, the same family member was re-evaluated one year following discharge on the CFI in order to approach the question of differential treatment effects on the level of high expressed emotion.

For purposes of this report, two types of relapse were evaluated. Type I relapse represented a change from being "nonpsychotic" at hospital discharge to "psychotic" according to RDC Criteria of schizophrenia or schizo-affective disorder. A Type II relapse represented an unequivocal exacerbation of persistent symptoms. Otherwise, among our multiple studies, less than 5% of the patients met the definition of Type III relapse, i.e., persistent but unchanged severe psychosis over time. Most symptomatic patients at discharge either relapsed or improved. Also not included in this report are Type IV relapses or patients with "mini-episodes," i.e., patients who had a mild exacerbation of symptoms not equal to the index episode, which responded in usually two or three weeks to increased surveillance or medication adjustment. (About 20% of patients in our various studies experienced a "mini-episode.") Definitions of relapse represented an unanimous team decision documented by rating scale criteria. In the few cases where the primary therapist and team disagreed, the case was reviewed by the investigator. In each instance, the investigator judged that the patient had relapsed (1 control, 2 experimentals).

Results

Treatment effects on relapse

Among the 88 treatment takers: 4 of 21 family therapy alone patients experienced a Type I or Type II relapse (19.0%); 4 of 19 social skills training patients relapsed (21.1%); 10 of 28 drug treated controls relapsed (35.7%) but none of the combined Family Therapy + Social Skills patients experienced a relapse by one year. Application of the maximum likelihood x^2 statistic indicated a main effect for family therapy, a main effect for social skills training and a strong trend toward an interaction, the latter test limited by the fact that the combined treatment cell had "bottomed out," i.e., had a 0% relapse rate. The main effect marginals are significant even when controlled for the effects of contrasting treatment (partials). A somewhat different picture emerged when the *entire* sample of "partial takers" and "full takers" was included: 22.7% of Family Therapy patients, 31.8% of Social Skills Training patients, 8.7% of the combined treatment cell and 45.7% of controls experienced a relapse. For the entire cohort, only a main effect of family therapy was demonstrated. Most convincing, when data were analyzed *only* for patients among whom maintenance medication was assured (83 takers; 90 takers plus partial takers), a single main effect of treatment on relapse was observed: family therapy significantly lowered the number of relapses among patients maintained on antipsychotic medication.

Treatment effects on the adjustment of survivors has been partially analyzed. To date, it is, for the most part, impossible to identify significantly different levels of adjustment among surviving patients. All groups of non-relapsed patients tend to improve over time, but not differentially. Isolated treatment effects that do emerge indicate a family therapy effect on "global judgments of illness" and the "amount of change" pre and post treatment. A significant trend favoring social skills training was observed on measures of "role performance" and the "quality of interpersonal relationships outside the home," findings very similar to our earlier major role therapy (MRT) study (HOGARTY et al., 1974).

Treatment effects on Expressed Emotion

A principal obstacle to inference making regarding the effects of treatment on high levels of expressed emotion can be traced to the fact that our "nested" control group method obstructed attempts to engage control families systematically over time in order to obtain a representative sample of repeat CFI and EE evaluations at one year. While only 23% of all experimental families were unable or unwilling to participate in the repeat CFI procedure, 54% of control families were unavailable for assessment. (The patient outcome of these refusing families, however, was generally good: only 21% of "refusing" experimental families experienced a patient relapse and 26% of "refusing" control families experienced a patient relapse.) We present the following data on the effects of treatment on EE levels only for the treatment "takers" since this cohort is less biased regarding main effects and interactions of treatment on relapse. Since all experimental treatments had a clear effect on lowering relapse, the contribution of lowered EE to this outcome could be directly approached.

We present data on the repeat CFI and EE evaluations and, as an approximate *estimate* of EE change in "uncooperative" families, a clinical team decision was made in 10 of 15 control families and in all 14 experimental families. Evidence that a "refusing" family had not changed EE status pre/post treatment was based upon frequent family telephone calls to the clinician indicating exaggerated concern or taking the "emotional temperature" of the patient; patient's reports of frequent hostility and criticism directed toward him/her; telephone calls from the family or from the patient (with the family in the background yelling at the patient) indicating that hostility and criticism continued to be directed toward the patient over the year of treatment.

We present data regarding the relationship between expressed emotion, treatment, and relapse in response to two important abiding questions:

1. Does the family psychoeducation and management strategy significantly lower the high EE of households over time, as contrasted to households with no direct family intervention?
2. Does the change or lack of change in EE status of the family relate to patient survival or relapse?

Table 3 presents the number and percent of households that changed from high levels of expressed emotion at hospital admission to low EE levels at follow-up, based upon the formal, repeat CFI assessments as well as the Team Estimates of EE change among uncooperative families. (In general, the CFI formal estimates are the same as the combined CFI plus Team Estimates for

Table 3: Household Change at One Year From High Expressed Emotion to Low Expressed Emotion among Treatment "Takers" (N = 88)

Method	CFI Interviews	CFI + Team Estimates	
Controls (N = 28)	5/13 (38.5%) unreliable	5/23 (21.8%)	23.8%
SST (N = 19)	3/13 (23.1%)	5/19 (26.3%)	
FT (N = 21)	7/18 (38.8%)	9/21 (42.8%)	39.0%
FT+SST (N = 20)	6/15 (40.0%)	7/20 (35.0%)	

the *experimental subjects.* As expected, the principal difference in CFI assessments versus Team Estimates is applicable only to *controls.*) If one accepts the change in the Social Skills Training alone condition (CFI) as representative of the change among control families (CFI + Team Estimates), there is evidence that Family Therapy does differentially lower the expressed emotion of households (about 42% vs 24% of families). However, though past studies tend to attribute most, if not all, change in expressed emotion from high to low to Family Therapy, there is also evidence that nearly one-quarter of families change from high to low *without* systematic education and management.

Table 4 illustrates the effects of EE status or its change on patient relapse and the differential contribution of the various treatments to this relationship. Two conclusions can be readily drawn from the table:

1. A change in household EE status from high to low, independent of treatment, is indeed related to patient survival. *No* patient living in a family which changed from high to low EE experienced a relapse by one year across all treatment conditions. Since more families changed from high to low in the family therapy conditions, this effect on family EE might indeed underly the prophylactic action of family therapy.
2. If a household remained high in expressed emotion, there is somewhat less of a basis for attributing a main effect on relapse to individual treatment modalities. It is only the *combined* treatment condition that exerts a clear prophylactic effect in the face of a persistent, high EE household.

In general, the same conclusions attributed to EE *household* status, treatment, and relapse can be made for *individual* relatives within the household as well: more individuals change from high to low in the family therapy cells; few patients relapse when living with an individual who changed from high to low; and more equivocal treatment effects can be found in families where all individuals remained high ... except for the combined treatment condition. Among the 126 significant adult relatives evaluated in this study, only 15% were originally judged at hospital admission to be low EE. Only one of these 19 relatives subsequently changed from low to high. Unexpectedly, the presence of a low EE individual in an otherwise high EE household did not lower the relapse rate.

Table 4: Household Expressed Emotion Status (Admission to One Year) and Patient Relapse by Treatment (Takers = 88)

| Method | High EE to Low EE | | High EE to High EE | |
| | CFI | CFI+Team Est. | CFI | CFI+Team Est. |
	Household (% Relapse)	Household (% Relapse)	Household (% Relapse)	Household (% Relapse)
Controls (N=28)	5 (0%)	5 (0%)	8 (75%)	18 (44%)
SST (N=19)	3 (0%)	5 (0%)	10 (20%)	14 (29%)
FT (N=21)	7 (0%)	9 (0%)	11 (27%)	12 (33%)
FT+SST (N=20)	6 (0%)	7 (0%)	9 (0%)	13 (0%)

Discussion

Among patients and families meeting criteria for treatment exposure, there is a clear effect of both *individual* and *family* approaches alone, and particularly in combination, in forestalling relapse relative to medication controls who received supportive therapy. Other studies of family therapy report 9-month relapse rates of 6% and 9% for family therapy and 44% and 50% for controls (FALLOON et al., 1982; LEFF et al., 1982). (Our own 9-month rates are approximately 5% and 25% for family therapy and controls.) Unlike other existing studies of family therapy, however, we were able to include a highly structured, *patient*-centered treatment as a contrasting, experimental condition, one based on the same model of schizophrenic pathophysiology as the family therapy approach. Both forms of family-centered and patient-centered treatment are effective in forestalling relapse among those who are exposed to therapy. The combination is singularly effective. Further, the outcome of medicated controls in our study is somewhat better than medicated controls in the two existing family therapy studies (FALLOON et al., 1982; LEFF et al., 1982). However, the relapse rate among our own controls (35%) is nearly identical to the rates published internationally for patients maintained on depot neuroleptics. In our study, the effect of a 35% relapse rate among controls is to further blur the contrast between experimental conditions and controls.

There has been considerable fanfare for the intuitively appealing and humane approach embodied in psychoeducational family therapies. But one should be cautious in avoiding inferences that family therapy is the *sole source* or *definitive* prophylactic treatment for schizophrenia. Social skills training appears less labor intensive and costly at face value, and it does represent an effective alternative aftercare treatment for schizophrenic patients when local resources are insufficient to mount an extensive family program. In combination with family therapy, there is an effect that is not possible with either treatment alone. The effects of social skills training seem similar to other patient-centered psychosocial strategies developed by us years ago, which were applied to a population of mixed and perhaps lower risk patients (HOGARTY et al., 1974).

Family therapy alone, on the other hand, appears to be relatively more advantageous for the larger sample of patients than social skills training alone on two accounts: (1) its ability to engage more patients in treatment via family connection and hence to buy time for the symptomatic patient to recover more fully in the early months post-discharge; (2) its ability to lower distinctly the high expressed emotion levels of the household – which translates into lower relapse rates for patients. Social skills training, on the other hand, would not likely be the treatment of choice in modern facilities hospitalizing patients for very brief periods of time and subsequently discharging such patients in a symptomatic state. Social skills training, based on our data and on reports of the therapists themselves, was not only ineffective for these actively psychotic patients at discharge, but was nearly impossible to apply. Nevertheless, if patients adequately recovered from their psychotic episode, the gains of social skills training in forestalling relapse occur largely in the context of families that remained high in expressed emotion.

In a report by LEFF et al. (1982), 50% of (12) high EE relatives participating in their family therapy condition changed from high to low expressed emotion, and the patients in these homes survived as well, a finding similar to our own. However, it is still noteworthy that one-quarter of families *not* educated and treated directly nevertheless changed from high to low in our own trial, and no patient relapsed in these households as well. The issue of causality, however, remains obscure. One-quarter of family therapy households change from high to low apparently due to direct intervention, but at least *another* quarter of families change from high to low for *other* reasons, perhaps because the patient is not psychotic and doing reasonably well. As such, in a proportion of cases, high expressed emotion might well be "reactions" to the patient's illness or adjustment, and not causes of the episode. Furthermore, additional analyses should reveal whether those families who change from high to low EE status are characterized primarily by selected components of EE pre treatment.

Otherwise, one must ask why patients in the combined Family Therapy/ Social Skills Training cell do not relapse, even in the face of persistently high expressed emotion. We have not yet analyzed "face-to-face" contact across treatment conditions, and perhaps the simple fact of being out of the house more often and into therapy might account for the low relapse rate. More directly, one of us has argued that family therapy, while clearly involving the patient as amply described in our volume (ANDERSON et al., in press), nevertheless did concentrate on the pain and suffering of other family members, while social skills training focused more directly on the pain and suffering of the patient. Perhaps the ideal treatment strategy does involve a professional who is very special to the family and another who is very special to the patient. It is unknown at the moment whether the *adjustment* of patients who reside in persistently high EE households is differently affected by treatment.

The generalization of our results must be tempered. In the United States, at least, data from our own study and that of FALLOON et al. (1982) indicate that expressed emotion, patient sex, and household type appear to be hopelessly confounded. Selection of "high-risk" patients for family therapy and other psychosocial strategies based on the designation of a high EE household tends to place under study a group of unmarried males (75% in this study), living in parental households. Data from an independent study of ours, which attempted to replicate EE, as well as data from studies of depot fluphenazine, suggest that low EE (largely schizo-affective) females remain at the same risk of relapse as high EE males. In other studies, female patients continued to relapse on depot fluphenazine at the same rate as male patients. Only in past studies involving oral neuroleptics do male patients relapse at rates greater than females – a phenomenon likely attributable to drug noncompliance (ANDERSON et al., in press).

Further, we are not talking about *prevention* of schizophrenic relapse at this time. Uncensured estimates of relapse into the second year of our study reveal that 25% of the family therapy patients, 35% of social skills patients, 22% of the combined treatment patients, and 57% of controls have experienced a relapse to date. Nevertheless, the data from this study (and at least from the study of LEFF et al. [1982]) clearly indicate a main effect of family therapy in forestalling relapse among patients for whom the receipt of antipsychotic medication is assured. (In the FALLOON et al. [1982] study, it is not clear to us whether relapsed patients had noncomplied with medication prior to their relapse.) After 30 years of study, there is a message of hope and promise to patients, their families, and therapists that the provision of a psychosocial therapy does, indeed, add something more to the prophylactic treatment of schizophrenic patients than drug alone. The treatment challenge and direction of the next decade will be to develop more *individual* psychosocial strategies based on the differential characteristics of various high risk groups, strategies which will be applied in the context of maintenance drug and family therapy.

Acknowledgement

This study was supported by Grant #MH30750 from the Psychosocial Treatment Research Branch of the National Institute of Mental Health (USA). Fluphenazine decanoate (Prolixin) was supplied by E. R. Squibb & Sons, Princeton, New Jersey.

The EPICS Schizophrenia Research Group variously shared in equally significant contributions to the treatment of patients and families, data collection, conceptualization of theory and treatment strategies, analysis and preparation of results. In alphabetical order they are:

Name and Degree	Position
Patricia BARTONE, R.N., M.S.N.	Nurse Clinician
Gertrude BAYER, A.B.D.	Research Associate
John CAHALANE, M.S.W.	Family Therapist
Mary CARTER, Ph.D.	Principal Research Associate
Rosemary CATHER, R.N., M.S.N.	Nurse Clinician
Susan COOLEY, R.N.C.S.M.N.Ed.	Nurse Clinician/Coordinator
Ann Louise DiBARRY, R.N., M.S.N.	Nurse Clinician
Kathy ERNDL, B.A.	Research Associate
Samuel FLESHER, M.Ed.	Behavioral Therapist Assistant
Deborah GREENWALD, Ph.D.	Behavioral Therapist
Carol JAVNA, Ph.D.	Behavioral Therapist
Sander KORNBLITH, Ph.D.	Behavioral Therapist
Michael MADONIA, B.A.	Research Associate/Data Analyst
Joseph P. McEVOY, M.D.	Research Psychiatrist
Athena McLEAN, M.A.	Research Associate
Mark R. MUNETZ, M.D.	Research Psychiatrist
Priscilla ORTLIP, B.A.	Research Associate
Douglas J. REISS, Ph.D.	Family Therapist
Katherine STOCKDALE, M.A.	Research Associate
Richard F. ULRICH, M.S.	Biostatistician
Elizabeth VENDITTI, M.A.	Assistant Behavioral Therapist
Bridget E. VIROSTEK	Administrative Assistant Sr.

Christine VAUGHN, Ph.D., graciously trained raters in the use of the CFI and the rating of expressed emotion.

Bibliography

ANDERSON, C. M.; REISS, D. J.; HOGARTY, G. E.: Schizophrenia in the family: A practitioners guide to psychoeducation and management. Guilford Press, in press.

FALLOON, I.; WATT, D. C.; SHEPPERD, M.: A comparative controlled trial of pimozide and fluphenazine decanoate in the continuation therapy of schizophrenia. Psych. Med. *8,* 59–70, 1978.

FALLOON, I. R. H.; BOYD, J. L.; McGILL, C. W.; RAZONI, J.; MOSS, H. B.; GILDERMAN, H. A.: Family management in the prevention of exacerbations of schizophrenia. New England Journ. of Med. *306,* 1437–1444, 1982.

GREENWALD, D.; KORNBLITH, S.; JAVNA, C.: A model of social skills training with schizophrenic patients. Pre-publication report. 1985.

HERSEN, M.; BELLACK, A. S.: Social skills training for chronic psychiatric patients. Comprehensive Psychiat. *17,* 559–580, 1976.

HOGARTY, G. E.: Depot neuroleptics: The relevance of psycho-social factors. J. Clin. Psychiat. *45,* sec. 2, 36–42, 1984.

HOGARTY, G. E.; GOLDBERG, S. C.; SCHOOLER, N. R.: Drug and sociotherapy in the aftercare of schizophrenic patients. III. Adjustment of non-relapsed patients. Arch. Gen. Psychiat. *31,* 609–618, 1974.

HOGARTY, G. E.; SCHOOLER, N. R.; ULRICH, R. F.; MUSSARE, F.; HERRON, E.; FERRO, R.: Fluphenazine and social therapy in the aftercare of schizophrenic patients: Relapse analyses of a two-year controlled study of fluphenazine decanoate and fluphenazine hydrochloride. Arch. Gen. Psychiat. *36,* 1283–1294, 1979.

LEFF, J.; KUIPERS, L.; BERKOWITZ, R.; EBERLEIN-FRIES, R.; STURGEON, D.: A controlled trial of social intervention in the families of schizophrenic patients. Brit. J. Psychiat. *141,* 121–134, 1982.

LIBERMAN, R. P.; KING, L. W.; DeRISI, W. J.; McCANN, M.: Personal effectiveness: Guiding people to express their feelings and improve their social skills. Champaign, IL: Research Press, 1975.

SCHOOLER, N. R.; LEVINE, J.; SERENE, J. B.; BRAUYER, B.; DIMOCIA, A.; KLERMAN, G. L.; TUASON, V. B.: Prevention of relapse in schizophrenia: An evaluation of fluphenazine decanoate. Arch. Gen. Psychiat. *37,* 16–24, 1980.

WALLACE, C. J.; NELSON, C. J.; LIBERMAN, R. P.; AITCHISON, R. A.; LUKOFF, D.; ELDER, J. P.; FERRIS, C.: A review and critique of social skills training with schizophrenic patients. Schizophr. Bull. *6,* 42–63, 1980.

86

Changing the Family Environment of Schizophrenic Patients

J. LEFF

A number of studies conducted in London, Los Angeles and Chandigarh, North India, have shown that certain emotional attitudes of relatives are significantly linked with the outcome of schizophrenia (LEFF & VAUGHN, 1985; LEFF et al., 1985b). These attitudes are measured by means of a semistructured interview, the *Camberwell Family Interview* (CFI) and a special rating technique for which a period of two to three weeks intensive training is required (VAUGHN & LEFF, 1976). The measures that are associated with the outcome of schizophrenia are "critical comments," "hostility," "overinvolvement," and "warmth." The first three measures are predictive of a poor outcome and are incorporated in an index named *Expressed Emotion* (EE). If relatives are high on EE, the relapse rate of Anglo-American patients over nine months following discharge was about 50 percent. The corresponding relapse rate in low EE homes was 15 percent or less, a significant difference. The relapse rates for schizophrenic patients in Chandigarh were lower in both high EE and low EE homes, but still significantly different. "Warmth" was predictive of a good outcome in the Anglo-American studies.

For patients living in high EE homes, regular maintenance with neuroleptics and reduction in social contact with the relatives both appeared to exert a protective effect. These findings led us to initiate a study of therapeutic intervention in high EE families in which the patients were in high contact with their relatives (LEFF et al., 1982, 1985a). This study showed, in common with another three trials conducted in America (LEFF, 1985), that it was possible to modify family attitudes in the desired direction, and that the relapse rate of the patients was reduced significantly as a consequence. All four trials employed a similar design, with patients being maintained on neuroleptics and being randomly assigned to family treatment or a comparison group. In two of the trials (LEFF et al., 1985a; FALLOON et al., in press), the beneficial effect of family treatment was shown to persist over two years after discharge from hospital.

In this paper I will attempt to convey the nature of high EE families and of our approaches to changing them. I will use clinical material to illustrate the elements of our therapeutic package.

We employed three main techniques in our therapeutic programme: an educational component, a relatives' group and sessions of family therapy conducted in the patients' home. The education was given in a formal way by reading from a prepared script. This was carried out in two sessions in the home at which the relatives, but not the patients, were present. The information covered the aetiology, symptoms, course, treatment and management of schizophrenia. The relatives were allowed unlimited time to ask questions. We did not consider that education ceased at the end of the formal sessions, but expected the process to continue in a less structured way throughout the therapeutic programme. This was born out by the results of a *Knowledge Interview,* which was administered to relatives immediately before and after the educational sessions, and for a third time at the nine-month follow-up (BERKOWITZ et al., 1984). Comparison of high EE relatives with low EE relatives showed that the latter were able to distinguish episodes of illness, between which the patient was his usual self. High EE relatives were unable to make this distinction so clearly ($p = 0.05$).[1] Furthermore, in contrast with low EE relatives, they believed that the condition from which the patient suffered was always present ($p = 0.01$). When the experimental relatives were compared with the control relatives, it emerged that more of the former knew that the diagnosis was schizophrenia, both immediately following the education sessions ($p < 0.01$) and at the nine-month follow-up ($p < 0.01$). At this point the experimental relatives knew considerably more about schizophrenia than the control relatives ($p = 0.002$). There were three additional gains that the experimental high EE relatives derived from the programme, when compared with their control counterparts: they were more likely to see the patient as an individual rather than "a schizophrenic" ($p = 0.03$), they knew more about the management of the condition ($p = 0.04$), and they were less pessimistic about the future ($p = 0.01$). This last point is of great value in demonstrating that the facts about schizophrenia are less gloomy than the relatives' fantasies.

The second main therapeutic element was the relatives' group. This was held every fortnight for an hour and a half and was run by two professionals. The group fluctuated in size and membership, since relatives were invited to join as the patients entered the study in sequence. On average, each relative attended once a month and most continued for nine months. They were welcome to keep coming after that period, and some continued to attend for over a year. The emphasis of the group was on the management of current problems, and themes were explored that were common to most, if not all relatives. Half the relatives were parents and the other half spouses, and there were differences in their respective concerns. For example, parents frequently voiced anxieties about "when I am gone", while spouses were concerned about deficiencies in the marital relationship.

The group exercised a number of different functions. Most relatives feel guilty about "producing" a schizophrenic in the family. Meeting others with similar problems helps to reduce this sense of personal responsibility. The group also acted as a forum for the expression of emotions, such as anger and guilt, which are better released in this setting than communicated to the pa-

---

1 All probability values are derived from FISHER's exact test.

tients. The presence of a number of relatives allowed the exertion of peer pressure on individuals to change. As LIDZ (1975) noted, "parents may be able to accept blunt comments about their behaviour from other parents that they would deeply resent and consider biased if made by a staff member." An example of this kind of interchange, which occurred in one of our group meetings, follows:

Mrs. M: We all want our children to be better and to behave normal and be like us, but all the time we're aware that they're ill and we're making up excuses, really, either for ourselves or for others, for people not to notice that our children are ill.

Mr. T (Indignantly): You can't treat people like that. They would know and you embarrass them by trying to do it.

A further function of the group was to enlarge the social network of the relatives. It has been shown that the social networks of relatives tend to decrease in size with duration of the patient's illness (ANDERSON et al., 1984). Social relationships were established between relatives in the group, and some of them developed these contacts outside of formal meetings.

Another area focussed on in the group was that of communication. High EE relatives are particularly voluble (KUIPERS et al., 1983) and find it difficult to listen to other people. It was often necessary in the group to prevent one relative dominating the discussion, but this was accomplished with humour if possible. Active listening was modelled by the therapists, as it is difficult to promote directly. A technique that was used occasionally was role play. A relative would be asked to play the part of his or her own schizophrenic family member, while another relative played his or her role. Relatives faced with a somewhat caricatured version of themselves could find this experience quite educational. On the other hand, acting the part of a patient could promote an emphatic understanding of the patient's dilemmas.

The family sessions in the home are more difficult to describe than the relatives' group, since each family has its unique problems. However, there were some emotional constellations which occurred frequently and are thus worth illustrating with clinical examples.

Case I: Tom

The patient, a man of 23 years, lived with his mother, stepfather and a younger brother. His mother was a powerful and dominating woman who had thrown her first husband out of the house because he was an alcoholic. She had brought up her two sons single-handly and had also made a successful career as a manageress. She had always seen Tom as the weaker of her two sons and appeared to have been overinvolved with him virtually from birth. He slept in her bed until the age of 15, when she became somewhat concerned about this situation and sent him off to Europe for a year on a student exchange. When he returned, his mother had acquired a new boyfriend who was to become his stepfather; Tom was banished to his own bedroom.

He developed his first episode of schizophrenia at the age of 22, but it took his parents a year to arrange his admission to hospital. During that time he showed progressively more negative symptoms, lying in bed all morning and allowing his hair to grow long. This infuriated his stepfather, who had been a professional soldier. Shortly before admission, Tom had thrown an ashtray through a window in the house. Following this, his mother had not left him alone in a room.

She was rated 3 on overinvolvement and made 11 critical comments, while the stepfather was not overinvolved but made 9 critical comments.

The education programme had a marked impact on stepfather's critical attitudes. Once he realised that Tom was ill, much of his criticism was muted; however, he then began to show overinvolved behaviour. Fortunately, he was aware of the dangers of this and the need to allow Tom his independence. These changes are evident from his own account.

"He's slipped right back into laying in bed in the mornings, and I've had to sort of be a bit firm again and chase him up in the mornings, but I'm doing it in a bit more polite manner because I realise that it's not all his fault probably. He can't help it. But before I thought that he could and he was playing up and so I took stronger measures of getting him out of bed. (He pulled him out by his hair). But now I don't."

"None of the things the others do are as good as I consider I do for him. But really I have to ease up sometimes because I'm starting to think for him, and that's bad. I realise that. I've got to control myself for thinking for him, because he'll be putting me in the same category as his mother, which is wrong because one of us has got to sort of keep away from him, so that he can see the difference, or find out the difference eventually."

Our aim was to strengthen the marital relationship, but in order to do this we had to take the focus off Tom. We were helped in this by his placement in a hostel. However, he was not happy there and left after a three-months stay to return to his family. His mother welcomed him back with open arms, but at least he agreed to attend a day hospital every day on a regular basis. He also began to spend more time with his friends in the evenings and at weekends, and pursued various hobbies. As a consequence, at the nine-month follow-up he was found to be in low contact with both parents. Furthermore, a repeat EE assessment at the same time showed that the mother's critical comments had fallen to one and her overinvolvement score to two, while the stepfather's critical comments were reduced to two. Thus, both parents had changed to low EE. Tom remained free of psychotic symptoms when assessed with the *Present State Examination* (PSE) at both the nine-month and the two-year follow-ups.

Case 2: Mary

The patient was a married woman of 53 years who had suffered a second episode of schizophrenia. She had been working as a civil servant, but retired early on the grounds of her poor health. Her husband, an engineer, had also retired, so that they spent almost all their time together. He was an intelligent, emotionally inhibited man, who was extremely intolerant of her irrationality. His immediate reaction to her psychotic episodes was to want to run away.

"Two brothers are doctors, but I wouldn't be a doctor, because I didn't think I had any patience with sick people. I didn't think I had the right attitude to them. I didn't feel sympathetic towards them. My natural inclination was one of irritation rather than help."

"If it happens again (his wife's illness) I'm off. I'm going. I'll ring up Dr. O. and say 'I'm bailing out'."

Initially, he made 9 critical comments and showed no overinvolvement. He attended every meeting of the relatives' group, and in addition we conducted family sessions in the home. Mary was persuaded to take up day classes, while fortunately he was offered a part-time teaching job by his old employers. Despite this increase in independent activities, the patient and her husband remained in high contact throughout the follow-up period. However, at the nine-month assessment, the husband made no critical comments at all, thus being categorised as low EE. We cannot entirely account for this dramatic change in his attitude as he was not open to exploration of his fears of his wife's madness. We can only assume that he gained more from the group and family sessions in the way of emotional support than was immediately apparent. Mary remained well throughout the two-year follow-up period.

In analysing the follow-up data for the trial, we first had to check on the effectiveness of the randomisation procedure. The 12 experimental patients were compared with the 12 control patients on a large number of items including the PSE data on admission, features of their past history, demographic characteristics, family history, occupational record and premorbid personality. The two groups differed significantly on only a single item: the experimental patients had a significantly ($p < 0.05$) greater duration of unemployment before admission than the control patients. This would be likely to impede our therapeutic aims for the experimental patients.

The research question our study was designed to answer was whether therapeutic intervention with the families could add to the beneficial effects of maintenance drug treatment. There is overwhelming evidence that patients off regular drugs relapse more frequently than those on medication. Therefore, we excluded from our analyses any patient who discontinued regular neuroleptic medication. Of the 24 patients in the trial, 21 were prescribed long-acting depot injections. During the first nine-month follow-up, all experimental patients remained on their drugs as prescribed, but two control patients discontinued their medication. One had been on oral drugs and remained well, while the other had been receiving long-acting injections and relapsed. The relapse rates for the remaining 22 patients are shown in Table 1. Relapse was defined as a return of schizophrenic symptoms in patients who had been free of them, or an exacerbation in those with persistent symptoms.

It can be seen that by nine months after discharge, half the control patients on drugs had relapsed, while only one experimental patient did so, a significant difference. However, we were not successful in achieving the aims of our intervention in all the experimental families. Of the thirteen experimental relatives, seven changed from high to low EE, representing six families, while contact also altered from high to low in six families. However, because of overlap between some of these families, we achieved one of our aims in nine of the twelve experimental families. No patient in any of these nine families relapsed. These data show that the therapeutic package was successful in lowering EE and/or social contact in the majority of families, and that these changes led to a significant reduction in the relapse rate of schizophrenia over nine months.

We were interested to determine whether these effects would persist over a longer period of time, so we conducted a two-year follow-up of the patients. Unfortunately, over this period a further three patients discontinued their medication, one from the control group and two from the experimental group. All three relapsed between one and four months after stopping their medication. The two-year outcome of those remaining on medication is shown in the Table. It can be seen that the difference in relapse rate between the experimental and control groups is even wider at two years than at nine months. Furthermore, in the families in which we achieved at least one of our therapeutic aims, only a single patient relapsed. From a consideration of the patients' activities during a typical week we were able to determine that the freedom from relapse was not achieved at the expense of their quality of life (LEFF et al. 1985a).

The professional attention given to the experimental families during the trial was not excessive. Up to the nine-month point, experimental families attended the relatives' group a median of 10.8 times, received a median of 4.7 family sessions in the home, and made phone calls to members of the intervention team lasting a total of 40 minutes on average. Between the nine-month and two-year follow-ups, family members attended the group a median of 1.1 times, were visited at home a median of 1.1 times and spent a mean of 32 minutes on the phone to team members. Throughout the two-year period no professional help directed at the problems of living with the patient was given to the relatives of control patients who remained on drugs. Hence the difference in outcome between the groups of drug-compliant patients can be ascribed to the therapeutic intervention received by the experimental families. However, it is not possible to determine whether it was the attention paid by professionals to the families that produced the benefit, or one or more specific aspects of the therapeutic package. This issue is being addressed in our current trial, in which family therapy is being compared with a relatives' group.

92

Table 1: Outcome of patients who remained on drugs

Group	Relapse Rates			
	9 months		2 years	
A Control	5/10	50%	7/9	78%
B Experimental	1/12	8%	2/10	20%
C Experimental in which aims were achieved	0/9	0%	1/7	14%
A vs. B	exact p = 0.032		exact p = 0.017	
A vs. C	exact p = 0.017		exact p = 0.020	

Bibliography

ANDERSON, C. M.; HOGARTY, G.; BAYER, T.; NEEDLEMAN, R.: Expressed emotion and social networks of parents of schizophrenic patients. Brit. J. Psych. *144*, 247–255, 1984.

BERKOWITZ, R.; EBERLEIN-FRIES, R.; KUIPERS, L.; LEFF, J.: Educating relatives about schizophrenia. Schizophr. Bull. *10*, 418–429, 1984.

FALLOON, I. R. H.; BOYD, J. L.; McGILL, C. W.; WILLIAMSON, M.; RAZANI, J.; MOSS, H. B.; GILDERMAN, A. M.; SIMPSON, G. M.: Family versus individual management in the prevention of morbidity of schizophrenia: 1. Clinical outcome of a two-year controlled study (in press).

KUIPERS, L.; STURGEON, D.; BERKOWITZ, R.; LEFF, J.: Characteristics of expressed emotion: Its relationship to speech and looking in schizophrenic patients and their relatives. Brit. J. Soc. Clin. Psychol. *22*, 257–264, 1983.

LEFF, J.: Family treatment of schizophrenia. In: GRANVILLE-GROSSMAN, K. (ed.): Recent advances in clinical psychiatry, Vol. 5. London: Churchill Livingstone, 1985.

LEFF, J.; KUIPERS, L.; BERKOWITZ, R.; EBERLEIN-FRIES, R.; STURGEON, D.: A controlled trial of social intervention in the families of schizophrenic patients. Brit. J. Psych. *141*, 121–134, 1982.

LEFF, J.; KUIPERS, L.; BERKOWITZ, R.; STURGEON, D.: A controlled trial of social intervention in the families of schizophrenic patients: Two year follow-up. Brit. J. Psych. (in press), 1985a.

LEFF, J.; VAUGHN, C.: Expressed emotion in families: Its significance for mental illness. New York: Guilford, 1985.

LEFF, J.; WIG, N.; GHOSH, A.; BEDI, H.; MENON, D. K.; KUIPERS, L.; KORTEN, A.; ERNBERG, G.; DAY, R.; SARTORIUS, N.; JABLENSKY, A.: Influence of relatives' expressed emotion on the course of schizophrenia in Chandigarh. Brit. J. Psych. (in press), 1985b.

LIDZ, T.: The origin and treatment of schizophrenic disorders. London: Hutchinson, 1975.

VAUGHN, C.; LEFF, J.: The measurement of expressed emotion in families of psychiatric patients. Brit. J. Soc. Clin. Psychol. *15*, 157–165, 1976.

Skills Training for the Community Adaptation of Schizophrenics

R. P. Liberman, H. E. Jacobs, S. E. Boone, D. W. Foy, C. P. Donahoe, I. R. H. Falloon, G. Blackwell, C. J. Wallace

Treatment and rehabilitation strategies for individuals suffering from schizophrenia can now be designed from a conceptual blueprint that explains and predicts the course and outcome of this major mental disorder. The variables comprising this blueprint are biobehavioral vulnerability; environmental protectors, potentiators, and stressors; and personal protectors. Conceptually, schizophrenia is viewed as a biomedical, stress-linked disorder that is moderated by the coping and competence of the individual, and the supportiveness of the environment.

This framework for understanding the variability in schizophrenic disorders, both across individuals and over time within an individual, emphasizes a dynamic interaction among determinants at the biological, environmental, and behavioral levels. Depending upon the balance of factors at any one time, transient intermediate states of psychobiological overload and hyperarousal can emerge, leading to prodromal symptoms or even to florid symptoms characteristic of the disorder. This multilevel and interactional model of schizophrenia is graphically represented in Figure 1. It should be noted that the symptoms of schizophrenia with their associated social and occupational impairments may be manifested for varying durations and in varying degrees of severity. Also, depending upon the time course and interplay among vulnerability, stress, protective, and potentiating factors, the correlation between psychopathology and psychosocial functioning may range from high to low.

Vulnerability-Stress-Coping-Competence Model of Schizophrenia

The symptoms and impairments in social role functioning that comprise schizophrenic disorders can be viewed as being in equilibrium with influences converging from the biological, behavioral, and environmental levels. For example, the appearance or exacerbation of schizophrenic symptoms may occur in a psychobiologically vulnerable individual when:

94

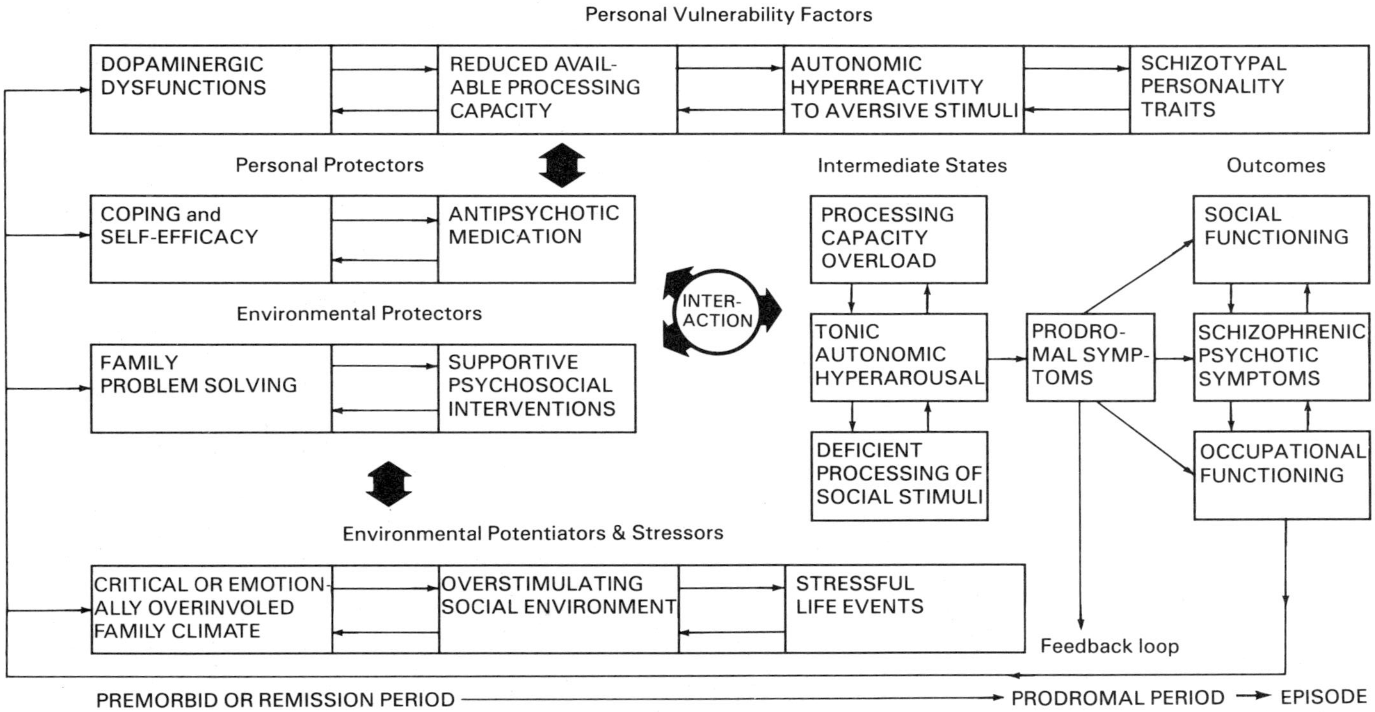

Figure 1: A conceptual framework for understanding course and outcome of schizophrenia with factors related to vulnerability, stress, coping and competence.

Personal Vulnerability Factors

| DOPAMINERGIC DYSFUNCTIONS | REDUCED AVAIL-ABLE PROCESSING CAPACITY | AUTONOMIC HYPERREACTIVITY TO AVERSIVE STIMULI | SCHIZOTYPAL PERSONALITY TRAITS |

Outcomes

SOCIAL FUNCTIONING

SCHIZOPHRENIC PSYCHOTIC SYMPTOMS

OCCUPATIONAL FUNCTIONING

Intermediate States

PROCESSING CAPACITY OVERLOAD

TONIC AUTONOMIC HYPERAROUSAL

DEFICIENT PROCESSING OF SOCIAL STIMULI

PRODRO-MAL SYMP-TOMS

Feedback loop

INTER-ACTION

Personal Protectors

COPING and SELF-EFFICACY

ANTIPSYCHOTIC MEDICATION

Environmental Protectors

FAMILY PROBLEM SOLVING

SUPPORTIVE PSYCHOSOCIAL INTERVENTIONS

Environmental Potentiators & Stressors

CRITICAL OR EMOTION-ALLY OVERINVOLED FAMILY CLIMATE

OVERSTIMULATING SOCIAL ENVIRONMENT

STRESSFUL LIFE EVENTS

PREMORBID OR REMISSION PERIOD ———— PRODROMAL PERIOD ——→ EPISODE

1. stressful events such as drug abuse or loss of a job overwhelm the individual's coping skills;
2. potentiating factors, such as high levels of intrafamilial tension or an over-stimulating treatment environment, evoke hyperarousal and deficiencies in the processing of information in an already compromised cognitive apparatus;
3. the individual cannot meet the behavioral demands of everyday life because the protective effects of medication have been lost through noncompliance;
4. social problem-solving skills have withered through disuse and withdrawal or, alternatively, have never been learned in the first place;
5. the individual's social support network weakens or collapses.

The interactional and multilevel model of schizophrenia is a bidirectional one and does not consign the patient to being a passive figure. Thus, appropriate dosing of neuroleptic drugs can abort a relapse; social skills can be strengthened through training and can protect a vulnerable individual from succumbing to stressful life events; family intervention and participation in a psychosocial self-help club can bolster social support and buffer the noxious effects of tension and stressors from the environment. Environmental and personal factors may even protect against a heightened biological diathesis.

Instead of viewing the pathogenesis of schizophrenia as arising mechanistically from biological and environmental determinants, it is useful to see individuals as active participants in the management and outcome of their disorder. The onset and course of a schizophrenic disorder is a reciprocal of the actions and behavioral repertoire of the individual, on the one hand, and biological and environmental processes on the other. A model of schizophrenia that encompasses "vulnerability-stress-coping-competence" highlights the ability of the individual to exercise behavioral competencies that can have an effect on his social environment and on his brain function.

For example, a person with good social and assertiveness skills can galvanize assistance and support from friends and relatives that, in turn, will aid in coping efforts, community survival, and instrumental problem solving. Repeated many times over the course of months and years, these mastery experiences may also favorably affect neurotransmitters or other aspects of central nervous system function. The intriguing work of KANDEL with simple neuronal systems in sea snails has documented that classical conditioning procedures produce both functional and structural changes in nerve cells; for example, environmental stimulation increases vesicles in the active zones of neurotransmitter release on the presynaptic neuron. Numerous other studies have confirmed the impact of environment and behavior on brain function.

After the onset of a schizophrenic disorder, the affected individual is presented with an enormous range of possibilities for action or inaction and for choice of options from among many available. While it is true that persons with schizophrenic vulnerability have a reduced capacity to act effectively on

96

behalf of their own personal development because of impairments in cognitive, emotional, and behavioral functions, they can exercise personal choice which affects the probability of adaptation or failure. Thus, the conception of our patients as acting upon their environments, their personalities, and indeed their biological substrates – and by so doing, altering the trajectory of their future status – should supplant the widely shared view of them as completely determined by their past histories, their psychobiological impairments, and their premorbid behavioral repertoires.

As mental health professionals, we can help our patients to improve their own contributions to their life span development. A "vulnerability-stress-coping-competence" model of mental disorder points us in useful directions for designing and implementing therapeutic interventions. Vulnerability can be compensated for by reducing environmental stressors, and by strengthening coping and competence in dealing with stress that inevitably accompanies life outside the cloistered existence of an institution. Psychotropic drugs, at doses that are optimal for restoring cognitive capacities, but do not produce interfering side effects, can eliminate or suppress symptoms that undercut efforts at coping and learning from one's environment.

Rehabilitation Strategies

With chronic mental disorders that produce severe impairments, complex disabilities and handicaps, it is understandable that a wide range of interventions will be necessary to achieve rehabilitation goals. Medication alone is rarely sufficient; likewise, psychosocial methods have little chance of success if isolated from the judicious use of psychotropic drugs. It is almost a truism among experienced clinicians that pharmacotherapy and psychosocial therapy should play supplementary and not competing roles in the comprehensive management of schizophrenic patients. Most experienced clinicians view neuroleptic therapy as accomplishing reconstitutive and prophylactic goals. In ameliorating the cognitive disorganization and disabling symptoms of psychosis, drugs enable the patient to make effective contact with the environment and engage in a therapeutic alliance with a therapist or psychosocial program. Continuity of care that integrates both maintenance medication and pursuit of personal, social and instrumental role goals has the best chance of restoring the individual with schizophrenia to a functional existence and reasonable quality of life.

Psychiatric rehabilitation can encompass three interlocking strategies for professional intervention:

1. Provision of appropriate types, doses and schedules of psychotropic medication.

2. Teaching the patient to develop or reacquire social and instrumental role skills.
3. Modifying the patient's social and physical environments to support whatever skills are in his/her repertoire or to compensate for continuing disabilities and handicaps.

Most chronically and severely mentally ill persons will require all three strategies for rehabilitation. A minority – such as those who are highly responsive to the benefits of antipsychotic drugs and who have excellent premorbid adjustment – may only need pharmacotherapy and time-limited assistance in re-establishing their family, occupational, and residential connections. Despite the best efforts at drug therapy and skills training, some chronically disabled patients may be unable to achieve symptom stabilization and remission or to learn and generalize social and independent living skills. For such refractory patients, alternate compensatory skills and prosthetic environments – such as functioning in a long-term sheltered workshop and supervised residential facility – might have to be the preferred focus of rehabilitative efforts.

With chronic psychiatric disorders, some amount of continuing symptoms and residual impairment makes necessary the acceptance of disability and the identification of lower, attainable goals. Learning how to cope with symptoms, manage medication, and utilize professional resources when necessary become important targets for rehabilitation. When deficits preclude gainful employment, the patient and family need assistance in generating alternative types of meaningful activity, social contacts, and daily structure. While persisting symptoms may limit the level of functional engagement in life, the reciprocal also holds, namely the more that rehabilitation improves the patient's social and role performance, the more likely his or her symptoms will be held in check. The rehabilitation professional is guided by the following basic assumptions:

- optimism that desirable change is possible, given the harnessing of principles of human learning to the needs of the patient;
- motivation for change can come from facilitative arrangement of the patient's rehabilitation and natural environments as well as from within the patient;
- building from the patient's assets and interests (including a supportive family environment), can produce small improvements that lead to significant functional changes and better quality of life.

Training skills for improved functioning in social, work, and family settings is an emerging technology that holds great promise for chronic mental patients. Skills training can take place in hospitals, community clinics, psychosocial clubs, workplaces, and the home. The focus of training can be the family, the individual, or a small group. Recent studies have shown that communication and problem-solving skills – in both instrumental and affiliative domains

– can be acquired by individuals suffering from schizophrenia (WALLACE et al., 1980). Moreover, these skills promote favorable outcomes in work adjustment, family relations, and symptoms (JACOBS et al., 1984; FALLOON et al., 1984). In one controlled study of behavioral skills training with families, relapse rates were reduced from 44% to 6% in nine months and from 83% to 11% in two years (FALLOON et al., 1984). Table 1 shows outcome data from this controlled study of behavioral family therapy. Imbedded in skills training methods are principles and techniques derived from social learning theory and operant conditioning (LIBERMAN et al., 1975; FOY et al., 1983). The remainder of this chapter will focus on one approach to skills training – that carried out in small groups of patients and aimed at improving conversational, problem-solving, medication self-management, friendship, and assertive skills.

Table 1: Comparison of outcomes between behavioral family management and individual therapy for schizophrenics (N = 18 in each group). All differences reaching statistical significance are noted by * (p < .05) or ** (p < .01). These data are taken from FALLOON et al. (1984).

	Family Rx	Individual Rx
Relapses (No. of Patients)		
Nine Months**	1	8
Two Years**	2	15
Target Symptom Ratings (Average Score)		
Nine Months**	2.25	4.10
Two Years**	2.55	4.75
Symptom Remission (No. of Patients)		
Nine Months*	10	4
Two Years	12	4
Time Spent in Rehospitalizations (Ave. Days)		
Nine Months	0.83	8.39
Two Years	1.8	11.3
No. of Patients Readmitted to Hospital		
Nine Months*	2	9
Two Years*	4	10
Household Tasks (Improvement)**	0.36	–.09
Work or Study (Improvement)**	0.36	–.14
Relationships Outside (Improvement)**	0.65	0.09
Cost per Unit of Effectiveness	$2.220	$5.167

Social Skills Training

There are three sources of empirical data that recommend social skills training as a means for improving patients' competence and ability to cope with stressors. Many studies have highlighted the importance of premorbid and post-morbid social competence as a predictor of outcome in major psychiatric disorders (LIBERMAN, 1982; PRESLY et al., 1982). This suggests that social skills training might improve the long-term prognosis by upgrading the post-morbid social competence of chronic patients. Second, the magnitude of deficits in social and living skills has been well documented in chronic psychiatric patients. For example, in one study major functional deficits in social and personal areas were found in over 50% of a sample of chronic psychiatric patients (SYLPH et al., 1978). A multi-hospital study of schizophrenic patients placed in foster homes after relatively brief hospitalizations found that relapse rates at one year after discharge were significantly higher among those patients who had pre-release deficiencies in social skills (LINN et al., 1980).

Methods of social skills training

Social skills training utilizes procedures based on principles of human learning to train specific interpersonal skills and to promote the generalization and maintenance of these skills. The procedures that have been developed to train interpersonal skills have been empirically tested and "packaged" for ready access by practitioners.

While many psychosocial programs claim to do social skills training, it is important to distinguish between nonspecific group activities that engage patients in "socialization," and methods which deliberately and systematically utilize behavioral learning techniques in a structured approach to skills building. Socialization activities can lead to acquisition of skills through incidental learning during spontaneous social interactions (TEST & STEIN, 1977). However, in this article we shall limit our definition of social skills training to those methods which harness the specific principles of human learning to promote the acquisition, generalization, and durability of skills needed in interpersonal situations (LIBERMAN et al., 1975). We believe that the systematic application of principles of learning yields superior outcomes and greater efficiency in the teaching of social and living skills.

The learning disabilities experienced by many chronic psychiatric patients require the use of highly directive behavioral techniques for training social skills. For example, most chronic patients have attentional and information-processing deficits. They show hyperarousal or underarousal in psychophysiological testing, and they experience overstimulation from emotional stressors or even from therapy sessions that are not carefully structured and modulated. Chronic patients often fail to be motivated by the customary forms of social and tangible rewards available in traditional therapy. In addition, they generally lack conversational ability, a basic building block for social competence. Schizophrenics, in particular, are deficient in social perception and have difficulty generating alternatives for coping with everyday problems such as missing a bus, making an appointment, or getting help with bothersome drug

100

side effects. Patients tend to make less eye contact, have more verbal dysfluencies, and use less vocal intonation, all of which may impair social learning.

It is important to tailor social skills training procedures to the needs of the individual patient, as all patients present different constellations of social abilities and deficiencies. Several training models are presently available to the clinician. Longest in use is a "standard package" for training skills, which includes instructions to the patient, the therapist modeling appropriate use of the skills, the patient role-playing interpersonal situations, and the therapist reinforcing and providing corrective feedback to the patient (LIBERMAN et al., 1975). Recently, training within an information processing framework has been shown to be effective for those patients capable of learning problem-solving strategies (FOY et al., 1983). Patients are taught to improve their perception of information in immediate interpersonal situations, process that information to choose a response, and send a response back to the other person. However, both of these approaches are ineffective for those patients with severe attentional deficiencies. A model using attention-focusing procedures that simplify the learning of complex skills, has been effective in training conversational skills in some seriously regressed, chronic psychiatric patients (LIBERMAN et al., 1985). The problem solving, information processing model will be presented in more detail in the following section.

Training interpersonal problem-solving skills

Inadequate performance in social situations may, in part, result from deficits in cognitive problem solving abilities. Chronic psychiatric patients have been found to be deficient in basic problem-solving skills (PLATT & SPIVACK, 1972; EDELSTEIN et al., 1980). In this social skills mode, components of problem-solving are focused on in training. Interpersonal communication is viewed as a three-stage process, requiring:

1. Receiving skills – attending to and accurately perceiving cues and contextual elements of interpersonal situations.
2. Processing skills – generating response alternatives, weighing the consequence of each alternative, and selecting optimal options.
3. Sending skills – using the chosen option for an effective social response, integrating both verbal and nonverbal skills.

As in the "standard" social skills training model, an interpersonal scene is role-played and videotaped. After the role-play the therapist asks specific questions to assess the patient's *receiving skills,* exemplified in the following dialogue:

Jim, a 38-year-old male, has been diagnosed as suffering from chronic schizophrenia. He has been hospitalized on several occasions, but he is currently an outpatient. Jim has just become part of a social skills training group, with a focus on heterosocial or dating skills. A role-play conversation between

Jim and Trudy, another patient, has just been completed and the therapist is about to assess and reinforce Jim's *receiving skills.*

T: That was good, Jim. You participated well in the conversation with Trudy. I think this will be a good start for training. I want to ask you a few questions first, though. Jim, what was Trudy talking about?

Jim: She was talking about walking on the beach and enjoying sunsets and cool drives in a car.

T: How did she feel?

Jim: I think she felt relaxed. She seemed comfortable with me.

T: Very good. What was your goal in this interaction, Jim?

Jim: I think it was to get to know Trudy better.

T: That is right. To get to know Trudy better and to feel comfortable enough to ask her for a date. You are doing very well so far Jim. You are paying attention and you have a good idea of what you need to work on.

The therapist asked specific questions of Jim to be able to assess if he was accurately perceiving the situation. After completing the *receiving skills* stage, *processing skills* are assessed and trained, if necessary. This stage involves generating response options and identifying positive and negative consequences of the potential options. For example, Jim has just completed a roleplay conversation with Trudy, in which he asked her for a date. In the following sequence Jim's *processing skills* are assessed and reinforced.

T: That was a very good conversation, Jim. You seemed relaxed, for the most part. What could you have done when Trudy said she already had plans for Saturday night?

Jim: I'm not sure. I guess she didn't want to go out with me.

T: That may not be right Jim. What could you have done to check that out?

Jim: Maybe I could have asked her out for another night.

T: Exactly. How do you think Trudy would have felt if you had asked her out for another night?

Jim: I guess that I am too interested in her.

T: Possibly, but more than likely she would have been flattered that you were really interested in her. What could she have done if she was interested in going out with you?

Jim: She could have said that she was busy for that night but she would like to go out with me another time.

T: Very good. How could you have achieved your goal of making a date with her?

Jim: I guess by being more persistent and not feeling rejected when she said she was busy.

T: Exactly right, Jim.

The therapist asked specific questions to gauge Jim's processing abilities and prompted alternative responses within Jim's repertoire of skills. The next step is to assess and train the patient's *sending skills*. The therapist and patient view the videotaped playback of the role-play which enables the patient to learn from himself as a model. The patient's self-evaluative skills are highlighted and reinforcement from the therapist as well as self-reinforcement are provided to enhance the patient's verbal and nonverbal performance.

T: I want to ask you some more questions now, regarding the conversation you just had with Trudy. How was your voice volume, Jim?

Jim: It was all right. Maybe it was too soft.

T: Good. I think you could have spoken a little louder also. That's something we can work on later. How was your facial expression?

Jim: I think it was good. I looked interested in Trudy and I was smiling quite a bit.

T: Right. Maybe you felt a little nervous but your face showed relaxation. What about your posture?

Jim: It looked all right to me.

T: Well, maybe you could have leaned closer to her more. That would show interest. Do you think you made enough eye contact?

Jim: I guess I was looking down a bit too much, but I did make some eye contact.

T: You did make some good eye contact. We can work on increasing the contact that you make. Jim, basically you are able to look at yourself on the screen and have a good idea of your strengths and weaknesses. That is a very good start.

The therapist again asked specific questions to determine how the patient perceived his *sending skills*. As in all stages of social skills training, reinforcement is given for appropriate responding. In all three stages of this model, the therapist may prompt or model correct responses or ask that the scene be role-played again. When the patient performs the *sending skills* at an acceptable level, assessment and training continue with a new scene.

In subsequent development of this problem-solving model, the scope of the approach has been expanded to a variety of areas of social and independent living other than conversational skills (Foy et al., 1983). A comprehensive array of "modules" are being developed to train skills in such areas as leisure and recreation, medication management, home maintenance, personal hygiene, and money management (WALLACE et al., 1985). Each module includes structured exercises for teaching small groups of patients specific functional skills, how to solve problems that may be encountered while attempting to employ these new skills, and how to practice the skills *in vivo*. Patients can enroll in one or more of these modules, depending upon the extensiveness of their deficits and the nature of the goals established for their treatment.

The content of a module is organized into scenes that recapitulate each of the interpersonal domains for cognitive and behavioral skills relevant to the goals of the module. For example, the medication self-management module contains scenes and associated exercises that are designed to inculcate knowledge and skills related to (a) learning about the benefits and side effects of medications, (b) acquiring the skills of medication self-administration, (c) coping with the side effects of medication, and (d) negotiating medication issues with physicians.

Each module is divided into separate skill areas with each area having specific behaviors that are taught to achieve personal effectiveness and competence. One skill area derived from the medication self-management module – negotiating drug doses and side effects with physicians – is illustrated in Figure 2.

Patients proceed through each module's training steps in a sequence, starting with an "introduction" that aims to highlight the values and advantages of the module to motivate subsequent participation. After acquiring the skills in the "training" phase, patients learn how to gather the tangible and social resources required to put the skills to use. For example, in order to negotiate medication side effects or dosage issues with the prescribing physician, a patient must be able to use a telephone to make an appointment to see the doctor

Each module is divided into separate *skill areas* with each area having specific behaviors that are taught for personal effectveness.

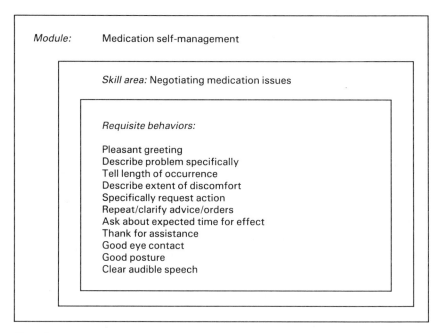

Module: Medication self-management

Skill area: Negotiating medication issues

Requisite behaviors:

Pleasant greeting
Describe problem specifically
Tell length of occurrence
Describe extent of discomfort
Specifically request action
Repeat/clarify advice/orders
Ask about expected time for effect
Thank for assistance
Good eye contact
Good posture
Clear audible speech

Figure 2

104

and find transport to take him to the doctor. After solving "resource management problems," patients anticipate "outcome problems" which might interfere with the successful implementation of the skills in the natural environment. Thus, patients learn how to deal with disappointing events such as the lateness or unpredicted absence of the physician at the appointment. The steps in this modular approach to training problem-solving skills are shown in Figure 3. This model of social skills training offers considerable promise for those patients who have the cognitive capacity for learning social skills in hour-long, small groups.

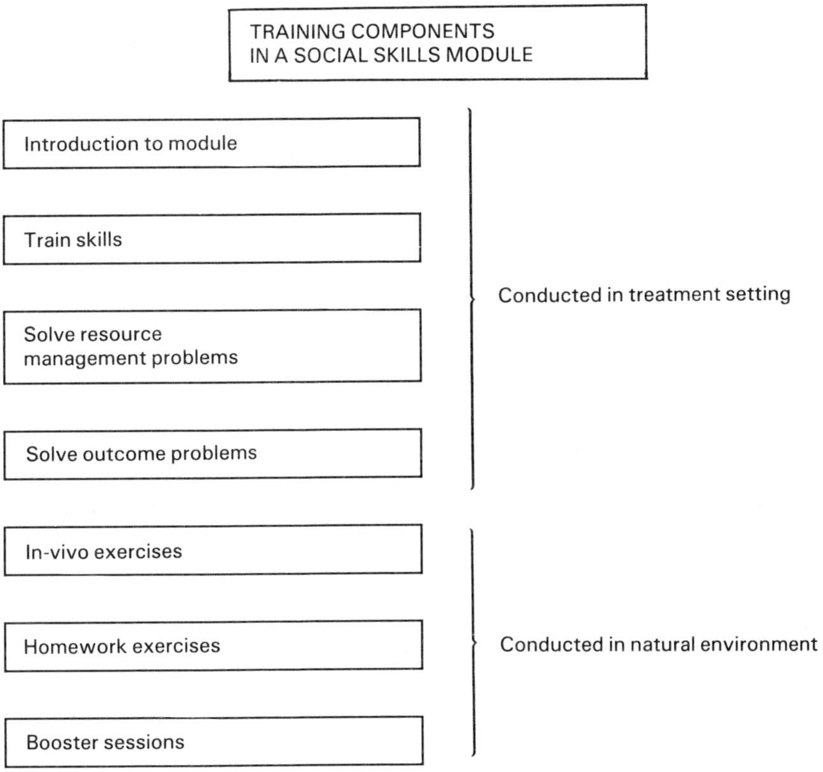

TRAINING COMPONENTS IN A SOCIAL SKILLS MODULE	
Introduction to module	
Train skills	
Solve resource management problems	Conducted in treatment setting
Solve outcome problems	
In-vivo exercises	
Homework exercises	Conducted in natural environment
Booster sessions	

Figure 3

Effectiveness of social skills training

Reviews of the empirical studies done on social skills training with schizophrenics have shown that a wide range of skills can be learned and maintained over short-term follow-up periods (WALLACE et al., 1980). In one controlled clinical trial, 28 carefully diagnosed male schizophrenic patients were randomly assigned to either intensive social skills problem-solving training or to holistic health therapy. A multidimensional evaluation was conducted before and after nine weeks of inpatient treatment and for 24 months in the community. Patients exposed to social skills training evidenced significantly greater acquisition, generalization, and durability of social skills; their social adjustment in the community was rated as better by relatives; and they experienced fewer relapses and rehospitalizations (WALLACE & LIBERMAN, 1985). Similar results have been obtained from skills-training programs in Italy (DEISABELLA & MENEGHELLI, 1983) and in Berne, Switzerland, by BRENNER and his colleagues in studies reported in another chapter of this book.

While social skills training has made considerable progress in enhancing skill levels of psychiatric patients, more work is needed in assessing and promoting generalization and long-term change.

Response generalization has been assessed in many clinical studies with results that have revealed intermediate to substantial generalization to untrained scenes and items (BELLACK et al., 1976; LIBERMAN et al., 1984; GOLDSMITH & McFALL, 1975; KELLY et al., 1980). The reason why response generalization has been so uniformly observed may lie in the strengthening of classes of responding as a by-product of training numerous related behaviors. In social skills training, a number of different role-play scenes and responses are practiced, resulting in various forms of the target skill being prompted and reinforced. For instance, an unassertive patient might practice sending burnt food back in a restaurant, confronting a person who cut in front of him in line, and saying "no" to unreasonable requests, among other scenes. This method of training to "multiple exemplars" of a particular skill has been recommended as a way to establish generalized responding (STOKES & BAER, 1977).

With schizophrenics and other severely impaired populations who suffer from cognitive deficits and a lack of initiative, generalization usually only occurs to a limited extent if efforts are not made to promote the performance of trained skills in naturalistic settings. For instance, a patient may be trained to reach criterion levels in skills that are important for having a good conversation, like appropriate self-disclosures and asking good questions. However, generalization may be impeded because certain factors are present in the training situation that may not be available in natural environments, such as:

1. The conversant in the role-plays is always attentive and he/she responds favorably when the patient asks a question or makes a self-disclosure.
2. The therapist reinforces the patient, with praise, tokens, or edibles, for making appropriate responses.
3. The therapist initially reinforces approximations of the correct response.
4. The therapist provides corrective feedback to the patients following inappropriate responses.

It may be expecting too much of the patient to utilize his/her newly learned skills in other environments and with other conversants, since other people are

106

not always attentive and responsive. Praise or rewards are rarely provided in natural communities for asking questions or making self-disclosures. Usually inappropriate responses are not corrected; rather, people tend to cut a conversation short if inappropriate things are said. Ideally, the skills would be maintained in other settings by the reinforcement qualities of engaging in interesting conversations. However, this step is generally not achieved without active programming.

One way to establish a solid link between training and naturalistic settings is by issuing homework assignments. Assignments to use trained skills in other settings and with other individuals have been utilized with positive results by a number of clinical researchers (FINCH & WALLACE, 1977; LIBERMAN et al., 1984; MCGOVERN & BURKHARD, 1976). This tactic has proved to be more effective when accompanied by prompts and reinforcement in the other setting. Friends, family members, nursing staff personnel, and peers can aid this process by prompting and reinforcing new social behaviors until they are established. Once the trained skills are well established and maintained by natural consequences in the environment, prompts and external reinforcement may be withdrawn. Gradually delaying reinforcement and making its delivery more variable will minimize the likelihood that newly learned patterns of behavior will be disrupted.

Training should not be separated from the patient's everyday world, but rather fully integrated with it. Whenever possible, therapy should be taken out of the clinician's office and practiced in homes, wards, workplaces, schools, stores, restaurants, and other environments where it is desirable to perform the target behaviors. Potent reinforcers (i.e., praise, money, edibles, and privileges) should be initially tied to successful performance of the behavior so that it is "worth doing"; only after the behavior is thoroughly ingrained and under the control of natural contingencies should prosthetic reinforcement be removed.

While it has been amply demonstrated that behavioral training produces incremental improvement in social competence, the data are far less convincing that such interpersonal strengthening actually reduces the probability of relapse or symptom exacerbation and increases community tenure and quality of life. Skills training imbedded within a family therapy context may prove to have greater impact on the long-term clinical status of chronic patients, such as in preventing relapse (LIBERMAN et al., 1984; FALLOON et al., 1984). Much more outcome research must be done to document the extent to which social skills training adds benefits to schizophrenic patients' long-term clinical and symptomatic outcomes, over and above antipsychotic medication. Since many patients have limited potential for acquiring and generalizing functional skills sufficient for fully independent living, there is continued value in developing rehabilitation approaches that emphasize environmental prostheses and social support.

Bibliography

ANTHONY, W. A.; COHEN, M. R.; VITALO, R.: The measurement of rehabilitation outcome. Schizophr. Bull. *4*, 365-383, 1978.

AZRIN, N. H.; BASALEL, V.: Job club counselors manual: A behavioral approach to vocational counseling. Baltimore: University Park Press, 1980.

BELLACK, A.; HERSEN, M.; TURNER, V.: Generalization effects of social skills training in chronic schizophrenics: An experimental analysis. Behav. Res. Ther. *14*, 391-398, 1976.

BROWN, G.; BIRLEY, J. L. T.; WING, J. K.: Influence of family life on the course of schizophrenia. Brit. J. Psychiat. *121*, 241-258, 1972.

CREER, C.: Social work with patients and their families. In: WING, J. K. (ed.): Schizophrenia: Towards a new synthesis. London: Academic Press, 1978.

DeISABELLA, G.; MENEGHELLI, A.: Un training di abilita sociali per la rehabilitazione di pazient psicotici cronici. Riv. Speriment. di Freniatria *5*, 1194-1204, 1983.

EDELSTEIN, G. A.; CONTURE, E.; CRAY, M.; DICKENS, R.; LUSELMINK, C. J.: Group training of problem solving with psychiatric patients. In: UPPER, D.; ROSS, S. M. (eds.): Group therapy: An annual review, Vol. 2. Champaign, IL: Research Press, 1980.

FALLOON, I. R. H.; LIBERMAN, R. P.: Behavioral family interventions in the management of chronic schizophrenia. In: McFARLANE (ed.): Family therapy of schizophrenia. New York: Guilford Press, 1983.

FALLOON, I. R. H.; BOYD, J.; McGILL, C. W.: Family care of schizophrenia. New York: Guilford Press, 1984.

FINCH, B.; WALLACE, C. J.: Successful interpersonal skills training with schizophrenic inpatients. J. Cons. Clin. Psychol. *45*, 885-890, 1977.

FOY, D. W.; WALLACE, C. J.; LIBERMAN, R. P.: Advances in social skills training for chronic mental patients. In: CRAIG, K. D.; McMAHON, R. J. (eds.): Advances in clinical behavior therapy. New York: Brunner-Mazel, 1983.

GOLDSMITH, J. B.; McFALL, R. M.: Development and evaluation of an interpersonal skills training program for psychiatric inpatients. J. Abnorm. Psychol. *84*, 51-64, 1975.

HAGEN, D. Q.: The relationship between job loss and physical and mental illness. Hosp. Comm. Psychiat. *34*, 438-441, 1983.

JACOBS, H.; KARDASHIAN, S.; KRIENBRING, R. K.; PONDER, R.; SIMPSON, A. R.: A skills-oriented model for facilitating employment among psychiatrically disabled persons. Rehab. Couns. Bull. *28*, 87-96, 1984.

KAZDIN, A. E.: Behavior modification in applied settings. Homewood, IL: Dorsey Press, 1984.

KELLY, J. A.; UREY, J. R.; PATTERSON, J. T.: Improving heterosocial conversational skills of male psychiatric patients through a small group training procedure. Behav. Ther. *11*, 179-183, 1980.

LEHMAN, A. F.; WARD, N. C.; LINN, L. S.: Chronic mental patients: The quality of life issue. Am. J. Psychiat. *133*, 796-823, 1983.

LIBERMAN, R. P.; KING, L. W.; DeRISI, W. J.; McCANN, M.: Personal effectiveness: Guiding people to express their feelings and improve their social skills. Champaign IL: Research Press, 1975.

LIBERMAN, R. P.: Social factors in schizophrenia. In: GRINSPOON, L. (ed.): Psychiatry: 1982 Annual review. Washington D.C.: American Psychiatric Press, 1982.

LIBERMAN, R. P.; FALLOON, I. R. H.; WALLACE, C. J.: Drug-psychosocial interactions in the treatment of schizophrenia. In: MIRABI, M. (ed.): The chronically mentally ill: Research & services. New York: SP Medical & Scientific Books, 1984.

LIBERMAN, R. P.; LILLIE, F.; FALLOON, I. R. H.; HARPIN, R. E.; HUTCHINSON, W.; STOUTE, T. M.: Social skills training for relapsing schizophrenics: An experimental analysis. Behav. Modif. *8*, 155-179, 1984.

LIBERMAN, R. P.; MASSEL, H. K.; MOSK, M.; WONG, S. E.: Social skills training for chronic mental patients. Hosp. Comm. Psychiat. *36*, 396-403, 1985.

LINN, M. W.; KLETT, J.; CAFFEY, F. M.: Foster home characteristics and psychiatric patient outcome. Arch. Gen. Psychiat. *37,* 129–132, 1980.
MCGOVERN, K. B.; BURKHARD, J.: Initiating social contact with the opposite sex. In: KRUM-
BOLTZ, J. D.; THORESON, C. E. (eds.): Counseling methods. New York: Holt, Rinehart & Win-
ston, 1976.
PLATT, J. J.; SPIVACK, G.: Problem-solving thinking of psychiatric patients. J. Cons. Clin. Psy-
chol. *28,* 3–5, 1972.
PRESLY, A. S.; GRUBB, A. B.; SEMPLE, D.: Predictors of successful rehabilitation in long-stay pa-
tients. Acta Psychiat. Scand. *66,* 83–88, 1982.
SNYDER, K. S.; LIBERMAN, R. P.: Family assessment and intervention with schizophrenics at risk
for relapse. In: GOLDSTEIN, M. J. (ed.): New directions for mental health services. Vol. 12.
San Francisco: Jossey-Bass, 1981.
STOKES, T. F.; BAER, D. M.: An implicit technology of generalization. J. Appl. Behav. Analy. *10,*
349–369, 1977.
STRAUSS, J.; HAFEZ, H.: Clinical questions and «real» research. Am. J. Psychiat. *138,*
1592–1597, 1981.
SYLPH, J. A.; ROSS, H. E.; KEDWARD, H. B.: Social disability in chronic psychiatric patients. Am.
J. Psychiat. *134,* 1391–1394, 1978.
TEST, M. A.; STEIN, L. I.: Special living arrangements: A model for decision making. Hosp.
Comm. Psychiat. *28,* 608–610, 1977.
VAUGHN, C. E.; LEFF, J. P.: The influence of family and social factors on the course of
schizophrenic disorders: A replication. Brit. J. Psychiat. *129,* 125–137, 1976.
VAUGHN, C. E.; SNYDER, U. S.; LIBERMAN, R. P.; FALLOON, I. R. H.; FREEMAN, W.; JONES, S.:
Family factors in schizophrenic relapse. Schizophr. Bull. *8,* 425–426, 1982.
VAUGHN, C. E.; SNYDER, K. S.; JONES, S.; FREEMAN W. B.; FALLOON, I. R. H.: Family factors in
schizophrenic relapse: A California replication. Arch. Gen. Psychiat. *41,* 1169–1177, 1984.
WALLACE, C. J.; NELSON, C.; LIBERMAN, R. P.; FERRIS, C.; LUKOFF, D.; FALLOON, I. R. H.: A
review and critique of social skills training with chronic schizophrenics. Schizophr. Bull. *6,*
42–64, 1980.
WALLACE, C. J.; BOONE, S. E.; DONAHOE, C. P.; FOY, D. W.: The chronic mentally disabled: Independent and living skills training. In: BARLOW, D. (ed.): Clinical handbook of psychological disorders. New York: Guilford Press, 1985.
WALLACE, C. J.; LIBERMAN, R. P.: Social skills training for schizophrenics: A controlled clinical
trial. Psychiat. Res. (in press), 1985.

109

The Efficiency of Therapeutic Relatives' Groups and Self-Help Groups for Prevention of Recidivism Among Schizophrenic Patients

G. Buchkremer, H. Schulze-Moenking

For purposes of rehabilitation it is considered reasonable to discharge schizophrenic patients after as short a hospital stay as possible or to treat them as outpatients. This does not remain without consequences for the patient's family: family members are frequently confronted with problems they feel unable to cope with. The intercourse of the family with the affected member is often characterized by uncertainty, anxiety, or vexation. Being overtaxed and helpless, the relatives frequently manifest specific patterns of emotional interactions (especially overinvolvement and excessive criticism), which significantly correlate with the frequency of relapses after discharge from the hospital (Brown et al., 1972; Vaughn & Leff, 1976a, b; Leff, 1981; Doane et al., 1985). These observations have led to the development of various concepts of therapeutic work with relatives of schizophrenic patients (Buchkremer & Lewandowski, 1984). The efficiency of these concepts will be investigated in this study with regard to prevention of recidivism.

In order to assess the efficiency of therapeutic concepts, the common hypotheses correlating emotional interaction styles and frequency of relapse will have to be defined more accurately. The following assumptions can be discriminated:

1) In a sufficiently high contact intensity an "overinvolved" or "supercritical" emotional expression behavior of the relatives of schizophrenics *induces* a relapse into acute psychosis (causality hypothesis). To adopt this hypothesis means to blame the relatives to a large extent for an unfavorable course of the illness.
2) If a patient shows schizophrenia-specific patterns of behavior indicating an increased risk of relapse, the relatives *react* to this with emotional overinvolvement (reaction hypothesis).
3) Both certain emotional interaction styles of relatives and an increased risk of relapse of schizophrenics show *correlations* with other factors influencing the course of the disease (correlation hypothesis). The reaction hypothesis as well as the correlation hypothesis tend to assign rather helpless roles to the relatives, with only slight possibilities of influencing the illness.

4) An increased risk of relapse in schizophrenic patients results from various mutually determining factors. Furthermore, there is an *interaction* between schizophrenia-specific behavioral patterns of the patient, reaction of the relatives, and other environmental factors, e.g., important life-events, social network, work situation, etc. (multiconditional hypothesis).

Based on the hypothesis of a multiconditional connection between emotional reaction styles of the relatives and risk of relapse concepts of therapeutic relatives' groups have been developed in order to prevent relapses in schizophrenic patients. In the elaboration of these concepts the multiconditional hypothesis has proved to be most fruitful, since it includes all other hypotheses, thus accounting best for the complexity of the factors triggering off the schizophrenic psychoses. Moreover, it assigns the relatives an important, but nevertheless limited, role in the prevention of relapses.

In the various approaches described in the literature the methodology of therapeutic work with relatives reveals major differences. The spectrum of therapeutic concepts covers sporadic crisis-oriented integration of the relatives into therapy (MUELLER, 1982), co-treatment of different families together with their affected family members (GOLDSTEIN et al., 1978; GOLDSTEIN & KOPEIKIN, 1981), psychoeducative (ANDERSON et al., 1981; BERKOWITZ et al., 1981) and problem-solving approaches (FALLOON, 1981; SNYDER & LIBERMAN, 1981; BERKOWITZ et al., 1981; MILLER, 1980). The extent of expert dominance in groups of relatives also varies greatly: In agreement with KATSCHNIG and KONIECZNA (1984), a decreasing degree of involvement of experts and an increasing proportion of relatives' dominance can be identified reaching from patient-centered relatives' groups past relative-centered relatives' groups to self-help groups.

In relatives' groups designed to prevent relapses, we can distinguish two main objectives:

1) *Reduction of emotional overinvolvement:* In the families of schizophrenics, social prejudices and feelings of helplessness due to lack of information frequently give rise to severe feelings of guilt and shame as well as incongruence in dealing with the patient. These attitudes often cause the families of schizophrenics to isolate themselves socially to an increasing extent and thus to focus their entire emotional involvement on the affected family member. For this reason, relatives' groups are meant to overcome feelings of guilt and shame as well as the tendency to social isolation. Therapeutic efforts reducing contact intensity between patient and emotionally overinvolved relatives serve the same purpose.

2) *Crisis management:* In therapeutic groups, relatives learn to discriminate schizophrenia-conditioned behavior from healthy behavior. Social withdrawal can thus be recognized as a symptom of illness and will no longer be interpreted as a manifestation of "ill will" on the patient's part. Detailed information on etiology, symptoms, prognoses, and possibilities of treatment given to the relatives by the group manager also helps to establish a

more realistic view of the patient's illness. These new experiences will have to be related to early experiences of the relatives concerning the onset and course of past psychotic diseases of the affected family member (ANDERSON et al., 1981; BERKOWITZ et al., 1981; BUCHKREMER & FIEDLER, 1982; GOLDSTEIN, 1981). Thus, the relatives can learn to perceive early symptoms of an imminent schizophrenic decompensation (cf. HERZ & MELVILLE, 1980) and exploit all possibilities of crisis management (GOLDSTEIN & KOPEIKIN, 1981).

Statement of the questions

Testing the efficiency of therapeutic relatives' groups and self-help groups with regard to prevention of relapses gives rise to the following complexes of questions:

1) Does psychiatric practice also allow a sufficiently reliable diagnosis of the family's emotional interaction style, which is considered a predictor for increased risk of relapse? The answer to this question determines whether theoretical knowledge obtained through extensive and relatively impracticable measuring practices can be converted into practicable concepts of therapy.
2) Can the above-mentioned objectives be achieved by the therapeutic relatives' groups and self-help groups? Above all, can emotional interaction styles be favorably altered, and can the relatives acquire an improved competence in crisis management?
3) What kind of influence do therapeutic groups exert on the course of the illness, in particular on the prevention of relapses?

Based on various published studies as well as our own investigations, we will now try to provide an answer to these questions.

Our own study covered 61 schizophrenic patients selected according to ICD criteria and included in an outpatient therapy project for relapse prevention. Thirty-seven received a therapy with mainly action- and cognition-oriented components, 24 served as control group. In addition to that, 13 families of the therapy group participated in therapeutic relatives' groups (BUCHKREMER & FIEDLER, 1982). With respect to prognosis (prognosis scale after STRAUSS & CARPENTER), medication and course of the illness, there were no differences between the patients of the therapy groups with and without relatives' groups and the control group. Focal points of the therapeutic program for the relatives were: visit at home, information on their relative's disease, recognition of early symptoms of an imminent relapse, crisis management, relief of guilt feelings, alterations of the emotional family climate (BUCHKREMER & FIEDLER, 1982).

Diagnosis of the emotional interaction style

In order to answer the first complex of questions, we examined whether theoretical results obtained through complicated measuring practices (and

112

documenting a correlation between the emotional interaction style of the relatives and the frequency of recidivism) could be replicated by less extensive and more practical survey methods.

A semi-structured interview *(Münster Family Questionnaire),* which took place at home, with all relatives and the affected family member present, was used to assess the emotional family atmosphere (BUCHKREMER et al., in preparation). Easy to learn and carried out only once, this family discussion allowed sufficiently reliable estimates with which the results of VAUGHN and LEFF (1976b) could be replicated. Surprisingly enough, patients confronted with a high degree of indifference by one or several family members also turned out to be in significantly more frequent need of rehospitalization. This result might indicate that chronically schizophrenic patients can face social isolation even within their own families and thus an increased risk of relapse similar to that of socially isolated patients (JOHNSTONE et al., 1979; COHEN & SOKO-LOVSKY, 1978; WATZL et al., 1985).

In order to simplify the diagnosis of the emotional family climate even more, we asked the schizophrenic patients (N = 61) to assess the emotional involvement of their relatives at the end of a three-month treatment phase. Again contrary to our expectations, the patients rating their relatives as over-devoted were rehospitalized significantly more often (p < 0.05) during the course of one year than the other patients. In their subjective opinion, the patients considering their relatives to be very critical experienced a significantly higher rate of relapses (p < 0.05) during the course of one year than the other patients. Therefore, the patients themselves appear to be able to recognize the strains resulting from the emotional interaction styles of their relatives.

A summarized answer to the first question will thus read as follows: Various studies using different methodologies reached the same conclusion, namely, that there is a correlation between the emotional interaction style of the relatives of schizophrenic patients and the frequency of relapse during a nine-month catamnestic period. There are indications that these findings – so far obtained employing methodologically very extensive procedures – can be replicated by simple and practicable measuring methods, making them available for psychiatric care in the future. However, more detailed research is required in order to create as valid and as reliable a diagnostic procedure as possible for registrating the emotional family climate, with means as simple as possible. Furthermore, it appears to be important to look not only at the problem of emotional overinvolvement, but also at the tendency of some families to confront the affected family member with indifference or deliberate social isolation.

Objectives of therapeutic relatives' and self-help groups

The next question to be answered is whether the therapeutic relatives' groups and self-help groups in the families of schizophrenics can reduce the emotional overinvolvement and improve crisis management.

113

By means of a treatment program, Kuipers et al. (1983) were able to reduce the extent of emotional overinvolvement and the number of critical comments of relatives in a relatives' group by a significant degree compared to a control group. The relatives' group attended to by Koettgen et al. (in press) also showed a great change in emotional interaction styles due to relatives' work, but its control group produced similar results.

The contact intensity between patient and emotionally overinvolved key person can apparently be reduced, too, as documented by Falloon (1982) in a controlled study.

In our own study patients and relatives were asked to answer a self-rating questionnaire after completion of therapy. This questionnaire comprised the following topics: relief of the relatives, attitude toward the patient, attitude toward the illness, dealing with the patient, the illness, and a possible relapse, alterations in the behavior of relatives and patients.

Our evaluation showed that according to their self-estimation, relatives who had participated in relatives' groups were able to achieve a significant improvement in dealing with schizophrenia, the affected person, and a possible relapse (Buchkremer & Fiedler, 1982). About two-thirds of the relatives believed that they would also be capable of using their newly-acquired knowledge in the future. After concluding the therapy group, nearly 75% of the relatives participating in therapy were convinced that their ability to distinguish schizophrenia-induced modes of behavior from others had improved. Seventy-five percent of the families participating in the relatives' groups felt that many of their problems had been alleviated by the group. All participants indicated having received valuable information from the group.

These positive estimations are reflected in the interview results of the patients. Schizophrenics whose relatives participated in a therapeutic relatives' group now felt that their relatives' understanding and support in preventing recidivism had improved significantly ($p < 0.05$). The patients explicitly attributed this change to the relatives' groups.

These assessments of patients and relatives could be repeated with similar significances six and twelve months after dissolving the relatives' groups. Furthermore, the contact intensity in patients whose relatives had participated in a group turned out to decrease during the course of the following six months ($p = 0.08$).

By definition, self-help groups evade scientific investigation much more easily, thereby preventing empirically verified results up to now. At present, a study supported by the German Ministry of Research and Technology is being carried out in Münster to investigate the effects of initiated self-help groups on the family climate and the course of the illness. However, it will take a year until this study produces the first empirically verified results. Meanwhile, previous experience indicates that relatives in self-help groups display the same strong need for information as those in therapeutic relatives' groups. However, self-help groups usually do not constitute themselves spontaneously; in most cases they have to be initiated by psychiatric professionals. In the course of time, "leader" personalities in the group take over the management of the group if the professional helpers withdraw sufficiently, allowing the group to make its own decisions. Adequate group cohesion develops rapidly under these circumstances. Self-help groups in urban centers can form an umbrella organization more easily.

To summarize, previous research results indicate that relatives' groups can alter the emotional family climate of schizophrenic patients positively in the sense of research hypotheses, and that they can also improve crisis management.

Influence on the course of the illness

Aside from relief and help for the relatives, therapeutic relatives' groups mainly intend to influence the course of the illness favorably, in particular to reduce the frequency of recidivism. Is this purpose indeed achieved?

GOLDSTEIN et al. (1978) were able to establish proof of the prophylactic effect on relapses if a crisis-oriented family therapy was carried out in combination with chronic pharmacotherapy. In a study on 24 families of schizophrenic patients, KUIPERS et al. (1983) reported that there were significantly less relapses over a nine-month observation period in the patients whose relatives participated in a treatment program. Improved problem-solving, fewer symptoms, and a reduction of the frequency and intensity of relapses could also be attained in patients treated with family therapy in a controlled study by FALLOON (1982).

In our own study (LEWANDOWSKI & BUCHKREMER, in press), the patients whose relatives had participated in the relatives' therapy suffered 50% less recidivism in the course of two years when compared to the patients not attending relatives' groups. Multiple manifestations were significantly more frequent in the patients without relatives' groups. We noticed furthermore that patients of relatives' groups reported psychotic symptoms that could be overcome without further therapeutic measures more than twice as often as patients without relatives' groups ($p < 0.04$). In this case, we are talking about subjectively experienced relapses that could be mastered within the family itself without psychiatric assistance.

Relating the number of stationary admissions before the beginning of therapy to the number of rehospitalizations two years after treatment (mirror method), the patients without a relatives' group showed a significant correlation ($p < 0.01$). The patients whose relatives participated in the therapy groups did not show this connection; there was merely a significant correlation ($p < 0.05$) with subjectively experienced relapses which did not require any psychiatric assistance. Therefore, it is presumably not so much the susceptibility of the patient to psychotic recidivism (vulnerability) that is favorably influenced by relatives' groups, but the capability for an improved crisis management strategy.

In conclusion, we can state that the hypothesis of a recidivism-reducing effect of therapeutic work with relatives is supported by several studies, including our own. The effect of self-help relatives' groups on the course of the disease, however, remains largely unknown.

Despite the described favorable effects of therapeutic work with relatives on the *course of schizophrenia episodes,* a final evaluation of the efficiency of relatives' groups is not yet possible. Too many questions still want an answer. For example, we still know too little about the effective components of relatives' groups and how long the effects of relatives' groups persist. Furthermore, it is important for psychiatric practice to evaluate the extent of expert involvement in relatives' groups. If it were to be demonstrated empirically that the relatives' groups must merely be initiated by experts in order to develop their full efficacy, relatives' groups might play a role similar to that of pharmacotherapy in recidivism prophylaxis in the standard treatment of chronic schizophrenic patients in the future.

Bibliography

ANDERSON, C. M.; HOGARTY, G.; REISS, D. J.: The psychoeducational family treatment of schizophrenia. In: GOLDSTEIN, M. J. (ed.): New developments in interventions with families of schizophrenics. San Francisco, Washington, London: Jossey-Bass Inc. Publishers, 1981.

BERKOWITZ, R.; KUIPERS, L.; EBERLEIN-FRIES, R.; LEFF, J.: Lowering expressed emotion in relatives of schizophrenics. In: GOLDSTEIN, M. J. (ed.): New developments in interventions with families of schizophrenics. San Francisco, Washington, London: Jossey-Bass Inc. Publishers, 1981.

BROWN, G. W.; BIRLEY, J. L. T.; WING, J. K.: Influences of family life on the course of schizophrenic disorders: A replication. Brit. J. Psychiat. *121,* 241–258, 1972.

BUCHKREMER, G.; FIEDLER, P.: Angehörigentherapie bei schizophrenen Patienten. In: HELMCHEN, H.; LINDEN, M. (Hrsg.): Psychotherapie in der Psychiatrie. Berlin, Heidelberg, New York: Springer, 141–144, 1982.

BUCHKREMER, G.; LEWANDOWSKI, L.: Therapeutische Gruppenarbeit mit Angehörigen schizophrener Patienten. In: ANGERMEYER, C.; FINZEN, A. (Hrsg.): Die Angehörigengruppe. Stuttgart: Enke, 1984.

BUCHKREMER, G.; SCHULZE-MOENKING, H.; LEWANDOWSKI, L.; WITTGEN, C.: Emotional atmosphere in families of schizophrenic outpatients. Relevance of a practice-oriented assessment instrument. In: GOLDSTEIN, M. J.; HAND, J.; HAHLWEG, K. (eds.): Treatment of schizophrenia: Family assessment and intervention (in press).

COHEN, D. J.; SOKOLOVSKI, J.: Schizophrenia and social networks. Schiz. Bull. *4,* 546, 1978.

DOANE, J. A.; FALLOON, I. R. H.; GOLDSTEIN, M. J.; MINTZ, J.: Parental affective style and the treatment of schizophrenia. Arch. Gen. Psychiat. *42,* 34–42, 1985.

FALLOON, I. R. H.: Communication and problem-solving skills training with relapsing schizophrenics and their families. In: LANSKY, M. R. (ed.): Family therapy and major psychopathology. New York: Grune & Stratton, 1981.

FALLOON, I. R. H.: Family management in the prevention of exacerbations of schizophrenia. A controlled study. New Engl. J. Med. *206,* 1982.

GOLDSTEIN, M. J.; RODNICK, E. H.; EVANS, J. R.; MAY, P. R. A.; STEINBERG, M. R.: Drug and family therapy in the aftercare of acute schizophrenics. Arch. Gen. Psychiat. *35,* 1169–1177, 1978.

GOLDSTEIN, M. J.: Family therapy during the aftercare treatment of abuse schizophrenia. In: LANSKY, M. R. (ed.): Family therapy and major psychopathology. New York: Grune & Stratton, 1981.

GOLDSTEIN, M. J.; KOPEIKIN, H. S.: Short- and long-term effects of combining drug and family therapy. In: GOLDSTEIN, M. J. (ed.): New developments in interventions with families of schizophrenics. San Francisco, Washington, London: Jossey-Bass Inc. Publishers, 1981.

HERZ, M. J.; MELVILLE, Ch.: Relapse in schizophrenia. Am. J. Psychiat. *137*, 801–805, 1980.

JOHNSTONE, E. C.; FRITH, C. D.; GOLD, A.: The outcome of severe acute schizophrenic illness after one year. Brit. J. Psychiat. *134*, 28–33, 1979.

KATSCHNIG, H.; KONIECZNA, T.: Typen der Angehörigenarbeit in der Psychiatrie. Psychiat. Prax. *11*, 137–142, 1984.

KOETTGEN, Ch.; SOENNICHSEN, I.; MOLLENHAUER, K.; JURTH, R.: Group therapy with the families of schizophrenic patients. Results of the Hamburg Camberwell Family Interview study II (in press).

KUIPERS, L.; BERKOWITZ, R.; EBERLEIN-FRIES, R.; LEFF, J.: Familienerfahrungen mit der Schizophrenie: Möglichkeiten der Modifikation. Nervenarzt *54*, 139–143, 1983.

LEFF, J. P.: Prevention of relapse of schizophrenia by social and pharmacological treatments. Bibliotheca psychiat. *160*, 15–21, 1981.

MILLER, W. H.: Systematic parent training. Champaign, IL: Research Press, 1980.

MUELLER, P.: Ambulante Behandlung akuter schizophrener Psychosen: Indikation, Vorgehen, soziale Folgen. In: HEINRICH, K. (Hrsg.): Schizophrene außerhalb der Klinik. Bern: Huber, 1982.

SNYDER, K. S.; LIBERMAN, R. P.: Family assessment and intervention with schizophrenics at risk for relapse. In: GOLDSTEIN, M. J. (ed.): New developments in interventions with families of schizophrenics. San Francisco, Washington, London: Jossey-Bass Inc. Publishers, 1981.

VAUGHN, C. E.; LEFF, J. P.: The measurement of expressed emotion in the families of psychiatric patients. Brit. J. Soc. Clin. Psychol. *15*, 157–165, 1976a.

VAUGHN, C. E.; LEFF, J. P.: The influence of family and social factors on the course of psychiatric illness: A comparison of schizophrenic and depressed neurotic patients. Brit. J. Psychiat. *129*, 125–137, 1976b.

WATZL, H.; WITTGEN, C.; COHEN, R.: "Expressed Emotion" – Leistungen und Probleme einer Forschungsrichtung – Über den Zusammenhang zwischen Familieninteraktionen und dem Verlauf von Schizophrenien. In: LZOGALIK, D.; EHLERS, W.; TEUFEL, R. (Hrsg.): Perspektiven der Psychotherapieforschung – Einzelfall, Gruppe, Institutionen. Freiburg: Hochschulverlag, 427–440, 1985.

117

Social Skills Training for the Treatment of Chronic Schizophrenics

A. S. BELLACK

One of the hallmarks of schizophrenia is severe impairment of social functioning. Deterioration of social relations is one of the defining diagnostic criteria specified in DSM-III (APA, 1980), and social isolation or withdrawal and marked impairment in major life role functioning are listed as prominent prodromal and residual symptoms. Clinical observation documents that schizophrenics are not simply withdrawn, but that they frequently appear to be "odd" and unable to relate in a "normal" manner. Even when gross symptomatology (e.g., hallucinations, delusions) is pharmacologically controlled or in remission, schizophrenic patients can be expected to have marked difficulties in social interactions (STRAUSS et al., 1974; SERBAN, 1975). Over the past 20 years, it has become widely accepted that poor social competence predates the onset of the disorder (STRAUSS et al., 1977; ZIGLER & PHILIPS, 1961, 1978) and there are considerable data suggesting that many adult schizophrenics exhibited maladaptive patterns of interpersonal functioning beginning in early childhood (LEWINE et al., 1978, 1980; WATT, 1978). Poor premorbid social competence has been related to the etiology of schizophrenia, as well as to treatment compliance and outcome. Moreover, level of premorbid competence remains one of the best prognostic indicators: the poorer the premorbid adjustment, the poorer the prognosis (STRAUSS et al., 1977).

In light of all these marked difficulties in social competence, one of the most promising approaches for improving social functioning and enhancing quality of life is social skills training (BELLACK & HERSEN, 1978; LIBERMAN et al., 1979). Social skills training is a structured learning program that teaches the skills necessary to develop a social network and reduce the stress resulting from interpersonal conflict and failure. A large number of studies has shown that skills training can be successfully applied to chronic patients (BELLACK et al., 1976; FINCH & WALLACE, 1977). However, few studies have focused on a well-diagnosed sample of schizophrenic patients in an ongoing clinical program. The research to be described below was designed to evaluate the effects of social skills training for chronic schizophrenic patients as part of a comprehensive partial hospital program.

Method

Subjects

Sixty-four schizophrenic patients at the Day Hospital Program at Western Psychiatric Institute and Clinic (WPIC) served as subjects. All were new admissions to the Day Hospital (i.e., within 2–4 weeks of beginning the protocol), most having been recently discharged from one of the inpatient units at WPIC or a local state psychiatric hospital. Diagnosis was independently confirmed by two M.D. or Ph.D. clinicians according to the FEIGHNER et al. (1972) criteria. The mean age of the sample was 32.7 years (range = 18–58). There were 38 males and 26 females, of whom 29 were black and 35 white. Only two of the patients were married. Mean I.Q. was 96.2 (range = 61–130). The subjects comprised a very chronic sample: they had a mean of 4.9 prior psychiatric hospitalizations, and the mean history of their illness was 10.84 years (range = 2–35).

Treatment groups

The core treatment for all subjects was the Day Hospital Program. Situated on a ward at WPIC, the program had an average daily census of approximately 25–30 patients. Patients were scheduled for 7 hours per day, 3–5 days per week. Following the social learning theory model, the program was highly structured and had an educational-rehabilitative focus. Patients spent approximately 5 hours per day in therapeutic activities, which consisted primarily of various educational and therapy groups. These groups were all focused and task oriented, but they did not follow a specific manual or curriculum. Each patient was assigned a care coordinator, who provided individual therapy and helped the patient to develop a schedule tailored to his or her idiosyncratic needs. The therapy was primarily supportive and focused on solving problems in daily living. All patients were administered neuroleptic medication by the same psychiatric staff in accord with current clinical practice. Both depot and ingestibles were prescribed as needed.

Subjects were randomly assigned to Day Hospital only (DH), as described above, or to day hospital plus Social Skills Training (SST). Subjects in the SST condition received 3 hours per week of group social skills training as part of their schedule, in lieu of 3 hours of one of the other group therapies. The skills training was conducted in small groups by two M.A. or B.A. level therapists, in accordance with a highly structured treatment manual (BEIDEL et al., 1981). In recognition of the severe social functioning deficits characteristic of chronic patients, the training focused on basic skills thought to be necessary for these patients to establish a social network and reduce stress in interpersonal encounters: (a) initiating, maintaining, and ending brief conversations; (b) standing up for one's rights and reducing unreasonable requests; and (c) expressing positive feelings, such as praise and appreciation. In addition, "special topics" such as dating skills and job interview skills were covered when applicable to more than one group member. Finally, training was provided in social perception: attending to cues provided by interpersonal partners.

SST involved five procedures. Subjects were first given specific, clear Instructions on how and why to perform targeted responses. Therapists then Modeled the appropriate way to perform the response. Subjects then took turns Role Playing the response, first with a therapist and then with one another. After each role play, the therapists provided specific Feedback and Positive Reinforcement. At the conclusion of each session, subjects received specific Homework assignments to facilitate practice of new responses in the environment. Training was graduated in difficulty within and across sessions to insure that subjects achieved success.

Subjects in both groups (DH and SST) received 12 weeks of treatment. At the end of that period they were discharged to an appropriate community mental health facility for outpatient treatment. For the most part, this entailed continued medication supervision with minimal psychosocial treatment.

Measures

Subjects were assessed with a variety of widely used instruments, including: the *Hopkins Symptom Checklist* (DEROGATIS et al., 1974), the *Wolpe-Lazarus Assertiveness Scale* (WOLPE & LAZARUS, 1966), the *Psychiatric Status Schedule* (SPITZER et al., 1970), and a *Behavioral Role Play Test* (BELLACK & MORRISON, 1982). The *Psychiatric Status Schedule* was administered by an experienced psychiatrist who was blind to the subject's treatment group. The *Role Play Test* consisted of 18 brief role-play interactions with members of the research staff. Responses were videotaped and subsequently rated on a variety of dimensions by trained raters who were blind to the subject's treatment group. Subjects were assessed before treatment, at the conclusion of treatment, and again 6 months later. We attempted to conduct a 12-month follow-up, but too few patients were available to permit valid conclusions. However, we were able to collect data on rehospitalization during the 12 months following treatment for most subjects. Those data will be reported below.

Results

The DH and SST groups were initially examined to determine if they were equivalent on age, sex, race, IQ, and history of prior hospitalizations. A series of chi square analyses and *t* tests revealed no significant differences on any of these variables. Three (of 20) subjects in the DH group were lost due to psychiatric hospitalization during the course of treatment, and two dropped out for other reasons. Three (of 44) subjects in the SST group were hospitalized and 12 others dropped out. Neither of these differences was significant (on chi square tests). A series of *t* tests comparing patients who completed treatment with those who did not revealed no differences at baseline on any measure (i.e., drop-outs were not more symptomatic, older, etc.).

The initial evaluation of the comparative efficacy of the two treatments was conducted with a series of *t* tests on pre-post change scores. These analyses were almost uniformly non-significant, reflecting a consistent lack of differences. However, examination of the data suggested that this finding was due, in part, to the fact that both groups improved. Therefore, we conducted a series of pre-post (correlated) *t* tests in which each group was examined separately. As shown in Table 1, subjects in the SST group did not report themselves to be improved on the *Hopkins Symptom Checklist*. However, the independent evaluator rated them as substantially improved on the *Psychiatric Status Schedule* (PSS). There were significant differences on each subscale and on the Total score. SST subjects also showed specific gains in social skill. They rated themselves as significantly more assertive on the *Wolpe-Lazarus Assertiveness Scale*. Performance on each item of the *Role Play Test* (RPT) was scored for Overall Skill on a 5-point Likert-type scale. Scores were analyzed separately for positive assertion items, negative assertion items, and conversation skill

Table 1: Pre-Treatment vs. Post-Treatment Analyses

	SST		DH	
	t	p value	t	p value
Hopkins Symptom Checklist				
Total Score	.78	NS	1.70	.06
Somatization	1.35	NS	1.05	NS
Obsessive Compulsive	.24	NS	2.08	.03
Interpersonal Sensitivity	.54	NS	.28	NS
Depression	1.34	NS	2.96	.01
Anxiety	.27	NS	1.67	.06
Psychiatric Status Schedule				
Total	2.89	.004	2.59	.01
Subjective Distress	2.23	.02	1.63	.07
Behavioral Disturbance	2.27	.02	2.00	.04
Impulse Control Disturbance	1.14	NS	1.05	NS
Reality Testing Disturbance	1.72	.05	2.61	.01
Wolpe-Lazarus Assertiveness Inventory	2.97	.003	.82	NS
Overall Social Skill	4.92	.001	1.08	NS

items. Reliability, calculated on 25% of subjects, was above .80 for each subset. Subjects receiving SST showed highly significant improvement on each set of items, as well as on an overall score reflecting all 18 items.

Subjects in the DH group also improved, but not as uniformly (see Table 1). They registered significant gains on the Obsessive Compulsive and Depression Scales of the Hopkins, and the Anxiety and Total scales reached borderline levels of significance. The independent evaluator rated them as significantly improved on the Behavioral Disturbance, Reality Testing, and Total scales of the PSS. All other scales on each instrument, including the Wolpe-Lazarus, were not significant.

The next series of analyses was designed to assess the durability of treatment effects. Seven DH and 20 SST subjects were available for the 6-month follow-up assessment. Change scores were calculated for each subject from post-treatment to the 6-month follow-up. The DH and SST groups were then compared by a series of t tests. The results are presented in Table 2. In contrast to the pre-post analyses, the SST group was consistently better. They either continued to improve or maintained their gains on most measures, while the DH group either maintained gains or lost them.

Table 2: Post-Treatment to 6-Month Follow-Up

| | Mean change | | | |
	SST	DH	t	p value
Hopkins Symptom Checklist				
Total Score	.275	-.132	3.07	.005
Somatization	.134	-.074	1.68	NS
Obsessive Compulsive	.525	-.155	2.92	.01
Interpersonal Sensitivity	.278	-.182	3.10	.006
Anxiety	.313	-.082	2.43	.02
Depression	.123	-.164	1.62	NS
Psychiatric Status Schedule				
Total Score	9.90	-6.42	2.98	.008
Subjective Distress	10.45	-6.28	2.77	.01
Behavioral Disturbance	9.55	1.00	1.69	NS
Impulse Control Disturbance	9.40	-.857	2.39	.02
Reality Testing Disturbance	11.15	-3.28	2.68	.01
Wolpe-Lazarus Assertiveness Inventory	.650	.285	.15	NS
Overall Social Skill	.091	-.20	.85	NS

On the Hopkins, SST was significantly better on Total score, Obsessive Compulsive, Interpersonal Sensitivity, and Anxiety. They were significantly better on all PSS scales except Behavioral Disturbance, although a separate group correlated *t* test indicated that they were significantly improved even on that scale (t = 2.13, p < .05). There were no group differences on either the Wolpe-Lazarus or the Overall Skill scales, and neither group showed any significant changes on within group *t*-tests.

We attempted to conduct a 12-month follow-up, but were unable to get an adequate sample of patients to come in for the assessment. However, we were able to secure data on rehospitalization for almost all patients who completed the 3-month training program. Fourteen of the 29 subjects in SST were rehospitalized during the year. One was hospitalized five times (106 days), while all the others were hospitalized one or two times (range 3–50 days). Six of twelve DH subjects were hospitalized. One was hospitalized five times (120 days), and the remaining five had one or two hospitalizations (range 1–25 days). There were no differences between the groups on number of patients hospitalized or days in the hospital.

Discussion

These results provide considerable support for the efficacy of social skills training. The SST condition produced substantial improvement during treatment, and these gains were enhanced during the 6-month follow-up. These findings are notable in several respects. First, the effects of SST were not limited to changes on specific, narrow behavioral response components (e.g., eye contact, voice volume). They were evident on important areas of functioning and core symptoms, as denoted by gains on the PSS and Hopkins. Second, the effects were discernable over and above the core day treatment program, which was itself a viable therapeutic intervention. This underscores the independent contribution of the highly focused and structured training. Third, the effects were durable. The gains were enhanced or maintained over the 6 months following treatment. This finding must be interpreted with caution as there are fewer subjects available at the 6-month assessment. Nevertheless, the results do suggest that social skills training is more than an ephemeral intervention producing changes on meaningless behaviors. Rather, it can produce meaningful clinical changes.

In some respects, our results are discouraging. Almost 50% of the patients were rehospitalized at least once during the 12 months after treatment was terminated. While the interventions had positive effects, clearly they were not sufficient to rectify the severe and broad-based handicaps of these chronic patients. In retrospect and in light of recent data from other research, it seems apparent that our program was too limited. Patients attended the program 5 days per week for 12 weeks. But we did not provide evening or weekend social activities or any supplementary social service support. Furthermore, patients were terminated after 21 weeks and referred to an outpatient medication clinic. Thus, treatment was too brief and did not adequately deal with the broad range of handicaps and life-skill deficits characteristic of this population.

Our findings reflect a general problem with the customary approach to service delivery. Following an infectious disease model, we tend to think of time-limited interventions: treat and cure. We must shift to a chronic disease model. Like diabetes, schizophrenics may need life-long treatment. Intensive educational or rehabilitation programs must be intertwined with ongoing support systems and intermittent rehospitalization. Moreover, we must do a better job of insuring continuity of care. As was the case in our research program, the various elements of the treatment and social service systems generally do not work together to coordinate efforts. As a result, patients tend to get lost between the cracks in the system. It is vital that someone or some group help bridge the gaps between service providers, and provide some constancy over time. No one intervention will be adequate in isolation, and no short-term intervention can be expected to produce enduring effects.

One additional issue should also be addressed, albeit briefly. Subjects in the social skills training condition did not all respond equally well. As with any intervention, there was considerable individual difference, which was masked by the grouped data analysis. Unfortunately, the small numbers of subjects left in the social skills condition at the various post-treatment and follow-up assessments precluded differentiation of patient factors which led to success or failure. This is clearly a high priority for future research. Schizophrenia cannot be regarded as a homogeneous disorder, and social skills training is not suitable for all patients meeting diagnostic criteria. In fact, some of our patients were clearly able to perform effectively when they chose to do so. We must be able to determine who *needs* social skills training, who can *profit* from it, and *when* patients will be receptive to it.

Bibliography

AMERICAN PSYCHIATRIC ASSOCIATION: Diagnostic and statistical manual of mental disorders, 3rd edition. Washington, D.C.: APA, 1980.

BEIDEL, D. C.; BELLACK, A. S.; TURNER, S. M.: Social skills training for chronic psychiatric patients: A treatment manual. JSAS catalog of selected documents in psychology *11*, 36, 1981.

BELLACK, A. S.; HERSEN, M.; TURNER, S. M.: Generalization effects of social skills training in chronic schizophrenics: An experimental analysis. Behav. Res. Therapy *14*, 391-298, 1976.

BELLACK, A. S.; HERSEN, M.: Chronic psychiatric patients: Social skills training. In: HERSEN, M.; BELLACK, A. S. (eds.): Behavior therapy in the psychiatric setting. Baltimore: Williams & Wilkins, 1978.

BELLACK, A. S.; MORRISON, R. L.: Interpersonal dysfunction. In: BELLACK, A. S.; HERSEN, M.; KAZDIN, A. E. (eds.): International handbook of behavior modification and therapy. New York: Plenum, 1982.

DEROGATIS, L. R.; LIPMAN, R. S.; RICKLES, K.: The Hopkins Symptom Checklist (HSCL): A self-report symptom inventory. Behav. Scien. *19*, 1-15, 1974.

FEIGHNER, J. P.; ROBINS, E.; GUZE, S. B.: Diagnostic criteria for use in psychiatric research. Arch. Gen. Psychiat. *26*, 57-63, 1972.

FINCH, B. E.; WALLACE, C. J.: Successful interpersonal skills training with schizophrenic patients. J. Consul. Clin. Psychol. *45*, 885-890, 1977.

LEWINE, R. R. J.; WATT, N. F.; FRYER, J. H.: A study of childhood social competence, adult premorbid competence and psychiatric outcome in three schizophrenic types. J. Abnorm. Psychol. *87*, 271–294, 1978.

LEWINE, R. R. J.; WATT, N. F.; PRENTKY, R.; FRYER, J. H.: Childhood social competence in functionally disordered psychiatric patients and in normals. J. Abnorm. Psychol. *89*, 132–138, 1980.

LIBERMAN, R. P.; WALLACE, C. J.; VAUGHN, C. E.: Social and family factors in the course of schizophrenia: Towards an interpersonal problem-solving therapy for schizophrenics and their families. Conference on psychotherapy of schizophrenia: Current status and new directions. New Haven, April 9, 1979.

SERBAN, G.: Functioning ability in schizophrenic and normal subjects: Short-term prediction for rehospitalization of schizophrenics. Compreh. Psychiat. *16*, 447–456, 1975.

SPITZER, R.; ENDICOTT, J.; FLEISS, J.: The Psychiatric Status Schedule. Arch. Gen. Psychiat. *23*, 41–55, 1970.

STRAUSS, J. S.; CARPENTER, W. T. Jr.; BARTKO, J. J.: The diagnosis and understanding of schizophrenia. Part. III. Speculations on the processes that underlie schizophrenic symptoms and signs. Schizophr. Bull. *11*, 61–69, 1974.

STRAUSS, J. S.; KOKES, R. K.; KLORMAN, R.; SACKSTEDER, J. J.: Premorbid adjustment in schizophrenia. Concepts, measures and implications. Schizophr. Bull. *3*, 182–244, 1977.

WATT, C. G.: Patterns of childhood social development in adult schizophrenics. Arch. Gen. Psychiat. *35*, 160–170, 1978.

WOLPE, J.; LAZARUS, A. A.: Behavioral therapy techniques. New York: Pergamon Press, 1966.

ZIGLER, E.; PHILIPS, L.: Social competence and outcome in psychiatric disorder. J. Abnorm. Soc. Psychol. *63*, 264–271, 1961.

ZIGLER, E.; PHILIPS, L.: Social effectiveness and symptomatic behaviors. J. Abnorm. Soc. Psychol. *87*, 271–294, 1978.

125

Basic Symptoms and Coping Behavior in Schizophrenia

G. Gross

HUBER has drawn attention to the subjectively experienced basic symptoms by developing the concept of basic disorders and by concerning himself with the apparently uncharacteristic stages in the course of schizophrenia (HUBER, 1966, 1968, 1976, 1979, 1983). In the uncharacteristic pre- and postpsychotic, reversible or persistent, basic stages, basic symptoms are – from a psychopathological point of view – experienced and described by the patients themselves as disorders and impairments. These *substrate-close basic symptoms* (HUBER, 1966) constitute the real primary symptoms of schizophrenic illness. They remain subjective and are closer to the hypothesized somatic substrate than the complex psychotic endphenomena. Hypothetically speaking, basic symptoms are ascribed to impairments of selective information processing and to genetically determined biochemical disturbances in the limbic system ("limbo(thymo)pathy" – HUBER, 1971, 1983; GROSS & HUBER, 1985).

Basic symptoms are not specific in the sense of being exclusive to schizophrenia. They can also be observed in cyclothymic depressions, in the so-called schizoaffective psychoses, and in definable brain diseases, though not in healthy individuals or in psychoreactive disorders. For the clinical use of the concept, it is important that basic symptoms display extreme fluctuations, both in their manifestation and degree, depending on given situations or strains, and on an endogenous level, i.e., without a discernible cause; the basic stages constituted by them can show very different degrees of process activity (HUBER & PENIN, 1968; PENIN et al., 1982).

To standardize documentation of basic symptoms, we established the **Bonn Scale for the Assessment of Basic Symptoms (BSABS).** This rating scale is based on the subjectively experienced and reported complaints of 450 patients who had been hospitalized at least once in their lives with the diagnosis of schizophrenia, and who were re-examined by us after an average course duration of 22.4 years. Specifically, we studied 202 patients with irreversible postpsychotic basic stages (pure defective stage – HUBER, 1961), 64 patients with reversible postpsychotic basic stages (HUBER, 1966), and 184 patients with uncharacteristic prepsychotic prodromes (GROSS, 1969; HUBER et al., 1979; GROSS & HUBER, 1985).

The BSABS prescribes no special method of examination and dispenses with a quantitative graduation for documentation. The psychopathological exploration is not directed and structured only in the second part, without, however, providing for a standardized interview with fixed

126

phrasing and succession of questions. Since basic symptoms frequently occur phasically or paroxysmally, and since they fluctuate on a situational or endogenous level, documentation must be accorded a longer period of time before the actual exploration. As early as 1966, HUBER took the view that pure defective syndromes are often more likely to act as an inclination to failure and can remain almost completely compensated under favorable environmental conditions, which the findings of the Bonn Study confirm (HUBER, 1966, 1976, 1983).

Rooted in a Heidelberg checklist of 1962 (HUBER) with 78 items, the BSABS is not oriented to a traditional diagnostic grouping, nor is it constructed for a traditional diagnosis in an individual case. Rather, it is clinically descriptive, symptom- and syndrome-related, and avoids restrictive nosological references. Still, all the patients examined had definitely been diagnosed as being schizophrenics on the basis of SCHNEIDER's criteria.

In the BSABS, basic symptoms are registered in six main categories and 104 single items: dynamic deficiencies (A): *direct minus symptoms (DMS);* dynamic deficiencies (B): *indirect minus symptoms (IMS);* (C.1) *cognitive thought* and (C.2) *perception disorders;* (D) *coenesthesias;* (E) *central-vegetative and motor disturbances;* and (F) *coping mechanisms.* Each basic symptom is defined by means of distinct criteria, commented upon in a glossary and illustrated by typical statements.

For the clinical utilization of the concept of basic disorders, it is important that basic symptoms be accessible to inner perception and communicable. In the light of the course of the disease over decades, most patients are able to view their basic symptoms with critical detachment, to recognize their deficiencies as such, and to develop coping, shielding, and avoidance strategies, based on their unfavorable experiences in situations of comparative overstimulation. The patients learn how much strain they are capable of absorbing in social contacts and professional performance, avoiding situations that provoke or intensify their symptoms. Thus, their autism is often secondary (HUBER, 1971). Patients with basic symptoms try to manage their disturbances with manifold coping strategies (HUBER, 1966, 1979, 1983; GROSS & HUBER, 1985).

Taking into account all basic symptoms reported to us by our patients, we were able to differentiate several types of **coping mechanisms:**

1. Avoidance psychisms (F.1): The patients strive to avoid situations entailing subjectively experienced negative, i.e., potentially unpleasant and undesirable, consequences that would cause overtaxation. Sometimes such situations entail negative consequences only in particular stages of the illness, especially in phases of endogenous lability with increased impressionability, and generally not in stable periods without signs of process activity.

The following situations are avoided most frequently:

1. Confrontations with the past psychosis and the contents of the remitted productive-psychotic phase, e.g., while talking with the therapist. Reactualizing contents can cause symptoms to intensify or to reappear, since it acts as a current overstimulation.

2. Contacts with other persons, implicating a visual and/or acoustic overstimulation ("unspecific stress") through informations that are affectively

primarily neutral, but too numerous or too contradictory: e.g. being caught up in crowds or working under time pressure. Since the patients try to avoid these situations or at least to control them, they increasingly withdraw from social contacts in the sense of secondary autism (HUBER, 1971; GROSS & HUBER, 1985).

3. Emotionally affecting, usually negatively tinted behavior, conversations or discussions of or with others which do not immediately concern the patients personally, or real or fictitious events with negative portents, insofar as the patients are able to avoid them, e.g., reading the paper, listening to the radio, or watching television.

4. Strain through physical or mental demands.

Even though they are useful and often effective per se, these avoidance psychisms can lead to several modes of behavior that probably have to be evaluated as socially negative and undesirable, e.g., the above-mentioned "secondary autism."

2. Compensatory mechanisms (F.2): Patients try to compensate for their deficiencies or mitigate their effects through certain techniques or modes of behavior. They organize their work, deal with things one after the other, reduce their work speed ("compensatory narrowing and limiting"), or take breaks; they limit their apprehension span, restrict themselves to only one perceptional factor or to partial aspects of a procedure; and they shield themselves against other stimuli or try to distract themselves – e.g., through physical work – in order to mitigate the effects of increased impressionability.

3. Adaptive psychisms (F.3): Through habit and/or adaptation, the patients have adjusted to the basic deficiencies caused by the disease; they have submitted to them and do not suffer as much anymore. Or through their negative experiences they have developed a certain routine so that their avoidance mechanisms in certain situations are no longer so obvious.

4. Attempts to compensate basic deficiencies and the decreases in performance caused by them *by an effort of will* (F.4): Like patients in endogenous depressive phases with psychomotor inhibition, schizophrenics complain about needing more energy to do their work or having to fight the illness.

5. Practice mechanisms (F.5): Patients deliberately practice certain functions or performances they experience as weakened or impaired.

By means of the main categories of the BSABS, we would now like to consider the above-mentioned coping attempts in detail and illustrate them with typical statements.

The first main category of the BSABS, the **direct dynamic deficiencies** (A) or direct minus symptoms (DMS), includes complaints about increased physical and mental *exhaustibility* (A.1) and *decreased energy, resilience, and perseverance* (A.3). These primary disorders occur with physical or mental strain

128

the patient could cope with quite easily before the onset of the illness; they take the form of general weakness, weariness, or decreased capability. As a direct reaction to their deficiencies, the patients tend to not letting themselves make an effort (objectively: apparent drooping). In contrast to their premorbid behavior, they display an inclination to rest, they interrupt their activities for hours or even days at a time, and sit or lie down frequently.

Apart from these symptoms of exhaustibility and weariness, physical or mental strain can provoke *indirect minus symptoms* (IMS) such as inner restlessness and excitation, troubled sleep, obsessive brooding, coenesthesias, or central-vegetative disorders. Triggering factors can be physical work in and around the house or on the job, sports or such commonplace tasks as dressing, eating, or doing handiworks. Mental strains most frequently leading to symptom provocation include visitors, conversations, or activities that require close concentration, like reading difficult texts. Patients try to avoid such situations and additional workloads as well as excitement surrounding problems or emotionally affecting events, as they can provoke or intensify their symptoms.

> I have less energy than before, taking care of my household and children is a big strain, I get tired more rapidly and have to rest more often. – Compared to before, my capability is negligible. If I plan to do something important, I have to stay in bed until noon, so I can work at least two to four hours in a row in the afternoon. – Nowadays, I can keep up everything only for a short time, 15 minutes at the most. If I work longer, I get a very unpleasant burning feeling all over my body and I can't fall asleep. – It's not like before the disease anymore, my energy and my vigor are almost gone, and my working capability has diminished. I have to make a very big effort to be able to do my job, so my colleagues don't realize something is wrong. – I'm not persistent or patient anymore; handiworks, for example, make me all fidgety. I have to lay things aside I've just begun and take a break; I can't start again until quite some time afterwards or have to do something completely different. – I have to avoid big tasks because I get very dissatisfied about not being able to do them, which makes me feel restless inside. – As I'm always overtaxed because everything wears me out, I'm much more reticent than before; otherwise, my character hasn't changed.

Diminished maximum stress (A.8) means a lower tolerance threshold to new and unusual demands or affectively neutral everyday situations exceeding the individual information-processing capacity. The patients try to avoid situations with unexpected or surprising new demands that require a re-adaptation (novophobia in the sense of SUELLWOLD) (A.8.1). Dynamic deficits are expressed in descriptions like: such situation are stressful, overstraining, or overexerting. Because of previous experiences, the patients fear that these strains might lead up to troubled sleep, coenesthesias, inner restlessness and excitation, or even psychotic relapses. For this reason, they attempt to avoid additional workloads or unusual situations that involve changes of environment and quantitatively or qualitatively unfavorable stimulation (A.8.2), for instance, large crowds, conversations with or about other people, visitors, festivities, the hubbub in department stores or public transport, milling crowds downtown, or immediate optic and/or acoustic (over-) stimulation, e.g., through electronic media or noises. The patients cannot tolerate such information, as it is too numerous, too intensive and/or ambiguous and confusing.

129

I can't stand crowds, for example, in church. I can't even walk by crowds of people, nor do I accept invitations, since they are much too trying. – Actually, I would rather like to be among people, but the mere presence of people makes me uneasy. – I can't bear many people talking, especially not all at once, which is why I can't join in family celebrations, for example. – Department stores are unbearable, much too tiring, which is why I have to do all my shopping in very small stores. – The milling crowds downtown make me very uneasy and jumpy, and my well-being gets considerably worse. Traffic, too, excites my nervous system. Sometimes it gets so bad that I feel sick and can't think straight anymore. – Television is unbearable, the pictures change much too fast; so I've stopped it. – I can't listen to the radio, watch TV, or read for a longer period of time. If I do, I can't go to sleep anymore.

The diminished capability to work under time pressure (A.8.3) or to split attention (A.8.4) belong to the same main category of the BSABS. Patients are unable to meet various rapidly changing demands within a given amount of time. Therefore, they try to avoid such situations as far as possible, or to compensate for the deficiencies with certain modes of behavior.

I simply can't handle situations anymore where somebody wants this and somebody else wants that. I have to organize everything very carefully, do one thing after the other, just so I can manage. – I have to organize my work. If things start to pile up, I don't know where to start, which wears me out completely so I can't do anything at all. – Compared to before, when I actually enjoyed such situations, I can't work under time pressure anymore, which is why I avoid rushing things and have to do everything in peace.

In the second main category of dynamic deficiencies, the (B) **indirect minus symptoms (IMS),** the most important item is increased impressionability (B.2). Everyday events, emotionally negative minimal occasions (B.2.1), modes of behavior and expressions of others, or discussions and arguments with others immediately concerning the patient or close persons (B.2.2) are experienced more frequently and intensely as insulting, disparaging, or offending than before the onset of the illness. The suffering of others, too, i.e., real or fictitious negative information relayed by the media or memories of the previous disease (B.2.3), provoke indirect minus symptoms, especially obsessive brooding. In intraindividual comparisons, such events leave a more intensive and lasting impression than before the illness.

I can't bear bad news in the paper, on the radio, or on TV anymore. The same goes for exciting movies or books: They grieve me too much, I get excited and nervous, start to brood, and I can't get any sleep, so I try to shield myself from all this. – When I have been under mental strain during the day, I still have to think about these problems before falling asleep, and then I can't fall asleep. As a matter of fact, people should get a chance to talk to people with intellectual interests more often, so they could practice unwinding more easily. – While preparing the documents concerning my illness, I had the impression of experiencing certain phrases or words very intensively, not as usual, as if I had heard them. Of course, I know that there were no "voices," but the thoughts were so vivid that afterwards I didn't know whether I had heard them or not. – Nowadays, I am much too compassionate, not about my own suffering, but about that of others. I didn't use to let things touch me that deeply. My wife and my children have adjusted to this and keep excitement away from me if possible. – I have stopped reading the paper and watching TV because I can't stand it anymore. I feel like a nervous wreck afterwards, I get much too involved in everything, and I get so upset I can't sleep anymore. – I can't watch TV except on weekends, or else I can't get any sleep at all.

Exceeding the tolerance threshold of processing outside impressions can provoke psychotic symptoms. Indirect minus symptoms or psychotic phenomena can be caused both by conversations and mental dealing with certain problems in which the patient takes great interest, even though they do not have to be of personal concern. If the triggering situation persists or if impressions – whether emotionally negative or positive – are too intensive, the symptoms can change from uncharacteristic symptoms of step 1 to step 2 with comparatively characteristic symptoms into the productive-psychotic symptoms of step 3 (HUBER & PENIN, 1968; GROSS & HUBER, 1985).

The third main category (C.1) deals with **cognitive thought disorders.** Types 1 to 7 can be summarized under the heading of "losing control of thought processes" (HUBER, 1957, 1961, 1966, 1983).

In the subtype interference of thought (C.1.1), patients notice the intrusion of notions that have nothing to do with the current train of thought and can be tied to external impressions. They cause increased distractibility and disturbances of selective attentiveness.

I can't do piece-work anymore because my thoughts get mixed up and I lose my temper. – I can't do fulltime jobs anymore because I lose the thread much too fast and my thoughts can't keep up with the work I'm doing. Nowadays, I can only do very simple chores because I don't have to think so much doing them. – When I work for longer periods of time, I get extremely tired and my thoughts become all confused.

The patients try to counter the frequently registered disturbances of concentration (C.1.5) and of memory (C.1.8–C.1.11), and the subjectively experienced vacancy of mind or blocking of the current train of thought (C.1.4), by organizing their work, by shielding themselves, by reducing the speed of work, by finishing tasks immediately, by writing everything down, by controlling their activities, or by trying to improve lost abilities, e.g., concentration or memory, through training them.

I can't concentrate or get things done anymore unless the conditions are extremely favorable, so I have to shield myself against all other possible impressions. – I have to think really hard in order not to forget everything. So when I go shopping, I write everything I need down. In addition to that, I have to get everything done at once or write it down, or else I forget it all immediately. – In my new apartment, I simply can't remember what is behind all those cupboard doors. Therefore, I have pasted little labels with their contents onto the doors, which I didn't need before. – I've noticed that I had lost track of my complicated work as an accountant, which is why I had to take on a simpler job. – I have to pay very close attention if I want to remember something because I always lose the thread so fast. – After too much strain at work or lack of sleep, every thought takes up much more time than usual, and I have to start again and again.

Patients with disorders of receptive speech (C.1.6) either do not grasp the meaning of written or spoken words, sequences of words, or phrases, or only with great effort and incompletely (SUELLWOLD, 1977, 1983). They try to offset this disorder by reading more slowly from the start and taking into account that reading takes up more time than before the onset of the illness. Thus, a more or less far-reaching compensation for this disorder can be achieved by reading a text slowly or several times, or by reading it out loud.

Among others, there are also relations between cognitive basic symptoms and secondary coping reactions in the form of obsessive symptoms, mainly controlling compulsions. Because of the cognitive basic disorders, patients lose confidence in their own capabilities. Therefore, they attempt to cope with their disorders through obsessive controlling mechanisms. By their increasingly stereotypic nature, these anankastic phenomena can often acquire the character of disorders themselves (SUELLWOLD, 1982, 1983).

In case of disturbances of expressive speech (C.1.7) – the self-perceived complication of speech due to deficient actualization of fitting words, the patient may try to compensate this deficit by repeating incalculated phrases (SUELLWOLD, 1977, 1983). With an increase in such stereotypes, a patient's vocabulary can become destitute. If this symptom is markedly intensified, it can lead to the poverty of speech ANDREASEN describes in the SANS. Other attempts to cope with the impaired linguistic precision include avoiding conversations (resulting in secondary autism), confining oneself to general sentences, or displaying a striking taciturnity.

The patients try to counter *cognitive perception disorders* (C.2) in the form of blurred vision, hypersensitivity to light or visual stimuli in general (C.2.3), or in the form of changes in the intensity and quality of acoustic perception (C.2.7) with hypersensitivity to noise (C.2.8), by wearing new prescription glasses, sunglasses, or by avoiding situations that might involve loud noises.

Coenesthesias (D), the fourth main category, belong to the most frequent basic symptoms (70%) in all types of reversible or irreversible hypergic basic stages. Coenesthesias predominantly occur as paroxysms setting in with or without external stimuli and lasting for seconds, minutes, or hours. The linkage of coenesthesia, asthenia, and dysthymia is common and typical in all basic stages (HUBER, 1966). First described as schizophrenic physical sensations by HUBER in 1957, coenesthesias usually concur with decreased vitality, and show a phenomenal similarity to spontaneous sensations of the thalamus (HUBER, 1957, 1971, 1976).

Patients suffering from coenesthesias try to mitigate them with adequate countermeasures, or they avoid situations that are likely to trigger them off. For instance, they cool down or warm up affected parts of the body, or try to alleviate these qualitatively abnormal sensations, through certain movements or gymnastic exercises, fixed rules of conduct, or keeping a diet.

At night, I often get pains in my right lower belly, my legs feel completely stiff, and my body starts to itch and burn, so the only way I can sleep is with my feet hanging out of the bed. – I have to avoid eating certain foods, e.g., potatoes, since they cause a terrible burning inside my body, thighs, and feet, and my stomach and liver start to swell, so I can't get any sleep all night. I mustn't drink any liquor, either, as this makes the inner pain grow quite severe. – When I go for a walk, my legs turn like numb every 200 yards or so, it feels as if something were stagnating inside, and that hurts terribly. After I've rested for a while, the feeling goes away again. – When something has up-

132

set me, my forehead starts to hurt, it feels icecold, and I have to put on warm stupes to make it go away. – Especially when the weather changes, I get stomach aches, unbearable shooting pains in my chest and lungs and up my back, so that I have to pound my chest really hard to make the pain go away. – If I comb my hair the wrong way, I get violent pains below my scalp, which is why I've had to change my hairdo and comb my hair forward. – Especially when I've overstrained myself, I get a burning feeling in my muscles and toetips, like poison ivy, and there is a pressure in the area of stomach, liver, and gallbladder, but more often inside than towards the outside. I can relieve the pain and make the pressure go away by doing special exercises. – I'd like to work, but I can't because if I overexert myself, my hands and feet and my whole body start stiffening, and I can't move anymore. After two hours' rest, the feeling is gone. – I often get a violent throbbing on the inside of my thighs down to my feet. If that happens, I can't wear nylons anymore because they make it even worse. – I often get headaches, a sort of pressure in the middle of my head, a static kind of pain that makes it difficult to think, and it gets worse if I move my head, so I mustn't move my head until the pain is gone. – My feet often feel incredibly warm, as if they were steaming. I have to put them under running cold water or in a bucket full of cold water to cool them down.

The patients try to avoid the provocation of **central-vegetative disorders** (E.1), including troubled sleep (E.2) and intolerance of certain kinds of food (E.3), by changing their habits. In case of intolerance, for instance, they avoid the incompatible substances and their unpleasant consequences either by keeping certain diets or by changing their eating and drinking habits.

The patients' personal experiences with their disorders and their way of coping with them or of avoiding certain triggering situations to prevent them from occurring could provide us with valuable information for the *development of adequate therapeutical concepts.* These concepts would have to consider the different basic symptoms, their interindividually varying emphasis, and their intraindividual fluctuations. It is important to identify the situations that intensify basic deficiencies according to experience or provoke them in a disturbing degree to begin with. These findings form the basis of strategies enabling patients to avoid such situations as far as possible. The breakdown susceptibility under certain critical conditions, e.g., big workloads, emotional stimulation, or differing everyday situations, which overstrain the patient's information-processing capacity, not only causes a decrease in the patient's efficiency, it also allows the understanding of reactions and behavior that at first seem inexplicable to the environment and uncanny and threatening to the patient himself (HUBER, 1983; SUELLWOLD, 1977, 1983).

The different types of coping mechanisms are particularly important with regard to the development of therapeutical and rehabilitative concepts and to our dealing with the patients. Postpsychotic basic stages always mean a more or less marked degree of breakdown susceptibility. Experience shows us that schizophrenic patients are very susceptible to changes of the environment (HUBER, 1966). Triggering factors, such as physical or mental activities and demands, emotionally affecting events, or everyday situations, represent a risk in the intraindividual comparison to the premorbid situation. The danger of intensification and provocation of psychotic relapses can be mitigated through a combination of neuroleptic treatment and therapeutical concepts adequately structured with respect to intensity and quality. Our own results support the hypothesis that long-term prognosis is more favorable and complete remission more frequent, if an adequate drug treatment combined with supportive psychotherapy and specially developed forms of behavioral therapy commences as early as possible, taking into account the basic deficiencies of prodromes (GROSS et al., 1983; HUBER et al., 1979).

Bibliography

ANDREASEN, N. C.; OLSEN, S.: Negative vs. positive schizophrenia. Definition and validation. Arch. Gen. Psychiat. *39,* 789–794, 1982.

GROSS, G.: Prodrome und Vorpostensyndrome schizophrener Erkrankungen. In: HUBER, G. (Hrsg.): Schizophrenie und Zyklothymie. Ergebnisse und Probleme. Stuttgart: Thieme, 1969.

GROSS, G.: Bonner Untersuchungsinstrument zur standardisierten Erhebung und Dokumentation von Basissymptomen (BSABS). In: HUBER, G. (Hrsg.): Basisstadien endogener Psychosen und das Borderline-Problem. Stuttgart, New York: Schattauer, 1985 (in press).

GROSS, G.; HUBER, G.: Die Bedeutung diagnostischer Konzepte und Kriterien für die biologisch-psychiatrische Forschung bei schizophrenen und schizo-affektiven Psychosen. In: HOPF, A.; BECKMANN, H. (Hrsg.): Forschungen zur biologischen Psychiatrie. Berlin, Heidelberg, New York: Springer, 1984.

GROSS, G.; HUBER, G.: Das Konzept der Basissymptome in der klinischen Anwendung. In: JANZARIK, W. (Hrsg.): Psychopathologie und Praxis. Stuttgart: Enke, 1985.

GROSS, G.; HUBER, G.; SCHUETTLER, R.; HASSE-SANDER, I.: Uncharakteristische Remissionstypen im Verlauf schizophrener Erkrankungen. In: HUBER, G. (Hrsg.): Ätiologie der Schizophrenien. Stuttgart, New York: Schattauer, 1971.

GROSS, G.; HUBER, G.; SCHUETTLER, R.: Verlauf schizophrener Erkrankungen unter den gegenwärtigen Behandlungsmöglichkeiten. In: HIPPIUS, H.; KLEIN, H. E. (Hrsg.): Therapie mit Neuroleptika. Erlangen: perimed, 1983.

HUBER, G.: Pneumencephalographische und psychopathologische Bilder bei endogenen Psychosen. Monographien aus dem Gesamtgebiete der Psychiatrie und Neurologie, Bd. 79. Berlin, Göttingen, Heidelberg: Springer, 1957.

HUBER, G.: Die coenästhetische Schizophrenie. Fortschr. Neurol. Psychiat. *25,* 491–520, 1957.

HUBER, G.: Chronische Schizophrenie. Synopsis klinischer und neuroradiologischer Untersuchungen an defektschizophrenen Anstaltspatienten. Heidelberg, Frankfurt: Dr. Hüthig, 1961.

HUBER, G.: Reine Defektsyndrome und Basisstadien endogener Psychosen. Fortschr. Neurol. Psychiat. *34,* 409–426, 1966.

HUBER, G.: Verlaufsprobleme schizophrener Erkrankungen. Schweiz. Arch. Neurol. Neurochir. Psychiatr. *101,* 346–368, 1968.

HUBER, G.: Schlußbemerkung zum Stand der Ursachenforschung bei den Schizophrenien. In: HUBER, G. (Hrsg.): Ätiologie der Schizophrenien, Bestandesaufnahme und Zukunftsperspektiven. Stuttgart, New York: Schattauer, 1971.

HUBER, G.: Indizien für die Somatosehypothese bei den Schizophrenien. Fortschr. Neurol. Psychiat. *44,* 77–94, 1976.

HUBER, G.: Das Konzept substratnaher Basissymptome und seine Bedeutung für Theorie und Therapie schizophrener Erkrankungen. Nervenarzt *54,* 23–32, 1983.

HUBER, G.; GROSS, G.; SCHUETTLER, R.: Verlaufs- und sozialpsychiatrische Langzeituntersuchungen an den 1945 bis 1959 in Bonn hospitalisierten schizophrenen Kranken. Monographien aus dem Gesamtgebiete der Psychiatrie, Bd. 21. Berlin, Heidelberg, New York: Springer, 1979 (Nachdruck 1984).

HUBER, G.; PENIN, H.: Klinisch-elektroenzephalographische Korrelationsuntersuchungen bei Schizophrenen. Fortschr. Neurol. Psychiat. *36,* 641–659, 1968.

PENIN, H.; GROSS, G.; HUBER, G.: Elektroenzephalographisch-psychopathologische Untersuchungen in Basisstadien endogener Psychosen. In: HUBER, G. (Hrsg.): Endogene Psychosen: Diagnostik, Basissymptome und biologische Parameter. Stuttgart, New York: Schattauer, 1982.

SUELLWOLD, L.: Symptome schizophrener Erkrankungen. Uncharakteristische Basisstörungen. Monographien aus dem Gesamtgebiete der Psychiatrie, Bd. 13. Berlin, Heidelberg, New York: Springer, 1977.

SUELLWOLD, L.: Zwangsmechanismen und Basisstörungen. In: HUBER, G. (Hrsg.): Endogene Psychosen: Diagnostik, Basissymptome und biologische Parameter. Stuttgart, New York: Schattauer, 1982.

SUELLWOLD, L.: Schizophrenie. Stuttgart, Berlin, Köln, Mainz: Kohlhammer, 1983.

On the Importance of Cognitive Disorders in Treatment and Rehabilitation

H. D. Brenner

In more than eight decades of intensive schizophrenia research, none of the etiological factors perceived to be essential in various areas of research have been proven to constitute either a sufficient or even just necessary condition for the development of schizophrenic illnesses. The present state of knowledge does not even allow us to exclude the possibility that each of these factors plays merely a supplementary role in the genesis of schizophrenia. If this were the case, we would have to deal with *psychopathological manifestations of equivalent phenomenology but varying etiopathogenesis.* As a consequence of this uncertainty, we are now experiencing an increasing interest in integrative concepts of schizophrenia (cf. ZUBIN & SPRING, 1977; STRAUSS & CARPENTER, 1981; CIOMPI, 1982). Despite essential differences concerning their starting points, approaches, and emphases, they all converge toward a *Vulnerability-Stress Model* in which earlier assumptions are assimilated and developed (cf., e.g., the Diathesis-Stress Model of ROSENTHAL, 1970).

The current state of the discussion is depicted in a very simplified manner in the following diagram (cf. FALLOON et al., 1984):

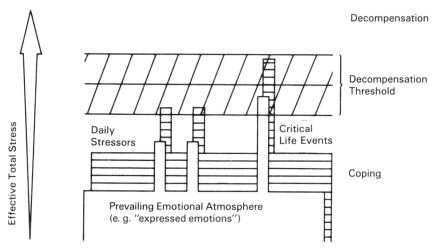

Figure 1: Components of the vulnerability-stress model of schizophrenia

In addition to acute daily strains, so-called critical "life events" are of particular importance as stressors. These may or may not be specific to the individual. They accumulate and interact in a complex way with chronically effective factors such as the prevailing emotional atmosphere, which can either intensify or weaken the effects of acute stress, or function as stressors by themselves. If the total strain exceeds a certain individually variable tolerance threshold in the sense of a person-related moderator variable (cf. BOEKER & BRENNER, 1983), this results – depending on the currently available possibilities for coping – in a breakdown of the (premorbid, at any rate deficient) order of the "psychische Bestände" (repertoire) (cf. VON UEXKUELL, 1979), manifested by psychotic modes of behavior. In this case, the range of coping possibilities can be described on different levels: for example, (1) with regard to cognitive processes as subjective evaluations of stress factors, or as cognitions in the sense of attribution theory, self-image, etc.; (2) with regard to prodromal and prepsychotic symptoms in the sense of the reactions intended to cope with them; (3) with regard to social competence as communicative and social skills; (4) depending on the social network as offering social support or hindrance in coping with stress.

Figure 1 also permits a schematic classification of the various *psycho-social intervention approaches*. For example, therapeutic interventions intending to influence the family environment attempt to ease the tension present in the emotional atmosphere, whereas approaches emphasizing training in social skills or supporting the self-stabilizing efforts of schizophrenics aim at raising the decompensation threshold by improving the ability for coping, albeit in different ways.

Vulnerability research itself has only just begun; there is still no consensus as to its conceptualization and integration into etiological models. Moreover, it will differ in the various areas of research. In the approach presented here, for instance, vulnerability can manifest itself in varying tolerance thresholds against stressors (thereby giving rise to direct relationships with specific characteristics in autonomous responsiveness and in the autonomous level of arousal; cf. STRAUBE, 1979), in an individually specific height of the decompensation threshold, and finally in deficits of social competence and the specific coping abilities. Thus, in accordance with this conception, vulnerability cannot be evaluated one-dimensionally, nor can it be described as orthogonally related to the remaining components of the model, even though ZUBIN and SPRING (1977) proceed in this manner in their model.

In processes leading up to a critical overtaxing of the vulnerable personality and consequently bringing about psychotic behavior, the main point of interest – with regard to the *clinical relevance* of the vulnerability model – consists in the nature of the interaction between currently effective stressors and existing vulnerability characteristics. Remarkably enough, the different conceptions of the vulnerability-stress model agree that a leading role in this process is played by cognitive disorders in the sense of disturbances in information processing, which have to be considered an expression of the vulnerability to schizophrenia, or rather the cause of an increased susceptibility to stress. This is an entirely plausible assumption, since several such disorders have repeatedly been found in risk populations, and in both active and remitted schizophrenics, so they can be regarded as vulnerability indicators (cf. NUECHTERLEIN & DAWSON, 1984b).

This makes it understandable that increasing attention is being drawn to the importance of disturbances in information processing for the treatment and rehabilitation of schizophrenic patients. However, none of the current conceptions of the vulnerability-stress model integrates these disorders in a sufficiently differentiated form. Thus, we still lack a deeper understanding of those processes that have very descriptively been characterized as "runaways," namely, the intermediate processes between pre-existing vulnerability characteristics and manifest behavior disorders. Accordingly, the corresponding therapeutic recommendations remain general and vague: shielding from stimuli, reducing the quantity of information, clear and unambiguous information, structuring, simplifying, and clarifying the dealings with patients and the whole therapeutic environment – these are all unspecific measures, which at the very best can lead to a facilitation of information processing, but do not directly influence the underlying disorders themselves. This is an unsatisfactory state of affairs and deserves greater attention both clinically and in research.

The concept of *information processing,* which originates with cognitive psychology, comprises all the processes that classify, combine, and evaluate information forming the basis of experience and behavior. Theories of human information processing attempt to follow the flow of information from intake past processing to the transformation into observable behavior, thereby considering the human organism an open cybernetic system. In this context, Figure 2 is not meant to represent a certain model of human information processing, but to illustrate the principles and hypothesis-generating potential involved as opposed to classical research with an exclusively clinical/phenomenological orientation.

Numerous studies about specific disorders in information processing as vulnerability characteristics have already been published. NUECHTERLEIN and DAWSON (1984b) recently gave an excellent review of these studies, which are essentially based on the primarily experimental-psychological and psychophysiological Anglo-American research into a "core psychological deficit" of schizophrenia (cf. BRENNER et al., 1983).

Especially difficulties in the following areas of information processing are described as basic cognitive deficits of schizophrenic patients: selection of relevant and rejection of irrelevant stimuli; maintenance or flexible shifting of focused attention; recognition, identification, integration, and storage of stimuli; the availability of earlier experiences for processes of comparison. Previous conceptions regarding specific disturbances in elementary cognitive operations or dysfunctions during given stages of information processing as a basis and explanation of all schizophrenic phenomena can no longer be main-

138

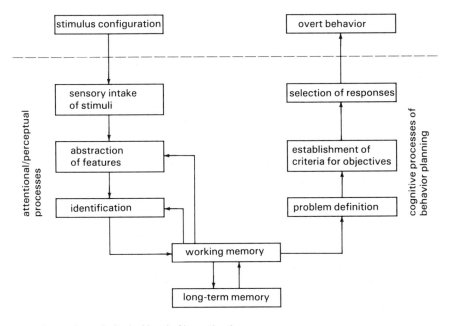

- experimental-psychological level of investigation

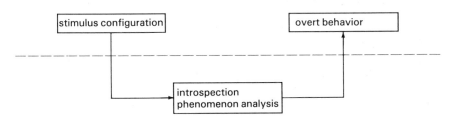

- clinical-phenomenological level of investigation

Figure 2: Cognitive functions in the processing of information

tained. Higher integrative, evaluative, and directive processes are much more likely to be impaired. Substantial progress in the direction of such an integrative understanding of these disorders has been realized by new conceptions of attention as a limited, unspecific processing capacity, which under normal circumstances can be flexibly shifted to specific tasks in accordance with the respective demands, on the one hand, and on the other hand by the concepts of simultaneous or parallel (as opposed to serial) information processing. While simultaneous processing makes use of quasi-automatic processes essentially based on fixed sequences of mental operations with direct access to long-term storage and requiring only little processing capacity, serial information processing requires a great deal of controlling and directive processing capacity, thereby limiting simultaneous processing possibilities for other cognitive operations. In recent years, these concepts have above all led to a modification of the traditional separation between attention and memory, and to an increasing interest in lasting dispositions or rules of involuntary attention. The emphasis was placed on abnormal allocation strategies dependent on deficits in automatic processing, on context probability, on momentary intentions, or on other demand characteristics.

In cognitive psychology, there is no dispute about basic disorders of information processing impairing not only higher mental functions such as judgement, but also emotions and overt behavior. In the area of schizophrenia research, BLEULER (1911) supported the opinion that primary disorders of elementary cognitive processes substantially contribute to the so-called thought disorders of schizophrenics. In the course of Anglo-American investigations into a core psychological deficit of schizophrenia, the relationships between cognitive disorders in the sense of deficits in information processing and symptoms of schizophrenic illness have been considerably expanded, especially with regard to schizophrenia-specific linguistic phenomena, delusions, and hallucinations as well as weak ego-boundaries. For instance, lack of availability of information stored in the long-term memory must lead to an inadequate coordination of thoughts, conceptions, and perceptions. In some cases, this might become so extreme that they are experienced as not one's own, perhaps as being produced externally (cf. BROEN & STORMS, 1967; HEMSLEY, 1977).

In the German-speaking world, HUBER and his colleagues, rooted in the "Grundstörungsdiskussion" (core deficit) of German psychopathology, took up these Anglo-American studies on the core psychological deficit (or rather deficits) in their *concept of basic disorders* ("Basisstörungskonzept"), albeit without including the current discussion of cognitive vulnerability characteristics (cf. HUBER, 1983; GROSS, this volume). According to their concept,

a neurochemical disturbance leads to an impairment of information processing in the transphenomenal area with a levelling of hierarchies of experience, and to a few basic disorders which are contained as common links – although with different shares – in the manifold and relatively substratum-close basic symptoms experienced by the patient, and in the schizophrenia-specific final and superstructural phenomena developing through amalgation with the anthropological matrix (HUBER, 1983, p. 23).

Thus, this approach is characterized by presupposing a common cognitive basic disorder in the transphenomenal area as a hypothetical link to prephenomenal abnormalities in somatic and particularly in neurochemical and neurophysiological brain functions.

L. SUELLWOLD (1977) deserves especial credit for systematically studying the clinically/phenomenologically registered basic symptoms on an experiential-psychological level, and for standardizing them by means of the *Frankfurt Complaints Questionnaire* as so-called "uncharacteristic basic disorders." On this basis, she described four disorder dimensions established through factor analysis: disorders in automated behavior, disorders in perception, depression and anhedonia, and stimulus overload. Not the least, her investigations demonstrated that the actual primary symptom formation in schizophrenic illness remains largely subjective. Observable characteristics often already belong to compensatory and coping behavior (cf. SUELLWOLD, this volume).

It seems to me that the concept of basic disorders ("Basisstörungskonzept") of HUBER and his colleagues can be criticized for two reasons. First, this concept proposes a one-directional sequence from neurobiochemical dysfunctions via disorders in information processing to substratum-close basic symptoms and finally to the manifest psychosis itself, without taking into account the systemic approach of other current conceptions of schizophrenia. Second, the direct leap from basic symptoms to the transphenomenal construct of the leveling of reaction hierarchies, which is meant to provide a global explanation for as many cognitive disorders as possible, does not correspond to the status quo of experimental schizophrenia research. It seems a precipitous evasion onto the metapsychological level, which cannot be understood unless we consider both the somatogenetic postulate HUBER supports so emphatically and his endeavor to connect the basic symptoms as closely as possible to the somatic substratum. However, the direct referral to neurophysiological explanatory models leaves important questions about intermediate processes unanswered. The concept of basic disorders, therefore, lacks a psychological foundation reaching beyond the area of subjective experience.

It is my conviction that such a foundation can only be attained through an investigatory approach that assigns a crucial role to the intermediating position of disturbances in information processing at the critical transition point between existing vulnerability characteristics and manifest symptoms of the illness, i.e., to the relationships between specific components of the cognitive system, and specific symptoms and patterns of symptoms. In this approach, the disorders in information processing, which have been discussed as vulnerability characteristics, must be included in the *analysis of the development and organization of schizophrenic behavior.* I am thinking in terms of a hierarchic consideration of the behavioral organization integrating relatively molecular functions into increasingly complex molar behavior. Independently of this problem, SPAULDING (1986) recently proposed such an analysis for severe behavioral disorders in adults. Figure 3 is meant to illustrate this approach. It is based on three major assumptions:

1. Schizophrenic patients display deficits on *different functional levels.*
2. The different functional levels are *hierarchically related* to one another.
3. Deficiencies on *molecular* levels lead to functional disturbances on *molar* levels.

In this approach, the term "basic disorder" refers to specific deficiencies of schizophrenics on the more molecular functional levels of the behavioral organization.

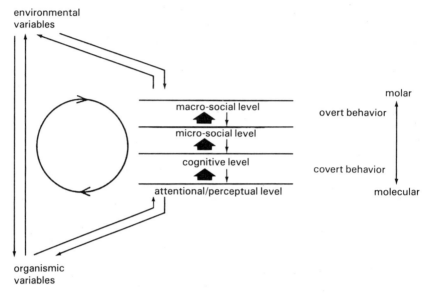

Figure 3: Schematic representation of the hierarchic development and organization of deficient behavior in schizophrenics

This approach allows us to conceptualize the different functional levels schematically into four categories:

1. the *attentional/perceptual* level. Most of the disorders in information processing described as vulnerability characteristics must be assigned to this level.
2. the *cognitive* level. This includes, e.g., disturbances in the formation and modulation of concepts, in prelinguistic associative processes, or in attributions.
3. the *micro-social* level. Essentially, this is the level of the so-called social skills, i.e., the overt behavioral functions taking place in the social context and being directly observable.
4. the *macro-social* level. This mainly involves the implementation of complex tasks in the sense of performing specific social roles.

As we know from experimental schizophrenia research, on each of the hierarchically subordinated levels there are numerous measurable deficiencies that can impair the functioning on the next higher level. More molar functions,

142

however, may have repercussions on elementary functions, too. For example, specific attentional disorders could occur only after a failure in a social situation, or improvements of micro-social and macro-social skills could lead to a normalization of inappropriate attributions. Such considerations make it clear that we must expect very complex processes to be involved in the manifestation of vulnerability-linked deficits. This manifestation is mediated by a large number of continuous factors; as part of this process, a specific deficit may lead to different patterns of behavior, and specific patterns of behavior may be caused by different deficits. Thus, the distinction between vulnerability-linked and symptom-linked deficits emphasized by various authors (CROMWELL & SPAULDING, 1978; NUECHTERLEIN & DAWSON, 1984a; SPAULDING, 1986) consists of different developmental stages of deficient processes rather than of disorders differing in principle. Likewise, the peculiarities described as vulnerability indicators on the level of instrumental and social skills and coping abilities are probably the result of elementary dysfunctions rather than of separate factors.

Furthermore, Figure 3 illustrates that the explanation of the variance involved in deficient behavior on a given level, which cannot be explained by molecular deficits, necessitates the inclusion of environmental and/or organismic variables interacting with all of the described functional levels as well as with each other. The organismic variables that have to be taken into account are primarily specific psychophysiological characteristics that investigations, mainly of electrodermal activity, have shown to be correlated not only with experimental-psychologically defined disorders in information processing, but also with unusual features of observable behavior. In turn, these are directly related to regulatory dysfunctions of the neuro-transmitter system and to disorders of the structural integration in the limbic system, hippocampus, and cerebellum (cf. STRAUBE, 1983). The most important environmental factors involved are discrete discriminative stimuli and social contingencies, situational stressors or mediators such as the prevailing emotional atmosphere or the social support network, as well as critical life events, which can interact with deficiencies described on the different functional levels in specific ways.

Thus, the vulnerability-stress model is fully represented in this approach. In the area of the hierarchic development and organization of behavior, disturbing influences from multiple sources, which can be assessed qualitatively as well as quantitatively, lead to deficiencies on the micro-social and macro-social functional levels, and this in different combinations. Some of these influences can be self-sufficient, others cannot, or only based on mutual accumulation and interaction. Beyond the limited behavioral aspect, an individual having difficulties controlling the intensity and processing of information is bound to display a reduced tolerance of interpersonal strain. Since our most intensive emotional experiences usually occur in family relationships, this is particularly true for intensive, ambiguous, or ambivalent communication within the family. On account of attentional and perceptual disorders, such situations are experienced as being more complex than they would be in case of normal information processing. Discrepancies between perception and imagination prevent the necessary integration, which directly intensifies the cognitive deficiencies. This also can happen indirectly, e.g., if the environment reacts with irritation or disapproval. If there is a build-up of such interactions, it can trigger off a total collapse of information processing.

Contrary to the concept of basic disorders ("Basisstörungskonzept") of HUBER et al., which displays too great an orientation toward nomothetic trait-theories and diagnostic models, this approach permits psychopathological research to conceptualize further investigations into the process of developing psychotic symptoms from the existing vulnerability characteristics. This is impossible on the empirical basis of subjectively experienced basic disorders alone, which in the best of cases are indicators for vulnerability-linked disorders taking effect. It is impossible because subjective experience does not allow a definite separation between primary disorder, processing, and coping reaction.

Although the gap between specific disorders in information processing and manifest psychosis is therefore still wide with regard to the pathogenetically relevant intermediary processes, the present knowledge concerning vulnerability-linked or symptom-linked deficiencies on the different functional levels of behavior permits us to draw important *conclusions for therapeutic interventions:*

1. The possibilities and efficiency of therapeutic interventions on a given functional level are influenced by simultaneously existing deficiencies on other functional levels. In particular, interventions on molecular levels may improve treatment possibilities on molar levels.
2. As a rule, therapeutic interventions should not be restricted to a single functional level, and interventions on different levels should be planned, carried out, and evaluated independently of one another.
3. On the molecular functional level, we can register vulnerability-linked deficiencies that are of special significance for the course of the illness because they exert a more permanent and basal influence than do disturbances on the more molar levels of overt behavior. Thus, they require attention even if they are not influencing micro-social and macro-social functions.

These statements are supported by numerous observations that improvements on the functional levels of overt behavior can be accompanied by deterioration on other functional levels, particularly by exacerbations of attentional, perceptual, and cognitive deficiencies (cf. HEMSLEY, 1977; SCHOOLER & SPOHN, 1982). Furthermore, they explain – at least partly – the ineffectiveness of certain therapy programs aimed at the level of overt behavior, or the common sudden loss of improvements already achieved. However, problems in generalizing and mediating social contingencies presumably also contribute to the latter of these two shortcomings.

144

With regard to the importance of basic disorders for treatment and rehabilitation, it is possible to differentiate schematically *three phases. Acute psychotic decompensation* is characterized by the collapse of all systematic information processing, which affects overt behavior in the sense of disorganization (cf. CROMWELL, 1978). The affected patient tries to use behavioral strategies that are supposed to reduce the related over-stimulation by limiting the reception of stimuli or by reorganizing attentional, perceptual, and cognitive processes. The main objective of this behavior is reducing excitation, not coping with tasks. In this case, treatment with neuroleptics is a matter of priority. In addition to that, however, help may be provided by methods that have been proposed by various authors, namely, the afore-mentioned unspecific measures to simplify and structure the information coming from the outside world. Nevertheless, a better understanding of the disorders in information processing would allow for more concrete recommendations to be made (cf. CHAPMAN, 1966; PLAUM, 1982; BRENNER et al., in press). For instance, the following recommendations can be given for conducting conversations: use of indirect exploratory techniques; as extensive an acceptance of the disruptive forms of behavior as possible; sitting face to face with the patient; reducing speech to bare necessities; speech should be calm, slow, and not too loud, and, if necessary, what has been said should be repeated using the same words and tone; if auditory perception is disturbed, sparse and concise gestures to clarify what is said; otherwise, strict avoidance of expansive gesturing, of playing with objects, excessive modulation of speech, etc.

In a *second phase,* the patient is sufficiently reorganized, in spite of the continuing productive symptoms, to make use of behavior strategies that are supposed to help avoid another complete breakdown of information processing. These strategies can sometimes convey the impression of being psychotic symptoms in themselves. Information processing remains extremely labile, and its disturbance is subjectively experienced in a rather severe way. Our experience makes us believe that it is helpful to address the subjective basic disorders we at first suppose and later ascertain with regard to the history of the decompensation, and to indicate possibilities of compensation and coping. This way, the patients feel understood in these experiences that have remained incomprehensible and uncanny for them, and which they had never been able to put into words. Merely addressing these disorders and indicating effective ways of coping with them is frequently sufficient to reassure the patient and to achieve an immediate reduction of psychotic symptoms. Although we still lack systematic investigations, recognizing and compensating or overcoming subjectively experienced basic disorders is – according to our experience – as important in this phase of the illness as in the stages preceding decompensation (cf. BRENNER et al., 1987; BOEKER, this volume).

Finally, in a *third phase,* there are only discrete psychotic symptoms or unspecific signs of disorganized behavior. Irrespective of whether the preceding loss of effective defense and coping mechanisms was of a functional nature, or whether there are already structural changes present, all treatment efforts must now be aimed at relapse prophylaxis and at completing insufficiently developed or lost behavior programs. With regard to the hierarchic development and organization of behavioral deficiencies ranging from specific elementary dysfunctions to peculiarities in overt behavior, it is therefore of primary therapeutic importance during this phase to take existing basic disorders into account.

Regardless of these different phases, a considerable number of patients, especially those with frequent psychotic decompensation followed by good social remission, might be subjected to a pronounced susceptibility to disturbance in information processing causing all by itself – in spite of undisturbed functioning on the molar level – the tolerance for stress to be reduced to a point critical for psychotic breakdown. In the case of these patients, therapeutic interventions on the functional level of overt behavior alone would be useless.

While therapy programs for deficiencies in overt behavior, for instance, training of social skills or teaching problem-solving strategies, are numerous, differentiated, and well documented (e.g., WALLACE & BOONE, 1984), there are much fewer descriptions of therapeutic approaches on the cognitive level. Apart from the self-instruction training of MEICHENBAUM and CAMERON (1974, 1975), approaches aimed at mastering and reducing manifest clinical symptoms deserve special mention (cf. FALLOON & TALBOT, 1981; FALLOON, this volume). Only rarely are the relationships between the different functional levels explicitly integrated in therapy programs, as has been proposed, e.g., in the cognitive analysis of the acquisition of social skills by WALLACE and BOONE (1984) or of problem-solving by SIEGEL and SPIVACK (1976). Finally, the number of papers on concerted therapeutic influencing of specific deficiencies on the attentional-perceptual functional level is extremely low. SPAULDING et al. (1986) recently reported attempts to exert direct influence by means of the operant reinforcement of attentive behavior or of self-instruction training.

Based on the conviction that therapeutic interventions limited to the schizophrenics' molar levels of behavior, i.e., without taking their basal attentional/perceptual and cognitive deficiencies into consideration, neglect fundamental disorders, we established a small working group, first in Mannheim (1976), then in Berne, in which we gradually developed a therapy program for the integrated training of cognitive, communicative, and social skills. Since then, we have constantly been attempting to examine and include new research results and experiences (BRENNER et al., 1980; STRAMKE & BRENNER, 1983; RODER et al., 1987; BRENNER et al., 1987; BRENNER et al., in press).

As illustrated in Figure 4, this therapy program consists of five subprograms concerned with practicing attentional/perceptual and cognitive functions followed by training social skills and problem-solving skills, always in groups of five to seven patients.

The five therapy programs individually stress the training of *cognitive differentiation, social perception, verbal communication, social skills,* and *interpersonal problem-solving.* Figure 4 also shows that the emphasis of therapeutic work slowly shifts from cognitive processes to general social competence and all the social skills connected with it. Both dimensions, however, are inseparably linked in every step of practical therapeutic work. As the therapy continues, emotionally

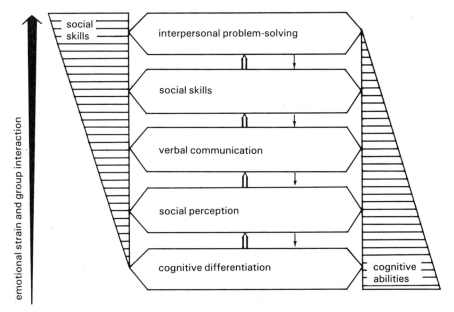

Figure 4: Schematic representation of therapy programs

charged material or themes are introduced more and more often, and group processes are intensified.

On account of the inseparable links between the cognitive and social dimensions, learning programs based on experimental psychology with their abstract stimulus material and their mostly meaningless task settings are not suited to therapeutic use. Correspondingly – and contrary to the necessities of investigations into pathogenetic processes – the therapeutic contents on the more molecular functional levels are not formulated with regard to individual dysfunctions, but rather to specific tasks in which schizophrenic patients regularly display deficiencies, even under different conditions using different methods of measurement.

All training programs require continuous practice of fundamental cognitive functions such as selective attention or shifts of attention, focused attention over a longer period of time, maintenance of a concerted readiness to react, etc. Specifically, the first subprogram of cognitive differentiation is concerned with functions such as concept formation (this kind of deficit refers to the formation of classes or concepts depending on unimportant features leading to unusual and overgeneralized combinations), abstraction ability and concept modulation (a fixation onto concrete thought would be such a deficit, e.g., taking proverbs literally), recall, as well as the formation and processing of associatively linked concept hierarchies. The second subprogram – social perception – aims above all at disturbances in processes of stimulus discrimination (e.g., size constancy, depth perception, figure-background differentiations, contrast perception) and at stimulus interpretation (e.g., context probability, familiarity, etc.) in perceiving and assessing social interactions. The subprogram of verbal communication is oriented according to the numerous findings about the strain on communication in the families of schizophrenics because of vague or contradictory information, talking at cross purposes, derogating other people's opinions, etc. Such strains arise primarily if the conversational situation becomes emotionally charged. Thus, the objective of this subprogram consists of enabling group members to respect the contributions of other members, to understand the thoughts of the others while disregarding one's own, to establish connections between one's own thoughts and those of others, and the training of the associative-semantic processes involved in the production of speech. The subprogram of social skills is best characterized by stressing the essential differences to the well-known techniques of behavior modification used in role-playing and self-assertiveness training, like detailed cognitive prestructuring and preparation; an only gradual transition to the principle of model-learning; at first merely informative and then motivational reinforcement; direct influencing of internal processes of self-regulation such as self-perception and evaluation, etc. Finally, the subprogram of interpersonal problem-solving attempts to convey more effective possibilities of coping with potential stressors, with the individual therapeutic steps closely connected to the cognitive analysis of the acquisition of problem-solving strategies.

For a detailed description of the therapy program and an extensive critical discussion of the evaluative studies carried out until now, the reader is referred to STRAMKE et al. (1983 a & b), BRENNER (in press), and BRENNER et al. (in press). The essential aspects of this therapy program have been adopted by several other working groups, some of whom have modified and subjected them to evaluative studies with comparable results (cf. KRAEMER et al., 1985; SCHMID, 1984; HERMANUTZ & GESTRICH, 1985).

Although the different studies still raise several methodological problems, it is possible to formulate a cautious *overall result:* (1) Corresponding psychological therapy programs for schizophrenic cognitive disorders seem suited to bring about improvements of the following assessed variables not only in moderately chronic patients, but also in those who have been hospitalized for many years: visual perception, short-term memory, attentional functions, nonverbal abstraction ability, verbal and cognitive differentiation capability, as well as social perception and problem-solving ability. (2) The data from catamnestic investigations carried out 18 months after the end of treatment – investigations in which determining the level of psycho-social functioning and ascertaining the readmission rate allows at least a summary assessment of the socially most relevant changes – provide evidence for a general relevance of these improvements in treatment and rehabilitation, i.e., for their generalization up to the macro-social functional level. (3) It still remains unclear, however, whether these therapeutic effects are based on a reduction of the cognitive disorders or on conveying and training effective compensation strategies (BRENNER et al., 1985). Probably these two levels are connected to each other by means of constant circular interaction processes.

Two further observations are founded on the basis of many years of therapeutic experience rather than on quantitative data: (1) In therapy (and presumably also in psychopathological research), the peculiarities of the information processing system can only be understood within the context of the development and present social environment of a given individual. Specific deficiencies are often related to factors external to the consideration of the hierarchic organization of these deficiencies. Thus, cause-effect relationships can only in the rarest of cases be determined exclusively through experimental and clinical features on the different functional levels. Moreover, improvements on a given functional level should not automatically be expected to be effective on other levels. Likewise, changes in overt behavior that are, for example, the result of training in problem-solving or social skills cannot be expected to be generalized onto the natural environment without transference of cues, instructions, and reinforcements. Such a transference can best be achieved by including individuals important to the patient as social mediators. (2) Deficiencies on the different functional levels hardly display stable interindividual interrelations. Patients apparently showing similar behavioral features may be suffering from quite different deficiencies on the attentional/perceptual and cognitive functional levels.

Based on the results of available investigations and the practical experience gained in the therapy of cognitive disorders, I wish to draw the following *conclusions* for further research and therapeutic work in this area: Developing and differentiating therapy programs founded on experience and intermediate evaluative studies with control-group designs has all in all proven its worth. With regard to the problems that still have to be solved, e.g., a greater understanding of the effects of therapy, which would permit greater specificity of therapeutic intervention, questions of differential indications for the complete program and the individual sub-program, etc., a closer connection between experimental psychopathology and therapy guided by hypotheses is necessary. It seems to me that this can only be achieved if single-case studies provide the basis for theoretical concepts and treatment programs to be integrated, aiming at the transitional area between existing vulnerability characteristics and disturbances in overt behavior. As part of this process, a multiple assessment of the deficiencies on a patient's different functional levels should lead to intervention programs guided by deductively derived and testable hypotheses regarding their hierarchic connections and external relations. The underlying theoretical assumptions would then either be validated, modified, or abandoned according to whether the corresponding treatment succeeds or fails. In my opinion, this is also the most promising way toward a further clarification of the nature of the intermediate processes between existing vulnerability characteristics and deficiencies in overt behavior. Pathogenetic and therapeutic research would thus enter into a relationship that promises much for the future.

Bibliography

BLEULER, E.: Dementia praecox oder die Gruppe der Schizophrenien. Leipzig: Deuticke, 1911.
BOEKER, W.; BRENNER, H. D.: Selbstheilungsversuche Schizophrener: Psychopathologische Befunde und Folgerungen für Forschung und Therapie. Nervenarzt *54*, 578–589, 1983.
BRENNER, H. D. (Hrsg.): Therapieprogramm zur Behandlung von Basisstörungen bei schizophrenen Menschen. Therapiemanual. München: Urban & Schwarzenberg (in press).
BRENNER, H. D.; STRAMKE, W. G.; MEWES, J.; LIESE, F.; SEEGER, G.: Erfahrungen mit einem spezifischen Therapieprogramm zum Training kognitiver und kommunikativer Fähigkeiten in der Rehabilitation chronisch schizophrener Patienten. Nervenarzt *51*, 106–112, 1980.

BRENNER, H. D.; REY, E.-R.; STRAMKE, W. G. (Hrsg.): Empirische Schizophrenieforschung. Experimentalpsychologische Ergebnisse und Beispiele ihrer Anwendung in Behandlung und Rehabilitation. Bern, Stuttgart, Wien: Huber, 1983.

BRENNER, H. D.; BÖKER, W.; ANDRES, K.; STRAMKE, W. G.: Efforts at compensation with regard to basic disorders among schizophrenics. In: LAASER, U.; SENAULT, R.; VIEFHUES, H. (eds.): Primary health care in the making. Berlin, Heidelberg: Springer, 1985.

BRENNER, H. D.; HODEL, B.; KUBE, G.; RODER, V.: Kognitive Therapie bei Schizophrenen: Problemanalyse und empirische Ergebnisse. Nervenarzt 58, 72–83, 1987.

BRENNER, H. D.; KRAEMER, S.; HERMANUTZ, H.; HODEL, B.: Cognitive treatment in schizophrenia: State of the art. In: HAHLWEG, K.; STRAUBE, E. (eds.): Schizophrenia: Models and interventions. Berlin, Heidelberg, New York: Springer (in press).

BROEN, W. E.; STORMS, L. H.: A theory of response-interference in schizophrenia. In: MAHER, B. A. (ed.): Progress in experimental personality research. New York, London: Academic Press, 1967.

CHAPMAN, J.: The early symptoms of schizophrenia. Brit. J. Psychiat. 112, 225–251, 1966.

CIOMPI, L.: Affektlogik: Über die Struktur der Psyche und ihre Entwicklung. Stuttgart: Klett-Cotta, 1982.

CROMWELL, R.: Attention and information processing: A foundation for understanding schizophrenia? In: WYNNE, L.; CROMWELL, R.; MATTHYSSE, S. (eds.): The nature of schizophrenia. New York: John Wiley & Sons, 1978.

CROMWELL, R. L.; SPAULDING, W.: How schizophrenics handle information. In: FANN, W. E.; KARACAN, I.; DOKORNY, A. D.; WILLIAMS, R. L. (eds.): The phenomenology and treatment of schizophrenia. New York: Spectrum Press, 1978.

FALLOON, I. R. H.; TALBOT, R.: Persistent auditory hallucinations: Coping mechanism and implication for management. Psychol. Med. 11, 329–339, 1981.

FALLOON, I. R. H.; BOYD, J. L.; McGILL, C. W.: Family care of schizophrenia. A problem-solving approach to the treatment of mental illness. New York: Guilford Press, 1984.

HEMSLEY, D. R.: What have cognitive deficits to do with schizophrenic symptoms? Brit. J. Psychiat. 130, 167–173, 1977.

HERMANUTZ, M.; GESTRICH, J.: Cognitive training and short-term outcome. Vortrag an der 15. Jahrestagung der Europäischen Gesellschaft für Verhaltenstherapie. München, 29. August bis 1. September 1985. (Publication in preparation.)

HUBER, G.: Das Konzept substratnaher Basissymptome und seine Bedeutung für Theorie und Therapie schizophrener Erkrankungen. Nervenarzt 54, 23–32, 1983.

KRAEMER, S.; SULZ, S. K. D.; SCHMID, R.; LAESSLE, E.: Kognitive Therapie bei chronisch schizophrenen Patienten. Vortrag an der 15. Jahrestagung der Europäischen Gesellschaft für Verhaltenstherapie, München, 29. August bis 1. September 1985. (Publication in preparation.)

MEICHENBAUM, D.; CAMERON, R.: The clinical potential of modifying what clients say to themselves. In: MAHONEY, M.; THORESEN, C. (eds.): Self-control: Power to the person. Monterey, CA: Brookscole, 263–290, 1974.

MEICHENBAUM, D.; CAMERON, R.: Training schizophrenics to talk to themselves: A means of developing self-controls. Behav. Ther. 4, 515–534, 1975.

NUECHTERLEIN, K. H.; DAWSON, M. E.: A heuristic vulnerability/stress model of schizophrenic episodes. Schizophr. Bull. 10, 300–312, 1984a.

NUECHTERLEIN, K. H.; DAWSON, M. E.: Information processing and attentional functioning in the developmental course of schizophrenic disorders. Schizophr. Bull. 10, 160–203, 1984b.

PLAUM, E.: Zum Leistungsverhalten schizophren Erkrankter. Psychiat. Praxis. 9, 35–41, 1982.

RODER, V.; STUDER, K.; BRENNER, H. D.: Erfahrungen mit einem integrierten psychologischen Therapieprogramm zum Training kommunikativer und kognitiver Fähigkeiten in der Rehabilitation schwer chronisch schizophrener Patienten. Schw. Arch. Neurol. Psychiat., 138, 1987.

ROSENTHAL, D.: Genetic theory and abnormal behavior. New York: McGraw Hill, 1970.

SCHMID, R.: Psychotherapeutische Zusatzbehandlung zur Verbesserung kognitiver Basisstörungen schizophrener Patienten: Eine Pilotstudie. Unveröffentlichte Diplom-Arbeit an der Ludwig-Maximilians-Universität, München, 1984.

SCHOOLER, C.; SPOHN, H.: Social dysfunction and treatment failure in schizophrenia. Schizophr. Bull. *8,* 85–98, 1982.

SIEGEL, J. M.; SPIVACK, G.: Problem-solving therapy: The description of a new program for chronic psychiatric patients. Psychotherapy: Theory, Research and Practice *13,* 368–373, 1976.

SPAULDING, W.: Assessment of adult-onset pervasive behaviour disorders. In: CIMINERO, A.; CALHOUN, K.; ADAMS, H. (eds.): Handbook of behavioral assessment (2nd ed.). New York: Wiley, 1986.

SPAULDING, W.; CANNELL, J. E.; HARGROVE, D. S.: Etiological hypotheses in a time series case study of multiple behavior problems. In press.

STRAMKE, W. G.; BRENNER, H. D.: Psychologische Trainingsprogramme zur Minderung defizitärer kognitiver Störungen in der Rehabilitation chronisch schizophrener Patienten. In: BRENNER, H. D.; REY, E.-R.; STRAMKE, W. G. (Hrsg.): Empirische Schizophrenieforschung. Experimentalpsychologische Ergebnisse und Beispiele ihrer Anwendung in Behandlung und Rehabilitation. Bern: Huber, 1983a.

STRAMKE, W. G.; HODEL, B.; BRAUCHLI, B.: Untersuchungen zur Wirksamkeit psychologischer Therapieprogramme in der Rehabilitation chronisch schizophrener Patienten. In: BRENNER, H. D.; REY, E.-R.; STRAMKE, W. G. (Hrsg.): Empirische Schizophrenieforschung. Experimentalpsychologische Ergebnisse und Beispiele ihrer Anwendung in Behandlung und Rehabilitation. Bern: Huber, 1983b.

STRAUBE, E. R.: On the meaning of electrodermal nonresponding in schizophrenia. J. Nerv. Ment. Dis. *167,* 601–611, 1979.

STRAUBE, E. R.: Kann die psychologisch-physiologische Grundlagenforschung einen Beitrag zur Therapie und Prognoseforschung liefern? In: BRENNER, H. D.; REY, E.-R.; STRAMKE, W. G. (Hrsg.): Empirische Schizophrenieforschung. Experimentalpsychologische Ergebnisse und Beispiele ihrer Anwendung in Behandlung und Rehabilitation. Bern: Huber, 1983.

STRAUSS, J. S.; CARPENTER, W. T., Jr.: Schizophrenia. New York: Plenum, 1981.

SUELLWOLD, L.: Symptome schizophrener Erkrankungen. Berlin: Springer, 1977.

UEXKUELL von, Th.: Lehrbuch der psychosomatischen Medizin. München, Wien, Baltimore: Urban & Schwarzenberg, 1979.

WALLACE, C. J.; BOONE, S. E.: Cognitive factors in the social skills of schizophrenic patients: Implications for treatment. In: SPAULDING, W. D.; COLE, J. K. (eds.): Theories of schizophrenia and psychosis. Lincoln, London: University of Nebraska Press, p. 283–317, 1984.

ZUBIN, J.; SPRING, B.: Vulnerability – a new view of schizophrenia. J. Abnorm. Psych. *86,* 103–126, 1977.

Assessing the Impact of Psychosocial Treatments for Schizophrenic Patients: Reliability, Validity, Responsibility

R. M. TURNER

The fundamental problems of assessing the impact of psychosocial treatments for schizophrenic patients are the development and utilization of adequate empirical measures of the abstract concept of psychosocial functioning. This is, of course, a basic problem in all areas of science, but it is particularly true in the social sciences. BLALOCK (1968) and SULLIVAN and FELDMAN (1979) have labeled the issue of obtaining meaningful indicators of psychological or socio-logical constructs *the measurement problem*. The solution of the measure-ment problem for assessing psychosocial treatments for schizophrenic pa-tients is far from being a straightforward and logical one. The question im-mediately arises: How do we best measure adequate psychosocial functioning as well as changes in psychosocial functioning in schizophrenic patients.

Psychometric theory has historically tackled the measurement problem by focusing upon the reliability and validity of psychosocial measurements. The aim of the psychometric approach is the development of empirical indicators of abstract constructs (e.g., adaptive psychosocial functioning) that truly measure the construct. The related notions of reliability and validity serve as mechanisms to help us gauge whether or not an empirical indicator truly measures the abstract concept.

Reliability assessment focuses upon estimating the extent to which random measurement error, or nonsystematic error, is influencing the indicator of psy-chosocial functioning. If an indicator is absolutely reliable, then a given in-dividual would obtain the same score at every measurement occasion – given no conditions have changed. No measurement is ever error-free, however. Even when measuring physical mass with a scale, there can be unsystematic vari-ations due to friction, altitude, and imperfections in the scale itself. Thus, in the final analysis, no indicators of psychosocial functioning will be totally reli-able. It is an issue of an acceptable degree of random error of a measure under specific conditions that helps to solve that part of the measurement problem.

The second component of the psychometric solution to the measurement problem comes under the heading of validity. Validity assessment attempts to determine whether an indicator measures the construct, and only the con-struct, it is supposed to measure and is not contaminated by other constructs. When error of measurement becomes nonrandom, or systematic, there is a reduction in the validity of the indicator.

Thus, from the psychometric theory point of view, when an indicator measures what it purports to measure and patients consistently obtain similar scores (again, given conditions have not changed) the measurement problem is solved.

There is a component of the measurement problem, however, the narrow psychometric view does not take into account. That component is responsibility. Responsibility to whom and about what? I mean responsibility to the schizophrenic patient and to society to assess the far-reaching social implications of the psychosocial treatment. The push of the behavioral and skills-training therapies has been to emphasize enhancing schizophrenic patients' ability to initiate, manage, and terminate conversations, to solve problems, to engage in less disruptive communications with family members, and to understand the importance of taking their medications. As a result of this treatment emphasis, assessment has most often focused upon ascertaining whether or not a specific skill change has occurred. KENDALL and NORTON-FORD (1982) termed this type of measurement the specifying level. Specifying-level measurement is crucial because we wish to know whether the treatment altered the target behavior. However, the responsibility viewpoint emphasizes that it is not sufficient to simply know the patient can initiate more conversations, but that we must know the meaning of the behavioral change in terms of the patient's interactions with family and friends as well as the overall symptomatic status. KENDALL and NORTON-FORD (1982) term this assessing at the impact level of the treatment.

Responsible measurement means then that we should attempt to identify improvements in deviant, maladaptive, and dangerous behaviors to the point that the patient is living a happier, symptom-free, growth-oriented lifestyle. To do this we need to incorporate impact-level measures of community functioning.

Furthermore, responsible assessment implies that we obtain measures of outcome from multiple points of view of the patient (STRUPP & HADLEY, 1977). The outcome of psychosocial treatments for schizophrenic patients needs to be assessed from the patient's, the mental health caretaker's, as well as the community's perspective.

Thus, the measurement problem is only truly solved when indicators are reliable, valid, and responsible. The remainder of this paper focuses upon describing several useful impact-level indicators of schizophrenic symptom and community functioning status, and reports on their reliability and validity when utilized by the patient, the clinician, and independent evaluators.

Impact-level instruments

The *Symptom Checklist 90* (SCL-90), the *Denver Community Mental Health Questionnaire* (DCMHQ), and the *Personal Adjustment and Role Skills Scale* (PARS) are the impact-level measures employed in the present investigation.

There are many other impact-level measures we could discuss, but we will restrict our discussion to these. HARGREAVES et al. (1975) provide an extensive overview of impact-level indicators. The above three measures, however, encompass a broad range of functional assessment across individual, family relations, and community dimensions. In addition, each specific measure was developed for, and traditionally used by, respondents in the roles of patient, significant other, and clinician/evaluator. In this study, all three measures were completed by an individual from each different perspective: each patient evaluated him or herself, a clinician evaluated each patient, and an independent evaluator rated each patient. Thus, instruments are fully crossed with perspectives.

SCL-90 (DEROGATIS, 1977)

This is a 90-item self-report inventory designed to assess symptomatic psychological distress. The subject indicates how much botherment each "complaint" has caused, using a 5-point scale ranging from "not at all" (0) to "extremely" (4). A sample item is: "sleep that is restless or disturbed . . . ." There are nine primary symptom dimensions: somatization, obsessive-compulsive, interpersonal sensitivity, depression, anxiety, anger-hostility, phobic anxiety, paranoid ideation, and psychotism. There is also an overall score, called the *General Severity Index* (GSI), which is generated from the average of symptom severity across all 90 items. Reported psychometric properties of the SCL-90 feature average alpha coefficients of .84 for the nine primary symptom dimensions (DEROGATIS et al., 1976). Test-retest coefficients of an average of .84 have also been reported (DEROGATIS, 1977). The SCL-90 is a measure appropriate for a normal to severe range of impairment, and has been frequently used as a measure of symptomatology in studies of psychopathology and treatment outcome (e.g. HAGEDORN et al., 1976; WEISSMAN et al., 1977).

DCMHQ (CIARLO & REIHMAN, 1977)

The DCMHQ is a 71-item multidimensional questionnaire designed to be administered in a structured interview by a clinician or evaluator. The subject indicates the frequency of specific behavioral events on a 4-point scale from "never" (0) to "constantly" (3). A sample item is: "When you are with your family, how often do you argue with them?" Thirteen subscales address the following dimensions of functioning: psychological distress, interpersonal isolation from family and friends, interpersonal aggression, work and home productivity, legal difficulties, public system dependency, alcohol and drug use, and client satisfaction. Psychometric properties of the DCMHQ feature alphas ranging from .52 to .70 (CIARLO & REIHMAN, 1977; BUTTERS et al., 1977), interrater agreements from .85 to 1.00, and test-retest coefficients of .60 to .83 (EDWARDS et al., 1978). The DCMHQ is a measure appropriate for a normal to severe range of impairment and, in fact, was developed for urban community mental health center inpatients and outpatients. It measures community adjustment and public system dependency across a broad range of domains.

PARS (ELLSWORTH, 1975)

The PARS is an informant (significant other) report measure of community behavior and adjustment of adult psychiatric patients. The PARS consists of 57 items for which the subject indicates on a 5-point rating scale the frequency of specific events (for example " ... been drinking to excess ... "), from "never" (1) to "always" (5). The following dimensions of adjustment are assessed: interpersonal involvement, anxiety-depression, confusion, substance abuse, household management, relationship to children, outside social, and employment. Psychometric studies report alphas ranging from .65 to .93, interrater correlations from .70 to .90, and one-week test-retest reliabilities averaging .88 (ELLSWORTH, 1975). The PARS is appropriate for a normal to incapacitated patient population, and has been frequently used to assess significant others' views of patient adjustment and treatment outcome (HARGREAVES et al., 1975; ELLSWORTH, 1978; PENK et al., 1980). It covers fewer areas of life functioning than the DCMHQ, but is not solely focused upon psychiatric symptoms, as is the SCL-90. The PARS focuses on frequency of events rather than severity.

Reliability and validity of responsible measures

In order to assess the reliability across different types of raters as well as to the convergent validity of these impact-level measures, we modeled this analysis after CAMPBELL and FISKE's (1959) multitrait-multimethod assessment procedure. The multitrait-multimethod approach has two components. First, the procedure utilizes multiple measures of the same abstract concept, given at one point in time, to determine the convergent validity of the measuring instruments. This process is much like the split-half reliability assessment of traditional psychometric theory. Two different measures of the same abstract concept should correlate significantly and converge into a unitary phenomenon. Second, the multitrait-multimethod procedure makes use of the notion of discriminant validity. Discriminant validity implies that if measures of a construct are valid, they should not correlate highly with measures of disparate constructs. For example, a measure of anxiety should not correlate highly with a measure of intelligence, if the measure of anxiety is valid. Taken together, CAMPBELL and FISKE's (1959) notions of convergent and discriminant validity incorporate aspects of experimental design rigor into multivariate statistical analysis. The plausible alternative hypothesis, that a given measure is not a valid index of a construct, is tested by incorporating measures of converse, rival constructs into the analysis. If significant correlations are obtained

155

between these purportedly different constructs, then the hypothesis alleging difference is falsified.

The investigation made innovative use of the multitrait-multimethod methodology. In this instance there are multiple perspectives and multiple methods. Convergent validity, in this case, refers to the notion that in measuring the concept level of functioning by different instruments within a given perspective, the different instruments ought to produce similar results. Reliability in this analysis was assessed by comparing the agreement rate for an indicator across perspectives.

The subjects were randomly selected from the patient population of four partial hospital programs in the greater Philadelphia area. Three of these programs were situated in urban and relatively impoverished inner-city neighborhoods, while the fourth was located in a suburban, semi-rural area. The subjects were randomly selected by the day program directors of four partial hospital programs, thereby achieving a full representation of their regular patient profile. There were a total of 146 patients selected across all four programs. The average age of patients was 44.8, with ages ranging from 19 to 80. Fifty-six percent of the sample was male; the racial composition was 42% Black and 58% Caucasian. The average educational level was 9.6 grades, while the greatest proportion (26%) were educated as far as the 12th grade. The majority of the patients (63%) had never been married, and 49% had the occupational status of "unskilled laborer." Eleven percent have never worked. The majority (78.3%) were covered by public medical assistance, and a small number (11.6%) were on Medicare. The living arrangements of the patients selected were representative of the programs' regular census in that 42% lived in boarding homes. Of these patients, 61% lived in large (10 or more residents) boarding homes. Only 35% lived with relatives.

The patient evaluations in each of the four partial hospitals proceeded in the same manner. Initially, there was a 1½-hour meeting among the staff clinicians and the independent raters to discuss the purposes of the project, the instruments to be used, and the procedure to be followed. A primary function of the initial meeting was to insure that patients would make self-ratings, and that the therapists and evaluators would make the clinical judgment of symptoms and role functioning on approximately the same day. The importance of coordinating the ratings to insure reliable results was stressed.

Next, the director of the partial hospital randomly assigned patients to an independent evaluator. Evaluators were kept blind as to the patient's diagnosis, history, etc. The only information available to the evaluators was the material they gleaned from the 1¼-hour interview with the patient. The evaluators each followed a standardized interview format developed from the *Social Adjustment Scale II* and the *Denver Community Mental Health Questionnaire*. WEISSMAN and her associates (SCHOOLER et al., 1980) devised the *Social Adjustment Scale II* for use with schizophrenic patients; its reliability and validity as an interview format are well established (WEISSMAN, 1975; WEISSMAN & BOTHWELL, 1976).

156

Immediately following the interview with the patient, the independent evaluator completed the DCMHQ, the SCL-90, and the PARS.

Following the interview with the independent evaluator, the patient was given copies of the SCL-90, the Denver, and the PARS to complete. The client was instructed by his/her case manager to complete the data forms before leaving the clinic that day.

Finally, the treating clinicians made clinical ratings of their clients' symptoms and community adjustment on the Denver, SCL-90 and PARS. Clinicians were allowed to refer to their own case notes and other client records in order to complete the questionnaires.

Canonical correlations were calculated between all combinations of perspectives and instruments. Table 1 presents the multi-perspective multi-instrument arrangement of the estimates of the proportion of variance in common for each possible perspective-instrument combination.

The values enclosed in the open-ended boundary markers on the diagonals of the "different perspective-same instrument" submatrices reveal the extent of overlap among differing perspectives of the same instruments. Seven of the nine estimates of concordant variance are significant, and the average shared variance among perspectives is .68. This suggests that the three measures utilized in this study are reliable across perspectives. This consensus is uniformly high for all three instruments studied here, although the cross perspective squared correlations involving the PARS were lower than those for either of the other instruments. The DCMHQ demonstrates the largest coefficients across perspectives.

The three diagonal matrices located along the diagonal of the total matrix present "same perspective-different instrument" squared correlations. The estimates of shared variance between pairs of instruments, within perspectives, range between .54 and .85. Seven of nine of the squared canonical correlations were significant. This indicates that the three outcome assessment procedures used are measuring a common phenomenon and corroborates their validity. The PARS and SCL-90 share the least variance in common and, consequently, would provide the greatest spread of coverage in an assessment battery.

Thus, in conclusion, assessment of the impact of psychosocial treatment of schizophrenia requires indicators that are reliable, valid, and responsible. It is not sufficient simply to measure skill changes: It is crucial to assess the broader meaning of psychosocial functioning.

Table 1: Multiperspective-Multiinstrument Analysis

Perspective	Instrument	Evaluator			Therapist			Client		
		SCL-90	Denver	PARS	SCL-90	Denver	PARS	SCL-90	Denver	PARS
Evaluator	SCL-90	(-)								
	Denver	.65***	(-)							
	PARS	.54***	.85***	(-)						
Therapist	SCL-90	.52***	.55	.35*	(-)					
	Denver	.48	.81***	.67***	.64	(-)				
	PARS	.43	.52***	.45***	.63***	.78***	(-)			
Client	SCL-90	.67*	.59	.51	.85	.98***	.76**	(-)		
	Denver	.73	.76*	.56	.93	.93**	.78*	.71	(-)	
	PARS	.81***	.69	.55**	.58	.89	.60	.65	.69***	(-)

All entries are squared Canonical Correlations. The Evaluator submatrix is based on 146 cases. The therapist submatrices are based on 71 cases. The three client submatrices are based on 42 cases.

—   p ≤ .10
*   p ≤ .05
**   p ≤ .01
***   p ≤ .001

Bibliography

BLALOCK, H. M.: The measurement problem: A gap between the languages of theory and research. In: BLALOCK, H. M.; BLALOCK, A. B. (eds.): Methodology in social research. New York: McGraw-Hill, 1968.

BUTTERS, E.; LOBB, J.; CIARLO, J. A.: The Denver Community Mental Health Questionnaire: Replication of the psychometric analysis and addition of the home productivity scale. Unpublished paper. Mental health systems evaluation project. University of Denver, 1977.

CAMPBELL, D. T.; FISKE, D. W.: Convergent and discriminant validation by the multitrait-multimethod matrix. Psychol. Bull. *56*, 81–105, 1959.

CIARLO, J. A.; REIHMAN, J.: The Denver Community Mental Health Questionnaire: Development of a multi-dimensional program evaluation instrument. In: COURSEY, R.; SPECTOR, G.; MURREL, S.; HUNT, B. (eds.): Program evaluation for mental health: Methods, strategies and participants. New York: Grune and Stratton, 131–167, 1977.

DEROGATIS, L. R.: SCL-90: Administration, scoring and procedures Manual-I. Baltimore: Clinical Psychometrics Research, 1977.

DEROGATIS, L. R.; RICKELS, K.; ROCK, A. F.: The SCL-90 and the MMPI: A step in the validation of a new self-report scale. Brit. J. Psychiat. *128*, 280–289, 1976.

EDWARDS, D. W.; MARVIS, R. M.; MUELLER, D. P.; ZINGALE, H. C.; WAGNER, W. J.: Test-taking and the stability of adjustment scales. Evaluation Quarterly *2*, 275–289, 1978.

ELLSWORTH, R. B.: Consumer feedback in measuring the effectiveness of mental health programs. In: GUTTENTAG, M.; STRUENING, E. L. (eds.): Handbook of evaluation research, Vol. 2. Beverly Hills, CA: Sage, 1975.

ELLSWORTH, R. B.: The comparative effectiveness of community clinic and psychiatric hospital treatment. J. Comm. Psychol. *6*, 103–111, 1978.

HAGEDORN, H. J.; BECK, K.; NEUBERT, S. F.; WERLIN, S. H.: A working manual of simple program evaluation techniques for community mental health centers. Rockville, MD: NIMH, 1976.

HARGREAVES, W. A.; ATTKISSON, C. C.; SIEGEL, L. J.; MCINTRYE, M. H.; SORENSON, J. E. (eds.): Resource materials for community mental health program evaluation: Vol. IV. Evaluating the effectiveness of services. N.T.I.S. Evaluation Study Report No. PB-249-046. Springfield, VA: N.T.I.S., 1975.

KENDALL, P. C.; NORTON-FORD, J.: Therapy outcome research methods. In: KENDALL, P. C.; BUTCHER, J. N. (eds.): Handbook of research methods in clinical psychology. New York: John Wiley and Sons, 1982.

PENK, W. E.; UEBERSAX, J. S.; ANDREWS, R. H.; CHARLES, H. L.: Client correlates of community informant adjustment ratings. J. Person. Assessm. *44*, 157–166, 1980.

SCHOOLER, N. R.; LEVINE, J.; SEVERE, J. B.; BRAUZER, B.; DIMASCIO, A.; KLERMAN, G. L.; TUASON, V. B.: Prevention of relapse in schizophrenia. Arch. Gen. Psychiat. *37*, 16–26, 1980.

STRUPP, H. H.; HADLEY, S. W.: A tripartite model of mental health and therapeutic outcomes: With a special reference to negative effects in psychotherapy. Am. Psychologist *32*, 187–196, 1977.

SULLIVAN, J. L.; FELDMAN, S.: Multiple indicators: An introduction. Beverly Hills: Sage Publications, 1979.

WEISSMAN, M. M.: The assessment of social adjustment: A review of techniques. Arch. Gen. Psychiat. *32*, 357–365, 1975.

WEISSMAN, M. M.; BOTHWELL, S.: Assessment of social adjustment by patient self-report. Arch. Gen. Psychiat. *33*, 1111–1115, 1976.

WEISSMAN, M. M.; SHOLOMSKAS, D.; POTTENGER, M.; PRUSOFF, B. A.; LOCKE, B. Z.: Assessing depressive symptoms in five psychiatric populations: A validation study. Am. J. Epidemiology *106*, 203–214, 1977.

The Role of the Patient in Recovery from Psychosis

J. S. Strauss, C. M. Harding, H. Hafez, P. Lieberman[1]

Introduction

There appears to be an historical tendency to swing from one extreme to the other when trying to understand scientific, political, or artistic phenomena. Views about mental illness are no exception.

In certain eras, mental disorder has been considered under the control or even the fault of the person who is ill. Collaboration with devils, lack of moral fiber, or inadequate coping skills have been cited (MILLON, 1969). In other eras, and at the opposite extreme, the mentally ill person has been viewed as the helpless victim of an external cause such as a "disease" or a pathogenic family or family member. The disease (as in the natural history model, KRAEPELIN, 1902) or the family (as with the schizophrenogenic mother theory, FROMM-REICHMANN, 1948) have been seen as separate from the person, who was unable to have any impact on them. Often the power of the polar opposite fault or helplessness orientations has been so pervasive during the eras in which they predominated that they have been perceived as universal truths rather than points of view. The net result of both viewpoints has been similarly paralyzing for the person with the disorder because of either the imputed blame or helplessness.

Currently, the pervasive belief appears to be that the psychotic patient is essentially helpless in the face of disease. This view together with the frequent effectiveness of medication, even if given against the patient's will, has contributed to many common treatment strategies. For example, medication clinics are often created to "manage" large numbers of psychotic patients with heightened efficiency and cost-effectiveness. Limited personal interaction in such settings is associated with little information about the disorder being given to the patient.

In the present disease-oriented era, however, there are some clinicians and investigators who attempt to find a midpoint between the helplessness and patient-in-control viewpoints. These attempts are reflected, for example, by those who consider how the disease and the person might interact to influence each other. Examples of such a viewpoint can also be identified in discussions

1 This report was supported in part by NIMH Grants No. MH34365, MH00340, and 40607. The authors wish to thank Laura ROGERS for her helpful suggestions.

160

about treating the whole person, considering both the disease and the person's feelings and coping capacities. But often it is not clear what "treating the whole person" means, and there are few models for accomplishing such a goal.

In fact, good data on the range of possibilities regarding roles the patient may have in recovery from psychosis are almost non-existent. Even the conceptual models and exploratory research that must precede such data are missing. Recently, however, increasing information has become available that could serve as a basis for systematic thinking about the role of the patient in recovery from psychosis. Sources of this information include autobiographical accounts, single-case reports, longitudinal studies of patients with severe psychiatric disorders, and systematic clinical descriptions (BOCKES, 1985; SECHEHAYE, 1951; BREIER & STRAUSS, 1983; BOEKER et al., 1984; COHEN & BERK, 1985; CHAMBERLIN, 1979; FEDER, 1982; BRUNDAGE, 1983; LOVEJOY, 1984; KAPLAN, 1964; HARDING et al., in press).

Based on such sources, this paper focuses on ways in which the patient afflicted with psychosis may influence the course of the disorder. It will offer a conceptual model to promote further research and enhance the ways in which clinicians can work with the patient's active participation in the treatment setting.

Levels of participation on a continuum

Level 1: Compliance

Conceptually, it may be best to view the potential range of patient roles in recovery from psychosis on a continuum from none to total. At the low end it is possible that the patient can do very little actively to help in the recovery process except to "comply" by following the clinician's orders, taking medications as prescribed, and perhaps avoiding excessive stress.

Viewed from a narrow version of the medical model, the efficacy of psychotropic medications and the harmful impact of certain environmental factors are sometimes interpreted as demonstrating the validity of the minimal patient role. Certainly the information that demonstrates the utility, although not the curative power, of medication is far more impressive than the available data showing that patients have a major active role influencing their disorders. The deleterious effects of certain types of family settings and stressful life events have also been suggested (e.g., VAUGHN & LEFF, 1976; BROWN & BIRLEY, 1968). Clearly, however, the useful impact of medications and the harmful impact of certain life situations for many psychotic patients do not necessarily mean that the patient as a person does not also have some active role in the course of the disorder. In fact, even patient compliance with medication and with directions to avoid certain kinds of stressful situations may reflect decisions on the patient's part to try the clinician's solutions in order to see if they work.

161

Level 2: Utilizing coping skills training

The next level in the continuum from total helplessness to total control is one in which the patient can in fact help promote recovery to a moderate degree. It may be possible that there is some psychosocial equivalent in the psychoses to exercises following knee surgery, things to learn and do to help rebuild strength and prevent recurrence. The data describing psychological processes of this kind following psychosis are fairly convincing, at least for some aspects of disorder and functioning. For example, the work of PAUL and LENTZ (1977) suggests that if the patient practices behaviors and new roles as part of a behavioral reinforcement program, even someone with extremely severe disorder may improve his or her functioning significantly.

At this level of patient involvement in the course of disorder, the available information relates primarily to improvement of functioning rather than of symptoms. And at least in the research already carried out, patients are still seen as relatively passive recipients of treatments, in this case behavioral/psychosocial treatments. These treatments are given in almost the same unidirectional manner as Level 1's prescriptions for drugs and directions for avoiding stress. But once again the patient has at least to consent to try this modality and to work in the direction of the therapist's goals. If those goals are not congruent with the goals of the patient, he or she may undermine the process. Attempts at collaborative treatment allowing more patient initiative at this level remain to be tested.

Level 3: The patient as a collaborator and innovator

There is yet a third level of the continuum of involvement, the most controversial one, but one that may also have the most potential regarding the patient's role in the healing process. There are many other aspects of a person beyond the ability to receive injectable medications, to comply, or to be trained. Areas of functioning exist that are in fact far above those of a common laboratory animal. It might be possible that goal-setting, creative problem-solving, innovative collaboration, and the construction of meaning can play important parts in recovery. Perhaps the even more ephemeral notions of courage, hope, and motivation fuel such processes. Long-term outcome data and consistent anecdotal evidence suggest that a person can provide a broad range of initiatives in the recovery from psychosis. But perhaps because these functions are so difficult to assess systematically, and because of the untested assumptions about how psychosis affects the person, these factors have been almost totally ignored in systematic research on the psychoses.

Autobiographical accounts provide one of the best sources to begin collecting information to advance our understanding in these areas. Although such sources have limitations regarding what is reported and the particular sample of patients who write them, the accounts are an extremely rich base for developing hypotheses (STRAUSS & CARPENTER, 1981). They describe patient experiences, often uniquely not limited to the kinds of issues the investigator or clinician traditionally focuses on or chooses to ignore.

To begin with, it is quite clear and somewhat embarrassing how pervasively patient initiative (whether effective or not) goes unnoticed. This initiative is found even in persons with psychosis (e.g., BREIER & STRAUSS, 1983; BOEKER et al., 1984; COHEN & BERK, 1985; CHAMBERLIN, 1979; FEDER, 1982; BRUNDAGE, 1983; LOVEJOY, 1984; KAPLAN, 1964). Psychotic patients attempt to do much more than comply or fail to comply with treatment regimens. Actually, our interest in the possibility of the patient's influencing the course of disorder in such ways comes not from our own theorizing or even our clinical experience, but from one of our research subjects who had been psychotic several times and had the initiative, insight, and courage to break through our semistructured interview focused on the impacts of the environment on disorder. She asked why we never inquired about what she did to influence her illness. The interviewer (STRAUSS) asked her, and subsequently we asked all our research subjects that question. And almost all of them told us that they had developed strategies that they felt helped control their psychotic symptoms. Our subjects were surprised that we might even be interested in such a possibility, since no one had ever asked them before. Similar findings were noted during a long-term follow-up study of schizophrenia (HARDING, in press).

What information do sources such as anecdotes, research, and clinical interviews provide about what patients do at the more complex levels that is relevant to recovery from psychosis? Starting one level beyond compliance and trainability described earlier, persons with psychotic disorders choose and arrange to be in or avoid certain situations, locations, and tasks. People with psychoses influence encounters or withdraw from encounters with other people. It appears that, to the extent to which environmental factors influence the course of disorder, patients' modulation and selection of environmental situations can affect the disorder as well.

At a more autonomous and complex level of initiative, information from one of our studies suggests other ways in which patients might control their psychotic symptoms. Seventeen out of 20 study subjects told us about ways in which they felt they were often able to control these symptoms. They described three mechanisms they used for this goal: self-instruction, reduced involvement in activity, and increased involvement in activity (BREIER & STRAUSS, 1983). Individual subjects seemed to pick the method that appeared to work particularly for them. Subjects also noted that there was a threshold of symptom severity beyond which their efforts to utilize control mechanisms were of no help.

There appears to be a still more complex level of patient initiative in the recovery process. The very issue of initiative raises the question of who it is that takes the initiative and who the source of that effort is. The questions of the origins of human action and the nature of "I" and free will involve complex philosophical problems (WITTGENSTEIN, 1961). But for purposes of clarifying the role of the patient in recovery from psychosis, it is best to view initiative from the standpoint of patient reports. In our study, patients often mentioned experiences related to their sense of themselves as integrated, self-directed people. They described (as almost all patients do) feelings of "falling apart" or "getting it together" or being "overwhelmed." In all such descriptions, as in the common term "nervous breakdown," the central factor is the sense of self in terms of integration and control.

KRAEPELIN (1902) and BLEULER (1950) both wrote about problems with integration of the self in schizophrenia, as have other psychiatrists and psychologists from many schools in discussing various types of psychiatric and psychological issues (e.g., MASLOW, 1968; ERIKSON, 1963). Even Kurt SCHNEIDER's first-rank symptoms can be readily viewed as instances in which the sense of self is damaged. This view is reflected in the delusions of being controlled by outside forces or being without boundaries. But amazingly, the notion of "self" now is relatively neglected in many current conceptualizations of psychosis and recovery, and it is almost totally neglected in research.

What can one learn from patients' frequent comments (when allowed the opportunity) such as "I felt that I just had to pull myself together," or "That was the last straw, and I just fell apart"? For one thing, patients' descriptions of such relatively sudden changes reflect a non-linear evolution of disorder, a phenomenon frequently noted clinically, documented with reliable instruments in one of our recent studies, and generally ignored and unexplained in research and theory (STRAUSS et al., 1985).

Do these processes reflect important actions or disruptions of the patient's "self"? Or is the patient in such instances erroneously considering a psychological "getting-it-together" or "falling-apart" as causes of phenomena that are actually biological in origin? Yet another possibility is that key psychological sequences including integration or disintegration of self are primary factors, with major biological correlates. No studies of even the phenomenology of such experiences have been carried out to begin clarifying these alternatives.

If sense of self, the ability to "get it together," and feeling "overwhelmed" are in fact important determinants of the recovery process or its failures, then many other factors influencing these and their determinants in turn become important. These other factors range from sleep to hope, from physical health to courage, from material resources to psychological energy and drive – and all the factors that influence them.

Thus, by selecting environments and involvements, by controlling symptoms or choosing not to, and possibly even by force of will influenced by such factors as courage and hope, it is possible that the patient has a major role in the recovery from psychosis.

But how good are the data from which these hypotheses are drawn? In considering some of the sources of information, there remains the old question posed by psychoanalysts and descriptive psychiatrists alike, whether the patient's view is really valid. The descriptive psychiatrist tends to focus on and accept the validity of reports about symptoms, even bizarre symptoms such as hallucinations and delusions, but not about experiences of coping and intentionality. The psychoanalyst may focus on and accept the validity of memories and fantasies, but also tends to de-emphasize these other topics. Professionals from both schools may actually agree that control of one's own symptoms and related issues such as hope, courage, motivation, and creative problem-solving are not likely to be useful in understanding the evolution of disorder.

The data, especially for the more complex aspects of patient initiative, are far from definitive; but they may reflect important processes. They offer some explanations for documented phenomena not otherwise understandable, and there is no good scientific evidence to consider them false. To paraphrase OS-LER, we should listen to the patients: they may be telling us something about the disease.

What are the implications of such a view? To return to the old polarizations, does it mean that a stiff upper lip or adequate courage and determination are sufficient to cure schizophrenia, or that anyone who remains ill does so from weakness of character? Those conclusions seem highly unwarranted. What does seem probable is that the patient as a person does, or at least can, take an active role in the recovery process at many levels. It is possible that the person has an active role at many levels in the worsening of disorder as well. We know very little about these processes or how important they might be since the field has vacillated from being contemptuous of such possibilities on one hand to totally embracing them on the other. The difficult tasks of systematic research and development of concepts and theory have remained all but neglected.

There are many clinical implications if the patient as a person does have a role in the recovery process. It would be extremely important for the clinician to provide education about the disorder, to help the patient find realistic amounts of hope, courage, determination, and to discover his or her own style of managing symptoms. Not having a clinician who could assist the patient with these areas would represent inadequate treatment.

We are beginning to learn how to educate patients and their families about severe psychiatric disorder (ANDERSON, 1977), but we know almost nothing about what is the most helpful amount of hope, courage, and determination for a given individual, or the various styles of using these, let alone how to assess or engender them. An attempt to deal more adequately with these issues will bring us into new areas as well as into rethinking the roles of meaning, identity, and the setting of goals.

There has been a tendency, often helpful, to reduce psychotic disorders to simple concepts by using a narrow version of the disease model or a particular psychodynamic theory. But in both cases there has been an unfortunate practice of ignoring a phenomenon that has been in front of us all the time: the possible multiple levels at which the patient as a person might have an active role in the process of recovery.

Bibliography

ANDERSON, C. M.: Family intervention with severely disturbed inpatients. Arch. Gen. Psychiat. *34,* 697–702, 1977.

BLEULER, E.: Dementia praecox or the group of schizophrenias. New York: International Universities Press, 1950.

BOCKES, Z.: Freedom means knowing you have a choice. Schizophr. Bull. *11,* 487–489, 1985.

BOEKER, W.; BRENNER, H. D.; GERSTNER, G.; KELLER, F.; MUELLER, J.; SPICHTIG, L.: Self-healing strategies among schizophrenics: Attempts at compensation for basic disorders. Acta Psychiatr. Scand. *69,* 373–378, 1984.

BREIER, A.; STRAUSS, J. S.: Self-control in psychotic disorders. Arch. Gen. Psychiat. *40,* 1141–1145, 1983.

BROWN, G. W.; BIRLEY, J. L. T.: Crises and life changes and the onset of schizophrenia. J. Health Soc. Behav. *9,* 203, 1968.

BRUNDAGE, B. E.: First person account: What I wanted to know but was afraid to ask. Schizophr. Bull. *9,* 583–585, 1983.

CHAMBERLIN, J.: On our own. New York: McGraw-Hill, 1979.

COHEN, C. I.; BERK, L. A.: Personal coping styles of schizophrenic outpatients. Hosp. Comm. Psychiat. *36,* 407–410, 1985.

ERIKSON, E. H.: Childhood and society. New York: Norton, 1963.

FEDER, R.: Auditory hallucinations treated by radio headphones. Am. J. Psychiat. *139,* 1188–1190, 1982.

FROMM-REICHMANN, F.: Notes on the development of treatment of schizophrenia by psychoanalytic psychotherapy. Psychiatry *11,* 263–273, 1948.

HARDING, C. M.; BROOKS, G. W.; ASHIKAGA, T.; STRAUSS, J. S.; LANDERL, P. D.: Aging and social functioning in once-chronic schizophrenic patients 21–58 years after first admission: The Vermont Story. In: HUDGINS; MILLER (eds.): Schizophrenia, paranoia and schizophreniform disorders in later life. New York: Guilford Press, in press.

KAPLAN, B. (ed.): The inner world of mental illness. New York: Harper & Row, 1964.

KRAEPELIN, E.: Dementia praecox. In: KRAEPELIN, E.: Clinical psychiatry – A textbook for students and physicians. New York: Macmillan, 1902.

LOVEJOY, M.: Recovery from schizophrenia: A personal odyssey. Hosp. Comm. Psychiat. *35,* 809–812, 1984.

MASLOW, A.: Toward a psychology of being. New York: VanNostrand, 1968.

MILLON, T.: Modern psychopathology: A biosocial approach to maladaptive learning and functioning. Philadelphia: W.B. Saunders Co., 1969.

PAUL, G.; LENTZ, R.: Psychosocial treatment of chronic mental patients. Cambridge, MA: Harvard, 1977.

SCHNEIDER, K.: Clinical psychopathology. New York: Grune & Stratton, 1959.

SECHEHAYE, M.: Autobiography of a schizophrenic girl. New York: Grune & Stratton, 1951.

STRAUSS, J. S.; CARPENTER, W. T., Jr.: Schizophrenia. New York: Plenum, 1981.

STRAUSS, J. S.; HAFEZ, H.; LIEBERMAN, P.; HARDING, C. M.: The course of psychiatric disorder: III. Longitudinal principles. Am. J. Psychiat. *142,* 289–296, 1985.

VAUGHN, C. E.; LEFF, J. P.: The influence of family and social factors on the course of psychiatric illness: A comparison of schizophrenic and depressed neurotic patients. Br. J. Psychiat. *129,* 125–137, 1976.

WITTGENSTEIN, L.: The Tractatus Logico-Philosophicus. New York: Routledge & Kegan Paul, 1961.

On Self-Help Among Schizophrenics: Problem Analysis and Empirical Studies

W. Böker

The potential for self-help among schizophrenics has lately been meeting with growing professional sensitivity after having been barely recognized, much less studied, for a long time. Earlier isolated casuistic reports about schizophrenic patients' attempts at coping are creating new interest, and autobiographical descriptions of the disease are being examined for patterns of self-help efforts. Moreover, the first systematic empirical studies on this topic are now appearing (among them, one conducted by the Berne Clinic), indicating that the existence of a potential for self-help can no longer be doubted.

Historical references

As early as 1911, E. BLEULER considered the symptom-forming and symptom-transforming approaches of schizophrenics to their psychoses as more or less successful or failed "attempts at adaptation." In Schreber's case, FREUD (1913) interpreted paranoid productions for the first time as an "attempted healing." KLAESI (1922) regarded even schizophrenic stereotypes as transformed and rigidified "attempts at self-healing." In 1926, BINDER differentiated between "disabling" and "defensive" psychisms. Seeing an analogy to neurosis, M. MUELLER (1930) described the mechanisms of blocking-off, repression, reinterpretation, isolation, and inactivation of psychotic experiences as "schizophrenic healing mechanisms." In 1959, JANZARIK spoke of a "stabilizing intentionality." And in 1960, KISKER mentioned "reordering attempts" by schizophrenic patients.

Published autobiographical accounts of schizophrenics, as collected, among others, by FREEDMAN (1974), WING (1977, 1978), and FALLOON and TALBOT (1981), represent a mine of information for our topic. In reviewing the medical histories of 616 schizophrenic patients, LANGE (1981) found indications of "strategies of adaptation, coping reactions, and self-healing attempts" in roughly 20% of all cases; of 97 schizophrenics studied by the author for this purpose, all had made self-help efforts at one time or another. In 1983, BOEKER and BRENNER reviewed the literature on this subject and discussed implications for research and therapy.

Definition and types

The first difficulty in analyzing the various self-help phenomena is delineating them from symptoms of the disease. The disorder observed in a patient often results from a combination of a schizophrenic symptom and the corresponding coping reaction.

LANGE uses the psychopathological example of "blocking": a patient experiences thinking as progressively more confused and stops in mid-sentence to restructure thoughts. In this case, the attempt at self-help presents itself in the form of a manifest symptom of the mental disorder. SUELLWOLD (1983a) conjectures that both the awkward repetitive modes of behavior and the sometimes agonizingly delayed patterns of movement and work so frequent in schizophrenics constitute attempts at self-control emerging as compulsive symptoms, i.e., a loss of resilience and initiative.

Self-help attempts can be classified based on the situation in which they occur, the degree of their complexity and efficiency, whether they are employed purposely by the patient, or whether they are rather the expression of unreflected, barely conscious efforts.

Accordingly, the scarce literature available formulates the concepts describing these phenomena with varying degrees of comprehensiveness. Here, we shall refrain from interpreting even the productive symptoms of the psychosis as "more or less failed or successful attempts at adaptation" (E. BLEULER, 1911) to a hypostatized basic disorder, or as "creative defense" (M. MUELLER, 1930), which makes them mostly unconscious "primary attempts at self-rescue." Rather, we focus our interest mainly on the patient's conscious approach to experiencing his/her psychosis and on the patient's coping with individual symptoms.

Coping with the illness as a whole can take the form of "global strategies" (LANGE, 1981): attempting self-analysis, resorting to philosophical/religious systems, formulating maxims, employing meditative techniques, studying scientific textbooks, indulging in painting and handiworks, literary productions, self-treatment with drugs, alcohol, or dietary measures. Various strategies of withdrawal and avoidance are especially frequent: a tendency to lead a pedantic life largely devoid of stimulation, apparently based on the patient's acquiescent understanding of his/her inability to deal with complex and challenging tasks.

Attempts to cope with individual symptoms cover the entire spectrum of psychotic disorders. Hallucinations, delusions, disturbances of the ego, impairments of routinized modes of behavior, and affective disorders all can become the focus of control and defense efforts. These efforts make use of numerous forms of coping, ranging from influencing the level of activity through attempted cognitive restructuring and personal initiative to passive retreat. In trying to hide symptoms from their environment, patients sometimes display a kind of "forced normalization."

Efficient forms of self-help can best be observed in cases in which the patient attempts to deal with delimitable individual disturbances. It is much more difficult to study and interpret global strategies, since they represent a complex reaction to a maze of premorbid impairments, handicaps directly dependent on the illness, and secondary effects.

Self-help, a learning process

Numerous case studies suggest that schizophrenics do not discover spontaneous self-help possibilities until several episodes of the illness have occurred. In the initial states of schizophrenia, they are so overwhelmed by the sudden new experience of psychotic distortions of reality that they are incapable of critical reflection or of viewing their psychosis with detachment. Only the recurring experience that increased excitation, sleep disturbances, lack of concentration, distorted perceptions, doubts about the existence of chance, or suspicious brooding on inconsequential details can announce a relapse into the psychosis turns these precedent initial symptoms into signals.

After analyzing cases of self-control of psychotic impairments in greater detail, BREIER and STRAUSS (1983) define three phases of the control process: first, patients notice that "something is wrong" about the way they experience reality and behave (self-monitoring); then, the change is identified as a symptom of the disease (self-evaluation), frequently with the help of other – healthy – people the patients more or less ask to assess the disorder in question; finally defense efforts start to function, efforts that consist, for example, of self-instruction and reducing or increasing one's personal activity.

The patient obviously attaches great importance to not being swept away immediately by the current of psychotic experiences, and to being able to pause and gain some distance. Accordingly, SUELLWOLD (1983b) recommends for the patient to learn to "recognize critical conditions and identify them as triggering factors of disorders." Citing SIMKO (1980), who regards even self-reflection as a significant compensatory possibility, SUELLWOLD considers it important to transform unconscious "routine reactions of avoidance" into "conscious measures of self-protection."

What has been said so far can be summarized in the form of consecutive stages of development:

1. First psychotic episode – complete defenselessness
2. Living through periodic relapses – experience with premonitory symptoms
3. Conscious perception of a new "disturbance"
4. Detachment and reflection
5. Evaluation of the disturbance as "recidivism signal"
6. Self-help attempt.

At this point, research can approach the problem from two equally promising directions:

169

1. Searching for the "critical conditions" that upset the psychic balance;
2. Analyzing the psychic "disturbance" preceding psychotic decompensation.

Thus, the preliminary and intermediate stages of acute psychotic episodes – which are almost or completely devoid of symptoms – become the focus of renewed interest as we try to find different forms of self-help.

GROSS et al. (1982) believe that "schizophrenic illnesses that remain latent or uncharacteristic for years or indeed decades are not rare at all; presumably they even number among the most frequent forms of schizophrenia." According to GROSS, the "experiential and phenomenal aspects of presyndromes, prodromes, basic stages, and purely residual states" intersect to a large extent, and the manifestation of such states is influenced by "individually variable mechanisms of compensation and coping."

We are convinced that many individuals who are prone to schizophrenia cope with psychotic "mini-episodes" by means of conscious or semiconscious self-help efforts, thereby forcing the illness back into its latent phase. As previously mentioned, these efforts are best studied in cases where the patient tries to deal with delimitable individual disorders. However, such studies need to be based on an empirically relevant *disorder model.*

Both the concept of "basic disorders" developed by HUBER et al. (cf. HUBER, 1983) and the "vulnerability concept" by ZUBIN and SPRING (1977) provide elements that could be operationalized as reference points for such a model.

Experiential basic disorders as risk indicators

Studies about the circumstances leading up to such mini-episodes, i.e., the nature of the above-mentioned "critical conditions," have yielded a large amount of information. In the course of the last few years, experimental psychological schizophrenia research has been able to prove that schizophrenics display cognitive disorders which experimental conditions allow us to observe even beyond clinically manifest episodes. Fluctuating in their intensity, these disorders affect attention, information processing, and memory, and precede as well as outlast clinically manifest symptomatology. They are designated as more or less tolerable deficiencies that can give rise to schizophrenia-specific psychotic symptoms if, for example, the patient is being overtaxed by stressful situations. Because they are thus practically considered to be basic and longer lasting disorders, they have been called "basic disorders" (HUBER, 1966, 1983; SUELLWOLD, 1977, 1981), even though under more careful examination, some of them appear to constitute complex disorders superimposed by "secondary reactions" (SUELLWOLD, 1982).

According to the studies of McGHIE and CHAPMAN (1961), CHAPMAN (1966), and notably SUELLWOLD (1977), the patients perceive such disorders subjectively, too. They report suffering from basic impairing experiences on the cognitive, psychomotoric, and affective level.

This increases the likelihood of some patients' gradually learning to recognize these deficiencies as risk indicators and – in a second step – to assess them as "danger signs" of an impending psychotic crisis as soon as a certain threshold of intensity is passed. Only this evaluative step opens the door to conscious self-help efforts, which could then be employed purposely and possibly even be enhanced in their efficiency through practice.

The concept of vulnerability and impairments of attention

ZUBIN and SPRING (1977) consider it a primary characteristic of schizophrenics to display a vulnerability to process stimuli from childhood on, rather than traits of an obscure, endogenous, process-like progressive disease in the traditional sense. As a relatively stable trait outlasting the course of the disease, vulnerability is distinguished from the actual psychotic episodes of schizophrenia, which represent unstable, changing states.

Vulnerability results from complex genetic deficiencies and dysfunctions of the CNS pertaining to infancy, the effects of which are overdeveloped by psycho-social factors as well as maturation and learning processes. The above-mentioned "basic disorders" – which are closely related to the "partial performance deficiencies," or early acquired minimal cerebral dysfunctions, brought out by LEMPP (1979) – constitute experimentally assayable and even subjectively detectable effects of vulnerability, the phenotype of which is still largely unspecific. In phases of stressful overtaxation of the cognitive system, the more or less tolerable basic disorders can presumably no longer be balanced, the psychological balance is lost, the psychosis becomes manifest.

The intensity of the risk a vulnerable person runs to become psychotic in stressful situations depends essentially on the degree of vulnerability, but it is also contingent on the number of stress factors and the efficiency of the coping methods available up to that point.

Certain cognitive performance deficits, e.g., the especially well-studied impairments of attention, may be used as operationalizable indicators of a probably important component of vulnerability with view to schizophrenia (SPRING & ZUBIN, 1978; CROMWELL et al., 1979; NUECHTERLEIN & DAWSON, 1984).

From the statements above we may infer an empirical research approach through which we could, on the one hand, experimental psychologically test a significant aspect of individual vulnerability at a given moment and on the other hand also uncover relations with subjective experiences of basic disorders and with autoprotective efforts of the patient. The degree of correlation between the concepts of basic disorders and vulnerability indicators is as yet unknown. Under no circumstance, however, must we interpret such an approach as being based on equating these two concepts.

Empirical investigations of the Berne Clinic

On the basis of these considerations, we studied 60 schizophrenics, 30 neurotics and 30 healthy control subjects, since 1983 (BOEKER et al., 1984; BRENNER et al., 1987; BRENNER et al., in press). We were concerned with the question whether there are regular correlations between objectifiable impairments of attention, subjectively experienced basic disorders, and autoprotective compensatory efforts as a reaction to such disorders. Of special interest to us were the form and frequency of possible self-help attempts that were consciously and purposefully dealing with basal performance deficits. Do schizophrenics prefer avoidance strategies or purposeful coping attempts? Do they display specific compensatory patterns in comparison to neurotics and healthy people, insofar as the latter also register impairments of attention and other basic disorders?

Test subjects

60 schizophrenics (39 men, 21 women, average age 31.1 years, average duration of illness 91.3 months, average number of hospitalizations 4.5) were studied during a phase of remission after an acute psychotic episode. The control groups consisted of 30 neurotics (12 men, 18 women, average age 29.6 years) and 30 healthy individuals (17 men, 13 women, average age 32 years).

Method

All subjects were submitted to reaction time measurements with optic and auditory stimuli based on a combination of the "cross-over" and the "cross-modality-shift" paradigms (SUTTON & ZUBIN, 1965; SHAKOW, 1965, 1979; GERSTNER, 1981) and the "span-of-apprehension" test (NEALE, 1971; ASARNOW & MACCRIMMON, 1978). Subjectively experienced basic disorders were ascertained by means of the *Frankfurt Complaints Questionnaire* (FBF, original version SUELLWOLD, 1977). A semi-standardized interview of about one and a half hours' duration was used to inquire about conscious compensatory attempts in reaction to these disorders. The subjects' attempts were divided into problem-solving-oriented coping reactions and non-problem-solving-oriented avoidance reactions and related to four disorder dimensions determined through factor analysis by SUELLWOLD and her collaborators (SUELLWOLD, 1983a; SCHUENEMANN-WURMTHALER, 1983).

Results

As was to be expected, the schizophrenics differ significantly from healthy as well as neurotic subjects by their inferior performances in the reaction time measures and the span-of-apprehension test. The same applies to the number of positive answers in the FBF.

172

Table 1: Investigated Variables and Methods Applied

Variable	Vulnerability indicators	Subjectively experienced basic disorders	Compensatory behavior regarding basic disorders
Measuring methods	Reaction time: method of extreme conditions (GERSTNER, 1981) Span-of-apprehension test (NEALE, 1971; ASARNOW & MACCRIMMON, 1978)	Frankfurt Complaints Questionnaire (FBF) (SUELLWOLD, 1977)	Semi-standardized interview – disturbances in routinized skills – disturbances in perception – depression and anhedonia – stimulus overload

Table 2: Analysis of Variance of Reaction Time, Span-of-Apprehension Test, and Subjectively Experienced Basic Disorders (FBF) in Schizophrenics (N = 60), Neurotics (N = 30), and a Healthy Control Group (N = 30)

Variable	Group Schizo-phrenics av	sd	Neurotics av	sd	Control group av	sd	F	p
Reaction time (in 10^{-2} sec.)	77	50	30	18	30	19	21.34	< 0.001
Span-of-apprehension test (mistakes)	4.7	3.2	2.4	1.5	2.0	1.7	14.83	< 0.001
FBF (number of positive answers)	39.2	21.5	11.9	15.1	3.6	4.9	59.82	< 0.001

av = average   sd = standard deviation

Schizophrenics indicated compensatory attempts in reaction to more than two-thirds of the reported basic disorders. Contrary to our expectations, the problem-solving-oriented coping efforts vastly outnumbered the avoidance reactions. This disparity is particularly pronounced in the disorder dimensions "Disturbances in routinized behavior" and "Depression/Anhedonia," whereas it is least apparent in the dimension "Stimulus overload." The fewest compensatory efforts were reported in the dimension "Disturbances of perception."

We have characterized the problem-solving-oriented reactions with terms like "re-interpretation," "restructuring," "reality testing," "shift in behavior," or "search for behavioral patterns" (for examples see BOEKER & BRENNER, 1984; BRENNER et al., 1985).

Neurotics and healthy individuals also experience basic disorders and try to compensate for them. Interestingly enough, the healthy have a propensity for

Table 3: Survey of the Reported Basic Disorders and the Associated Compensatory Attempts with Regard to the Four Disorder Dimensions of the FBF

Compensatory attempt	Disorder dimension	Disturbances in routinized skills	Disturbances in perception	Depression and anhedonia	Stimulus overload	Total
Compensatory attempts: total		121	70	117	140	448
Problem-solving-oriented		93	54	92	93	332
Non-problem-solving-oriented		28	16	25	47	116
Quotient	compensatory attempts	121	70	117	140	448
	reported basic disorders	149	121	157	172	599

Table 4: Analysis of Variance (KRUSKAL-WALLIS) of Compensatory Attempts for Reported Basic Disorders in Schizophrenics (N = 60), Neurotics (N = 30), and a Healthy Control Group (N = 30)

Variable	Group	Schizophrenics		Neurotics		Control group		$x2$	p
		av	sd	av	sd	av	sd		
Total compensatory attempts		7.5	3.1	3.6	2.4	1.6	2.3	58.6	< 0.001
Basic disorders with compensatory attempts: Total basic disorders		69.9%		83.6%		70.1%		7.40	< 0.05
Problem-solving-oriented compensatory attempts		5.5	3.1	2.4	1.9	1.0	1.4	47.1	< 0.001
Problem-solving-oriented compensatory attempts: Total compensatory attempts		68.4%		58.8%		39.8%		7.89	< 0.05
Non-problem-solving-oriented compensatory attempts		2.0	1.3	1.2	1.2	0.6	1.3	27.4	< 0.001
Non-problem-solving-oriented compensatory attempts: Total compensatory attempts		31.6%		41.2%		60.2%		7.89	< 0.05

av = average   sd = standard deviation

174

avoiding the problem rather than purposely coping with an individual disorder (ratio 60%:40%), whereas neurotics display a relation of problem-solving-oriented to non-problem-solving-oriented behavior similar to the one established for schizophrenics (68.4%:31.6%), namely, 59%:41%.

With an increasing number of reported basic disorders on the one hand and an increasing number of compensatory attempts on the other, the problem-solving-oriented self-help efforts of schizophrenics gain an evident predominance over non-problem-solving-oriented efforts ($r = 0.43$, $p < 0.001$).

Contrary to our expectations, there was no significant correlation between the experimentally determined extent of attentional deficits and the number of subjectively experienced basic disorders. The number of reported compensatory efforts did not relate, either.

Table 5: Correlations (r = Spearman's Correlation Coefficient) Between Subjectively Experienced Basic Disorders (FBF) and Compensatory Attempts as well as Vulnerability Indicators (Reaction-Time Measures, Span-of-Apprehension Test) in Schizophrenics, Neurotics, and a Healthy Control Group

Group	Schizophrenics		Neurotics		Control group	
Variable	r	p	r	p	r	p
Problem-solving-oriented compensatory attempts	0.44	< 0.001	0.61	< 0.001	0.86	< 0.001
Non-problem-solving-oriented compensatory attempts	-0.07	n.s.	0.38	< 0.05	0.70	< 0.001
Reaction-time measurements (msec.)	-0.12	n.s.	0.17	n.s.	0.10	n.s.
Span-of-apprehension test (mistakes)	0.18	n.s.	0.11	n.s.	-0.04	n.s.

Even when we singled out the patients with the poorest performances on both the reaction time and the tachistoscopic measurements to form an extreme group and opposed this group to the schizophrenics indicating the largest numbers of attentional impairments on the FBF[1] we could not detect any significant correlations between those two groups. What we did find, however, was a large percentage of compensatory efforts that were non-problem-solving oriented, i.e., connected to passive avoidance reactions, above all in FBF-answers associated with "stimulus overload."

---

1 For this purpose, we prepared a subscale encompassing all the questions relevant to maintaining a certain (attentional) attitude, the questions being selected by several experts.

Discussion

The experimental psychological methods and the FBF we used in this study established a significant distinction between clinically diagnosed schizophrenics on the one hand and neurotics and healthy individuals on the other. Yet basic disorders also occur among the healthy and – distinctively more often – among neurotics; from a qualitative point of view, they are therefore not strictly schizophrenia-specific phenomena.

The question remains why the schizophrenics showing the objectively poorest attentional performances did not report the highest number of disorders in the respective subscale of the FBF, too. Originally, we had expected to find a significant correlation here, but it did not materialize. Taking into consideration the statements made in the section on "Self-help, a learning process," we might interpret this finding as follows:

The FBF answers reflect the awareness of subjectively suffering from specific impairments, an awareness that doubtlessly requires a certain ability for detached self-perception and critical evaluation of one's own personal capabilities. Could it be that these patients, being severely handicapped in their attentional functions are unable to accomplish this act of self-evaluation as well as other individuals, and that their subjective awareness of disorders is therefore also less well developed? Thus, they would not necessarily register more basic disorders, despite their marked attentional dysfunctions, and consequently would also not be in as good a position to compensate for their performance deficits in an active manner. This would again emphasize the importance of "self-monitoring" mentioned by BREIER and STRAUSS (1983).

According to our findings, experimentally testable attentional deficits as vulnerability indicators are thus not directly related to subjectively experienced basic disorders, which makes the significance of the intermediate cognitive processes become obvious. Only if we take those into account may we expect to gain further enlightenment on the nature of compensatory behavior.

On the whole, self-help efforts by schizophrenics are more frequent than expected. Subjectively perceived basal performance dysfunctions are evidently experienced and evaluated as "critical conditions" or emotional "danger signs" (cf. BRENNER et al., 1985). The compensatory attempts of schizophrencis deal with the source of anxiety in a much more marked and purposeful way than was previously assumed. Avoidance reactions are clearly outnumbered.

SUELLWOLD (1982), who studied 20 schizophrenics with a modified FBF (additional scale with 8 items under the heading "Measures that help me and improve my condition"), found the following consciously initiated self-help efforts:

1. If I avoid unrest around me
2. If I work slowly
3. If I concentrate on a few activities and omit everything else.

176

In accordance with our own results, the global statement "If I withdraw frequently" was denied in the overwhelming majority of cases.

Apparently, the healthy control subjects are hardly troubled by basic disorders. They consider them to be familiar concomitants of everyday occurrences such as fatigue, disinterest, or insecurity at work. Consequently, their compensatory efforts mainly include taking a break, trying to regain strength, or switching to another activity (action shifting). Avoidance reactions predominate (cf. BRENNER et al., 1987).

The neurotic patients in our study form an intermediate group; they see basic disorders above all as concomitants of their neurotic nuclear symptomatology. Their compensatory behavior consists in trying to resolve conflicts, e.g., by discussing them with the people involved, rather than in avoidance or withdrawal, which differentiates them from the healthy control group. Unlike schizophrenics, however, they rarely report clearly defined attempts at coping with individual disorders. In their case, experiencing a basic disorder did not seem to be accompanied by extreme emotional tension very often, either (cf. BRENNER et al., 1987).

Although our studies have established proof of self-help attempts by a large number of schizophrenics, they have so far failed to provide insights into the quantitative effectiveness of such attempts. Nevertheless, many compensatory efforts seem to calm and structuralize frightening alterations of the experiential field, if only for a short time. This way, some of the patients presumably succeed in mitigating risk situations and avoiding psychotic relapses.

The finding that an increase in subjective basic disorders entails an increase in specific problem-solving-oriented coping efforts leads us to the question whether this is of advantage to the schizophrenic patient. Continuous attempts at controlling and mastering frequently perceived performance deficits use up energy. In the case of a similar experience, a healthy individual will take a break or switch to another activity more often than not. Many schizophrenics, however, appear to become overly engrossed in coping with their deficits. This could explain many forms of schizophrenic "adynamia" as well as the "reduction of the energetic potential."

Since the majority of psychotic episodes seems to be preceded by prodromal symptoms for days or even weeks (CONRAD, 1958; HERZ & MELVILLE, 1980), and since many vulnerable individuals probably live in a near-psychotic labile state on the boundaries of manifest illness without decompensating for a long time, there is preventive importance attached to the timely observation and evaluation of such disorders, which most probably constitute early symptoms of a psychotic crisis and not "banal" fluctuations of the patient's condition.

If, for example, a reasonably stabilized patient begins to doubt the existence of chance again, and if this results in initial paranoid elaborations, this is bound to gain a larger significance than the patient's experiencing a general susceptibility to stimuli or lack of concentration.

The more we know about these changes in experience, which presumably vary from patient to patient and develop in circular stimulus-reaction spirals leading up to a psychotic crisis, the more easily we can help the patient to select and intensify those attempted autoprotective strategies that interrupt the vicious circle most effectively and most economically. If the patient succeeds in focusing energy on the most effective measures, then the experience of successful self-stabilization is liable to increase autonomy as well as self-respect, which are both massively impaired through long illness.

This is where the development of future therapy programs must set in: programs that make use of the available knowledge about risk factors and control and counter measures in the sense of preventive training. However, there is still too little known about the specificity and effectiveness of such programs.

Bibliography

ASARNOW, R. F.; MacCRIMMON, D. J.: Residual performance deficit in clinically remitted schizophrenics: A marker of schizophrenia? J. Abn. Psychol. 87, 597–608, 1978.

BINDER, H.: Zur Psychopathologie der Zwangsvorgänge. Berlin, 1929.

BLEULER, E.: Dementia praecox oder die Gruppe der Schizophrenien. Leipzig: Deuticke, 1911.

BOEKER, W.; BRENNER, H. D.: Selbstheilungsversuche Schizophrener: Psychopathologische Befunde und Folgerungen für Forschung und Therapie. Nervenarzt 54, 578–589, 1983.

BOEKER, W.; BRENNER, H. D.: Über Selbstheilungsversuche Schizophrener. Schweiz. Archiv f. Neurologie, Neurochirurgie und Psychiatrie 135, 123–133, 1984.

BOEKER, W.; BRENNER, H. D.; GERSTNER, G.; KELLER, F.; MUELLER, J.; SPICHTIG, L.: Self-healing strategies among schizophrenics: Attempts at compensation for basic disorders. Acta Psychiatr. Scand. 69, 373–378, 1984.

BREIER, A.; STRAUSS, J. S.: Self-control in psychotic disorders. Arch. Gen. Psychiat. 40, 1141–1145, 1983.

BRENNER, H.D.; BOEKER, W.; ANDRES, K.; STRAMKE, W.G: Efforts at compensation with regard to basic disorders among schizophrenics. In: LAASER, U.; SENAULT, R.; VIEFHUES, H. (eds.): Primary health care in the making. Berlin, Heidelberg: Springer, 1985.

BRENNER, H. D.; BOEKER, W.; MUELLER, J.; SPICHTIG, L.; WUERGLER, S.: Autoprotective efforts among schizophrenics, neurotics and controls. Acta Psych. Scand. 75, 1987.

BRENNER, H. D.; KRAEMER, S.; HERMANUTZ, H.; HODEL, B.: Cognitive treatment in schizophrenia: State of the art. In: HAHLWEG, K.; STRAUBE, E. (eds.): Schizophrenia: Models and interventions. Berlin, Heidelberg, New York: Springer (in press).

CHAPMAN, J.: The early symptoms of schizophrenia. Brit. J. Psychiat. 112, 225–251, 1966.

CONRAD, K.: Die beginnende Schizophrenie: Versuch einer Gestaltanalyse des Wahns. Stuttgart: Thieme, 1958.

CROMWELL, R. L.; DE AMICIS, L.; HAYES, T.; BRIGGS, D.: Reaction time crossover, a vulnerability index: Mean reaction time, a symptom severity index. Psychopharmacol. Bull. 15, 24–25, 1979.

FALLOON, I. R. H.; TALBOT, T.: Persistent auditory hallucinations: coping mechanisms and implications for management. Psychol. Med. 11, 329–339, 1981.

FREEDMAN, B. J.: The subjective experience of perceptual and cognitive disturbances in schizophrenia. Arch. Gen. Psychiat. 30, 333–340, 1974.

FREUD, S.: Psychoanalytische Bemerkungen über einen autobiographisch beschriebenen Fall von Paranoia (Dementia paranoides) (1909-1913). Ges. Werke Bd. VIII, 4. Aufl., Frankfurt: Fischer, 1964.

GERSTNER, G.: Eine experimentalpsychologische Untersuchung zur beeinträchtigten Aufmerksamkeit bei Schizophrenen am Beispiel von Reaktionszeiten. Diplomarbeit (unveröffentlicht) am Psychologischen Institut der Universität Mannheim, 1981.

GROSS, G.; HUBER, G.; SCHUETTLER, R.: Larvierte Schizoprenie? In: HEINRICH, K. (Hrsg.): Der Schizophrene außerhalb der Klinik. Bern, Stuttgart, Wien: Huber, 1982.

HERZ, M. I.; MELVILLE, Ch.: Relapse in schizophrenia. Am. J. Psychiat. *137*, 801–805, 1980.
HUBER, G.: Reine Defektsyndrome und Basis-Stadien endogener Psychosen. Fortschr. Neurol. Psychiat. *34*, 409–426, 1966.
HUBER, G.: Das Konzept substratnaher Basissymptome und seine Bedeutung für Theorie und Therapie schizophrener Erkrankungen. Nervenarzt *54*, 23–32, 1983.
JANZARIK, W.: Dynamische Grundkonstellationen in endogenen Psychosen. Berlin, Göttingen, Heidelberg: Springer, 1959.
KISKER, K. P.: Der Erlebniswandel der Schizophrenen. Berlin, Göttingen, Heidelberg: Springer, 1960.
KLAESI, J.: Über die Bedeutung und Entstehung der Stereotypien. Berlin: Karger, 1922.
LANGE, H. U.: Anpassungsstrategien, Bewältigungsreaktionen und Selbstheilungsversuche bei Schizophrenen. Fortschr. Neurol. Psychiat. *49*, 275–285, 1981.
LEMPP, R. (Hrsg.): Teilleistungsstörungen im Kindesalter. Bern, Stuttgart, Wien: Huber, 1979.
MUELLER, M.: Über Heilungsmechanismen in der Schizophrenie. Berlin: Karger, 1930.
MCGHIE, A.; CHAPMAN, J.: Disorders of attention and perception in early schizophrenia. Brit. J. Med. Psychol. *34*, 103–116, 1961.
NEALE, J. M.: Perceptual span in schizophrenia. J. Abnorm. Psychol. *77*, 196–204, 1971.
NUECHTERLEIN, K. H.; DAWSON, M. E.: Information processing and attentional functioning in the developmental course of schizophrenic disorders. Schizophrenia Bull. *10*, 160–203, 1984.
SCHAUB, A.: Bewältigungsstrategien bei schizophrenen Patienten. Diplomarbeit, Bonn, 1984.
SCHUENEMANN-WURMTHALER, S.: Empirische Untersuchungen zum Frankfurter Beschwerde-Fragebogen. Inaugural Diss. Univ. Frankfurt a.M., 1983.
SHAKOW, D.: Mental set in schizophrenia, studied in a discrimination reaction setting. J. Personality and Social Psychol. *1*, 88–95, 1965.
SHAKOW, D.: Adaptation in schizophrenia. The theory of segmental set. New York, Wiley, 1979.
SIMKO, A.: Reflexiv-kompensierend verarbeitete Residualsymptome in schizophrenen Defektpsychosen. In: HUBER, G. (Hrsg.): Schizophrenie – Stand und Entwicklungstendenzen der Forschung. 4. Weissenauer Schizophrenie-Symposium, 59–67, 1980. Stuttgart, New York: Schattauer, 1981.
SPRING, B. J.; ZUBIN, J.: Attention and information processing as indicators of vulnerability to schizophrenic episodes. J. Psychiatr. Res. *14*, 289–301, 1978.
SUELLWOLD, L.: Symptome schizophrener Erkrankungen – Uncharakteristische Basisstörungen. Monographien aus dem Gesamtgebiet der Psychiatrie, Bd. 13. Berlin, Heidelberg, New York: Springer, 1977.
SUELLWOLD, L.: Basis-Störungen: Ergebnisse und offene Fragen. In: HUBER, G. (Hrsg.): Schizophrenie. Stand und Entwicklungstendenzen der Forschung. Stuttgart: Schattauer, 1981.
SUELLWOLD, L.: Zum Einfluß von Sekundärreaktionen auf die Langzeitentwicklung schizophrener Psychosen. In: BECKMANN, H. (Hrsg.): Biologische Psychiatrie. Stuttgart, New York: Thieme, 1982.
SUELLWOLD, L.: Subjektive defizitäre Störungen bei schizophrenen Erkrankten. In: BRENNER, H. D.; REY, E.-R.; STRAMKE, W. G. (Hrsg.): Empirische Schizophrenieforschung. Bern, Stuttgart, Wien: Huber, 1983a.
SUELLWOLD, L.: Schizophrenie. Stuttgart, Berlin, Köln, Mainz: Kohlhammer, 1983b.
SUTTON, S.; ZUBIN, J.: Effect of sequence on reaction time in schizophrenia. In: WELFORD, A. T.; BIREN, J. E. (eds.): Behavior, aging and the nervous system. Springfield, IL: Charles C. Thomas Publishers, 562–597, 1965.
WING, J. K.: Schizophrenie in Selbstzeugnissen. In: KATSCHNIG, H. (Hrsg.): Die andere Seite der Schizophrenie – Patienten zu Hause. München, Wien, Baltimore: Urban & Schwarzenberg, 1977.
WING, J. K.: Schizophrenia – towards a new synthesis. London: Academic Press / New York: Grune and Stratton, 1978.
ZUBIN, J.; SPRING, B.: Vulnerability – a new view of schizophrenia. J. Abn. Psychol. *86*, 103–126, 1977.

Cognitive and Behavioural Interventions in the Self Control of Schizophrenia

I. R. H. FALLOON

Recent advances in the management of florid episodes of schizophrenia have led to the assumption that most persons suffering from this disorder experience relatively rapid remissions enabling efficient restoration of community functioning. However, carefully conducted long-term follow-ups of cohorts of schizophrenic patients have revealed that the rate of full remission of florid delusions and hallucinations remains a relatively infrequent phenomenon, perhaps no more than one-fifth of all cases (FALLOON et al., in press). The majority of persons continue to experience psychotic phenomena, albeit in a less intense manner, for several years after the onset of their condition.

Despite the low frequency of complete disappearance of delusions and hallucinations the handicaps associated with schizophrenia appear to have diminished considerably during the past three decades with two-thirds of all patients returning to community functioning within the normal range. The number of cases severely incapacitated has been halved since 1950.

The apparent contradiction between incomplete clinical recovery and complete social recovery may surprise observers schooled in the KRAEPELINIAN tradition where the diagnosis of schizophrenia was linked to deteriorating social status, and has led to questioning the appropriateness of the original diagnoses of such cases. However, the tradition of the BLEULERS, (both of whom remarked upon the relatively high rate of social remission, especially where effective psychosocial support was provided) leads us to seek the psychological mechanisms that appear to underly this lack of concordance between clinical and social status.

In contrast to Eugen BLEULER's (1911) efforts to link the social outcome of schizophrenia to an underlying "basic disorder" upon which florid delusions, hallucinations and thought interference were mere epiphenomena I propose to examine schizophrenia along more straightforward behavioral lines, more akin to the observations of Prof. Manfred BLEULER (1972).

This model considers that the florid psychotic phenomena are at the basic symptoms or *impairment* associated with schizophrenia, and remain evident in at least 60% of all cases. Persistence of such symptoms, often with reduced intensity, contributes to the *disability* noted in many persons who appear to have made "good" recoveries from acute florid episodes, as well as in those where the persistence of florid symptoms is more overt. The disability of schizophrenia is less specific than the florid symptoms and is manifest in an impairment of psychological functions. A reduction in cognitive functioning

180

that includes attention, information processing, perceptual acuity, decision making and problem solving (HEMSLEY, 1982; NUECHTERLEIN & DAWSON, 1984) has been found consistently in studies of psychological disability in schizophrenia.

Changes in affective expression have been well documented, but when contrasted with the changes noted in depressive illness have shown less specificity for schizophrenia. Indeed, it is evident that depressive symptoms are an almost constant feature of florid schizophrenia (KNIGHTS & HIRSCH, 1981) and that they tend to parallel the course of psychotic symptoms in terms of remission and exacerbation. Thus, the so-called "negative" symptoms of schizophrenia are extremely difficult to discriminate from the florid picture, particularly where it persists. The pseudo Parkinsonian side effects of neuroleptic drugs further confuse this picture of affective impairment. Cases with greater severity of persisting delusions, hallucinations and thought interference are, therefore, most likely to have higher levels of depression and be treated with higher doses of neuroleptic drugs, and thereby to show more "negative" symptoms. Thus, attempts to attribute the disability of schizophrenia to a "negative" syndrome or deficit state appear to ignore the persistence of "positive" or florid psychotic features. In a careful survey, in which patients were interviewed with the PSE in their own homes after treatment of florid episodes of schizophrenia 92% of patients with significant "negative" symptoms revealed persistent delusions, hallucinations or thought interference. In many cases the patients were able to describe how their florid symptoms contributed to the "negative" features, especially the continued need for social withdrawal.

However, it should be noted that a substantial proportion of these cases disclosed the persistence of their florid symptoms only when systematically questioned in their own homes, and were reported as consistently free of florid psychotic symptoms at their aftercare clinics.

It is concluded that the *disability* observed with schizophrenia chiefly consists of impaired cognitive and affective functioning, and that this disability is largely secondary to delusions, hallucinations and thought interference. The extent of the disability observed is due only in part to the severity of the florid symptoms. In as much as neuroleptic drugs may reduce the severity of florid symptoms, cognitive and affective disability may be improved. However, an unwanted feature of drug therapy, particularly in moderate or high doses, is cognitive impairment and affective blunting. For this reason an overvalued concern with the complete remission of all psychotic phenomena may contribute paradoxically to increased disability. Another factor contributing to the level of disability associated with symptoms is the person's ability to compensate for the impairment. Greater premorbid cognitive capacity (intelligence, perceptual and problem solving skills) may help, as well as the ability to develop effective coping mechanisms to deal with the disability. In a study of persons suffering from persistent auditory hallucinations it was noted that all subjects employed some cognitive or behavioural strategies to attempt to reduce the disability caused by their symptoms (FALLOON & TALBOT, 1981).

The disability that remains despite compensatory efforts is likely to contribute to an individual's handicaps in his social functioning in the community. However, as WING (1978) has clearly indicated, persons who suffer from schizophrenia may show handicaps in their social functioning quite unrelated to the disorder. Such handicaps, such as schizoid personality, or lack of educational or vocational attainment may have contributed to social handicaps in the absence of schizophrenia. The onset of schizophrenia undoubtedly compounds such premorbid features and may contribute to higher levels of resultant handicap. But it is important not to conclude that the severity of the illness can be equated with the severity of the social handicap.

It is evident that impaired cognitive and affective functioning *(disability)* may contribute to difficulties in social functioning. Social relationships will be impaired where a person lacks the ability to clearly perceive and process aspects of non-verbal communication, for example where a friendly smile is perceived as a threatening gesture. Affective withdrawal may similarly impede the development of friendships and work relationships. Indeed it has been noted that many patients with schizophrenia can function adequately in performing the specific tasks required of a job, but their difficulty in developing adequate social relationships among their work colleagues tends to prove a major stumbling block.

Other factors that contribute to the social handicaps associated with schizophrenia include the availability of opportunities – for example, the availability of suitable jobs. And finally, the presence of adequate social network support. The value of family and friends in assisting individuals to overcome the handicapping features of schizophrenia and in assisting persons to maximize their social functioning potential is well recognized, although few studies have focused on this positive aspect of family functioning.

In summary (see Table 1), it is proposed that the florid symptoms of schizophrenia frequently persist and provide a continued source of *impairment* that contributes to psychological disability. Effective compensation of the resulting *disability* may minimize *handicaps* of social functioning, which themselves depend upon premorbid social attainment and environmental support factors and resources.

Implications for management

This formulation, based upon a multilevel assessment of clinical, psychological and social features, gives rise to several areas where therapeutic intervention may benefit the patient. To date, most successful efforts to reduce the morbidity of schizophrenia have concerned direct attempts to reduce the florid symptoms, usually by drugs, or attempts to enhance social functioning through rehabilitation. Attempts to intervene at the psychological level have been less successful and have seldom focused on coping functions specific to the symptoms of schizophrenia. It could be argued that the benefits of family-

Table 1: The impairments, disabilities and handicaps associated with schizophrenia

Impairment	
● thought interference	
● false perception	
● distorted information processing	
● motor abnormality	

Disability	
● cognitive dysfunction:	attention perceptual acuity decision making problem solving
● affective dysfunction:	recognition of social cues non-verbal expression reduced sensitivity to reinforcement
● behavioural dysfunction:	motor performance

Handicap	
● social relationships:	family friends workmates
● work activity	
● leisure activity	

based approaches to stress management have been attributable in part to an enhancement in the ability of the patient to cope with persisting symptoms with the support and assistance of family members (FALLOON, 1985).

The remainder of this talk will examine some of the efforts that have been made to apply psychological treatment to enhancing the coping with the florid symptoms of schizophrenia.

Thought interference

A major feature of schizophrenia is the interference with a person's train of thought. This usually takes the form of experiencing alien thoughts being in-

183

serted into one's stream of consciousness, or the unexpected disappearance of thoughts from one's mind. Such phenomena occurring frequently constitute a major source of cognitive disability. In a less pronounced form they may impede perception, attention and problem solving functions.

MEICHENBAUM & CAMERON (1974) employed a cognitive training procedure to teach chronically impaired patients to enhance their perceptual, attention and problem solving skills. This involved patients giving themselves instructions while performing tasks. Extended training produced significant improvements on a variety of cognitive and language measures, but no specific measures of thought interference were employed.

Systematic training in cognitive skills has been developed by BRENNER and his colleagues in Berne (BRENNER et al., 1982), and WALLACE & LIBERMAN in Los Angeles (WALLACE et al., 1980). In both these programs efforts have been directed towards enhancing social perception and communication skills. Specific changes in thought interference have not been measured.

A young woman who suffered almost constant thought insertion was able to gain modest relief from a combination of thought stopping – shouting "STOP!" aloud, and later under her breath – and slowing down her speech with controlled breathing exercises. Remarkably, she remained quite free from thought interference when engaged in a problem solving task in which she wrote notes at each step of the process. It was apparent that the highly structured nature of the task that captured this patient's attention reduced her cognitive disorganization.

ADAMS et al. (1981) reported training a patient in recognizing irrelevant thoughts and to eliminate them with a combination of thought stopping and refocusing on external stimuli in the immediate environment. He was instructed to induce such thoughts and then switch them off. A final, important component involved instructions to avoid verbalizing his irrelevant thoughts.

To date, the intrusive alien thoughts of schizophrenia have received much less attention than the somewhat similar unwanted thoughts of the obsessive-compulsive syndrome. Even less is known about the contingencies surrounding thought blocking or withdrawal phenomena, which seem much less persistent since the advent of effective drug therapy. Nevertheless further research is needed to develop strategies to assist those persons who remain disabled from thought interference phenomena despite optimal drug management.

Delusions

The central feature of a delusion is its patent absurdity that is impervious to all other experiences and compelling counter arguments (JASPERS, 1913). Such rigid definitions would appear to leave little room for self control strategies. However, persisting delusions held with absolute conviction are now relatively rare in treated cases of schizophrenia of recent origin.

184

Attempts to modify firm beliefs with psychological interventions have met with limited success. WATTS et al. (1973) obtained significant changes in the intensity of delusions in three chronic paranoid patients. They avoided direct confrontation, which appears to merely heighten the belief, confirming the old adage "never believe a rumour until it is convincingly denied!". Instead a problem-solving approach was used in which the patient was encouraged to examine each delusion and to consider all the arguments in support of the beliefs and all the arguments against them. Worthwhile reductions were obtained, although the delusions remained intact.

MILTON et al. (1978) contrasted a confrontational approach with problem-solving in a small controlled study in chronic schizophrenia. Both approaches resulted in small, but significant changes in the intensity of the beliefs, with further significant reductions in the problem-solving group some six weeks after treatment. There was some evidence that confrontation produced an increase in delusional intensity in several cases.

LAMONTAGNE et al. (1983) successfully employed thought stopping to reduce the intensity of delusions of persecution.

The complexity of persisting delusional beliefs has been highlighted in recent studies (HARTMAN & CASHMAN, 1983; BREIER & STRAUSS, 1983). It is unlikely that any single strategy will prove effective for all cases. An individualized functional analysis of the contingencies surrounding the occurrence of these thoughts and their subsequent disappearance is an essential step in seeking strategies to assist patients to cope with them. HARTMAN & CASHMAN (1983) describe such an approach in which three persistently deluded patients employ a variety of cognitive and behavioural strategies to reduce the social and interpersonal handicaps associated with their delusions. In one case the focus was on relieving the distress associated with the belief, another on real-life exposure to situations where persecution was feared, and the third on developing more adaptive cognitions and correcting a negative self-image. All cases showed substantial improvements in their delusions and affect as a result of these procedures. Persecutory delusions bear considerable similarity to severe phobias – in this case irrational fears of people. We have successfully employed a graduated desensitization approach to several persistent cases. This involves defining a hierarchy from least to most feared interpersonal situations, training in anxiety management strategies, then self-controlled graduated exposure to feared situations. Family members have been trained to assist patients in this approach, to minimize confrontation, and to maximize support for the patient's positive efforts. They are trained to avoid arguments about the delusions while clearly stating their own beliefs.

It is evident that moderate or high doses of neuroleptic drugs block the habituation process substantially, so that successful desensitization has been achieved in cases who have been on minimal or no drugs. The interactions between neuroleptic drugs and psychosocial interventions is of crucial importance to the development of effective therapeutic regimens. To date research on this issue is sparse (FALLOON & LIBERMAN, 1983).

185

In cases of bizarre beliefs we have employed a strategy of problem solving that starts with the assumption that the belief is indeed a *real problem* for the patient. Solutions to this problem are then found by brainstorming, systematically evaluated, and a detailed plan worked out. In one such case an anxious woman who lived with her elderly mother and believed that she would be raped by the devil was greatly relieved when her mother fixed the back-door lock on their house and repaired the broken latch on her bedroom window. However, such simple environmental manipulations seldom produce such dramatic results and more complex repeated problem solving is usually necessary to enhance the ability of patients and their relatives to cope with persisting delusional beliefs.

When such methods fail to relieve persistent delusions interventions directed towards coping with the associated handicaps are sought. These include strategies such as teaching patients and their families to minimize discussion about the delusion, particularly in social interaction and public settings. Eugen BLEULER (1911) remarked that he had observed that patients over the age of 30 showed better control over their behaviour, even in the presence of powerful delusions, they "do not lose their grip on things nor do they really deteriorate; except during acute thrusts many of these patients are perfectly capable of working". Undoubtedly the same holds true today. The behavioural psychotherapist seeks to build upon the effective coping behaviour that patients currently exhibit, not merely to eliminate their seemingly ineffective efforts.

Hallucinations

Reports of strategies for reducing the frequency of persistent auditory hallucinations are numerous. For the most part the methods have been empirically based with only limited analysis of the contingencies surrounding the hallucination.

They have included aversive conditioning (BUCHER & FABRICATORE, 1970; ANDERSON & ALPERT, 1974; LAMONTAGNE et al., 1983; WEINGARTNER, 1971; ALFORD & TURNER, 1976; TURNER et al., 1977; MOSER, 1974); relaxation and desensitization (LICK & HEFFLER, 1977; ALUMBAUGH, 1971; SLADE, 1972); reduction of attention of associates to patients' external signs of hallucinations (ALLYON & KANDEL, 1976; HAYNES & GEDDY, 1973; NYDEGGER, 1972; PATTERSON et al., 1976); increased information processing tasks (ROSENTHAL & QUINN, 1977; SLADE, 1974); control of the onset of hallucinations and thought stopping (FISHER & WINKLER, 1975); reinforcement strategies (ANDERSON & ALPERT, 1974); engagement in social interaction (ALFORD & TURNER, 1976; TURNER et al., 1977).

While all these strategies have proven effective in reducing the frequency of reported persistent hallucinations during treatment sessions they have been of limited clinical benefit.

186

FALLOON & TALBOT (1981) reported clinically useful reductions in auditory hallucinations in two patients with self-administration of a painful stimulus (snapping a rubber band worn around the wrist). This self-control method enabled patients to cope with frequent hallucinatory intrusions so that they were able to engage actively in vocationing training. In both these cases it was clear that the patients usually enjoyed their voices, but after having deliberately induced them they were often unable to switch them off and attend to external stimuli.

The provision of external auditory stimuli by means of stereo radio and music (FEDER, 1982), white noise (SLADE, 1974), television (MAGEN, 1983) had reduced the intensity of auditory hallucinations. The advent of portable personal radiorecorders may provide a potentially valuable coping aid for responsive patients who are able to attend to constructive activity whilst listening to music or spoken word. However, in a systematic study of 10 different auditory stimuli MARGO and his co-workers (1981) concluded that it was the active information processing that accompanied auditory input that contributed to a reduction in the intensity of hallucinations not merely the sound itself. Thus, the development of effective strategies may be a much more complex matter than it first appears.

The broad range of strategies that have provided reduction, albeit usually transient, of hallucinations appear to have one element in common – all seek to divert the person's attention away from the hallucination. The lack of long term benefits suggests that unless methods are devised to enable such diversionary strategies to be maintained beyond the treatment sessions such approaches are of little practical value.

Moreover, most of these coping strategies are responses to the occurrence of hallucinations. A less frequently employed approach is to train patients to recognize the contingencies surrounding the onset of the hallucinations and to devise strategies for preventing their onset. One patient we treated was able to pinpoint the onset of his voices to times when he felt anxious and apprehensive. He was observed to be hyperventilating at this time. He was trained to recognize this hyperventilation and to take slow, shallow breaths. The frequency of his hallucinations became minimal. Interestingly he noted that physical exercise that induced breathlessness continued to trigger off hallucinations. However, understanding this process reduced the anxiety associated with vigorous physical activity and he was able to enjoy a range of sporting activities despite the presence of hallucinations.

Physiological changes may contribute in a similar manner to exacerbations of hallucinations and delusions that occur regularly during the premenstrual phase of the menstrual cycle of women (CATER et al., 1985). Awareness of the association between these cyclical exacerbations and menstrual physiology may enable sufferers to find ways to cope with these symptoms without the anxiety they tend to arouse.

Other biological factors that may be accessible to self-control strategies for schizophrenia include tobacco smoking, excessive caffeine intake and abuse of stimulant drugs. These chemicals appear to counteract the tranquillizing effects of neuroleptic drugs and may provoke florid symptoms. Education of patients and their relatives about the nature of schizophrenia and the part played by these factors on the course of the illness may assist in the self control of the condition.

Reduction in the handicaps associated with hallucinations may be achieved through more tolerant societal attitudes towards such phenomena. It has been argued that the better outcome of schizophrenia in the developing countries may be partially explained by the increased tolerance, in some cases amounting to reverence, for persons who experience hallucinations (AL-ISSA, 1976).

Recent specific efforts to educate patients and their friends and relatives about the nature of schizophrenia have led to more tolerant attitudes and reduced fear associated with the disclosure of such experiences (FALLOON, 1985). One young man who feared that his girlfriend would find out that he heard voices rehearsed ways of explaining his experience to her. His mother suggested that he could tell her that he had a special ability to dream when he was wide awake. When he told his girlfriend she appeared upset at first and then burst out laughing and told him that she had been in a psychiatric hospital once and had had the same experience of hearing peoples' voices when nobody was about, but she had been terrified that he wouldn't want to have anything more to do with her if she told him.

A recent report describes an educational group approach in which persons experiencing persistent hallucinations explain their various strategies for coping and assist one another to find effective ways of managing their disabilities (KANAS, 1984). Such open discussions help dispel the links between hallucinations and devils, witchcraft and exorcism, torture and incarceration that have played a prominent role in European religion and culture till the present. The view that schizophrenia is a frightening, progressively dementing, incurable cancer of the mind remains widely prevalent. In my opinion, such cultural notions must be replaced urgently. This may necessitate major public education campaigns that highlight the manner in which the vast majority of people who develop schizophrenia can learn to cope with their disabling symptoms, with the skilled assistance of professionals to provide optimal drug and psychological treatments, their families and friends to provide caring supportive homes, and their fellow sufferers to suggest new self-control strategies to assist in the management of refractory thought interference, hallucinations and delusions.

Bibliography

ADAMS, H.E.; MALATESTA, V.; BRANTLEY, P.J.; TURKAT, I.D.: Modification of cognitive processes: A case study of schizophrenia. J. Cons. Clin. Psychol. *41*, 460–464, 1981.
ALFORD, G.S.; TURNER, S.M.: Stimulus interference and conditioned inhibition of auditory hallucinations. J. Beh. Ther. Experim. Psychiat. *7*, 155–160, 1976.
AL-ISSA, I.: Behavior therapy and hallucinations: A sociocultural approach. Psychotherapy: Theory, Research and Practice *13*, 156–159, 1976.

Allyon, T.; Kandel, H.: "I hear voices but there's no one there": A functional analysis of auditory hallucinations. In: Eysenck, H. J. (ed.): Case studies in behaviour therapy. Henley-on-Thames: Routledge & Kegan Paul, 1976.

Alumbaugh, R. V.: Use of behavior modification technique toward reduction of hallucinatory behavior: A case history. Psychol. Record *21*, 415–417, 1971.

Anderson, L. T.; Alpert, M.: Operant analysis of hallucination frequency in a hospitalized schizophrenic. J. Beh. Ther. Experim. Psychiat. *5*, 13–18, 1974.

Bleuler, E.: Dementia praecox or the group of schizophrenias. New York: International Universities Press, 1911.

Bleuler, M.: Die schizophrenen Geistesstörungen im Lichte langjähriger Kranken- und Familiengeschichten. Stuttgart: Thieme, 1972.

Brenner, H. D.; Stramke, W.; Hodel, B.; Rui, C.: A treatment program for impaired cognitive functions aimed at preventing chronic disability among schizophrenic patients: Results of a two years field study. Paper presented at the World Psychiatric Association Symposium, Baltimore, MD, 1982.

Breier, A.; Strauss, J. S.: Self-control in psychotic disorders. Arch. Gen. Psychiat. *40*, 1141–1145, 1983.

Bucher, B.; Fabricatore, J.: Use of patient-administered shock to suppress hallucinations. Beh. Ther. *1*, 382–385, 1970.

Cater, R. E.; Falloon, I. R. H.; Palmer, R. N.: Premenstrual exacerbation of schizophrenia. Brit. J. Soc. Clin. Psychiat. in press, 1985.

Falloon, I. R. H.: Family management of schizophrenia: A study of clinical, social, family and economic benefits. Baltimore: Johns Hopkins Univ. Press, 1985.

Falloon, I.R.H.; Liberman, R. P.: Interactions between drug and psychosocial therapy in schizophrenia. Schizophr. Bull. *9*, 543–554, 1983.

Falloon, I. R. H.; Talbot, R. E.: Persistent auditory hallucinations: Coping mechanisms and implications for management. Psychol. Med. *11*, 329–339, 1981.

Falloon, I. R. H.; Watt, D. C.; Shepherd, M.; Smeeton, N.: A five-year epidemiological study of the course of schizophrenia. Psych. Med. Monogr. London: Cambridge Univ. Press (in press).

Feder, R.: Auditory hallucinations treated by radio headphones. Am. J. Psychiat. *139*, 1188–1190, 1982.

Fisher, E. B.; Winkler, R. C.: Self-control over intrusive experiences. J. Cons. Clin. Psychol. *43*, 911–916, 1975.

Hartman, L. M.; Cashman, F. E.: Cognitive-behavioural and psychopharmacological treatment of delusional symptoms: A preliminary report. Beh. Psychother. *11*, 50–61, 1983.

Haynes, S.; Geddy, P.: Suppression of psychotic hallucinations through time-out. Beh. Ther. *4*, 123–127, 1973.

Hemsley, D. R.: Cognitive impairment in schizophrenia. In: Burton, A. (ed.): The pathology and psychology of cognition. London: Methuen, 1982.

Jaspers, K.: Allgemeine Psychopathologie. Heidelberg: Springer 1973 (9. Auflage).

Kanas, N.: Self-control of psychotic productions in schizophrenics. Arch. Gen. Psychiat. *41*, 919–920, 1984.

Knights, A.; Hirsch, S. R.: «Revealed» depression and drug treatment for schizophrenia. Arch. Gen. Psychiat. *38*, 806–811, 1981.

Lamontagne, Y.; Andret, N.; Elie, R.: Thought-stopping for delusions and hallucinations: A pilot study. Beh. Psychother. *11*, 177–184, 1983.

Lick, J. R.; Heffler, D.: Relaxation training and attention placebo in the treatment of severe insomnia. J. Cons. Clin. Psychol. *45*, 153–161, 1977.

Magen, J.: Increasing external stimuli to ameliorate hallucinations. Am. J. Psychiat. *140*, 269–270, 1983.

Margo, A.; Hemsley, D. R.; Slade, P. D.: The effects of varying auditory input on schizophrenic hallucinations. Brit. J. Psychiat. *139*, 122–127, 1981.

Meichenbaum, D. H.; Cameron, R.: The clinical potential and pitfalls of modifying what clients say to themselves. In: Mahoney, M. J.; Thoresen, C. E. (eds.): Self-control: Power to the person. Monterey, CA: Brooks-Cole, 1974.

189

MILTON, F.; PATWA, V. K.; HAFNER, R. J.: Confrontation vs. belief modification in persistently deluded patients. Brit. J. Med. Psychol. *51,* 127–130, 1978.

MOSER, A. J.: Covert punishment of hallucinatory behavior in a psychotic male. J. Beh. Ther. Experim. Psychiat. *5,* 297–299, 1974.

NUECHTERLEIN, K. H.; DAWSON, M. E.: Information processing and attentional functioning in the developmental course of schizophrenic disorders. Schizophr. Bull. *10,* 160–203, 1984.

NYDEGGER, R. V.: The elimination of hallucinatory and delusional behavior by verbal conditioning and assertive training: A case study. J. Behav. Ther. Exp. Psychiat. *3,* 225–227, 1972.

PATTERSON, R. L.; LIBERMAN, R. P.; BAKER, V.: A problem in the behavioral assessment of the frequency of hallucinations. Unpublished report, Camarillo Neuropsychiatric Research Institute, 1976.

ROSENTHAL, D.; QUINN, O. W.: Quadrupet hallucinations. Arch. Gen. Psychiat. *34,* 817–827, 1977.

SLADE, P. D.: The effects of systematic desensitization on auditory hallucinations. Beh. Res. Ther. *10,* 85–91, 1972.

SLADE, P. D.: The external control of auditory hallucinations: An information theory analysis. Brit. J. Soc. Clin. Psychol. *13,* 73–79, 1974.

TURNER, S. M.; HERSEN, M.; BELLACK, A. S.: Effects of social disruption, stimulus, interference, and aversive conditioning on auditory hallucinations. Beh. Modification *1,* 249–258, 1977.

WALLACE, C. J.; NELSON, C. J.; LIBERMAN, R. P.; AITCHISON, R. A.; LUKOFF, D.; ELDER, J.; FERRIS, C.: A review and critique of social skills training with schizophrenic patients. Schizophr. Bull. *6,* 42–63, 1980.

WATTS, F. N.; POWELL, G. E.; AUSTIN, S. V.: The modification of abnormal beliefs. Brit. J. Med. Psychol. *46,* 359–363, 1973.

WEINGARTNER, A. H.: Self-administered aversive stimulation with hallucinating hospitalized schizophrenics. J. Cons. Clin. Psychol. *36,* 422–429, 1971.

WING, J. K.: The social content of schizophrenia. Am. J. Psychiat. *135,* 1333–1339, 1978.

The Philosophy and Practice of Self-Help for Relatives of the Mentally Ill

H. KATSCHNIG, T. KONIECZNA

Introduction

During the past 15 years, self-help organizations for relatives of the mentally ill in general and of schizophrenics in particular have been increasingly founded all over the world. A predecessor of this development is the "Unité Nationale des Amis et des Familles des Malades Mentaux" (UNAFAM), an association of friends and relatives of the mentally ill in France, established as early as 1963. In 1972, the "National Schizophrenia Fellowship" was founded in the United Kingdom; this organization essentially prompted the creation of similar associations in many other countries. The Austrian relatives' association "Hilfe für Psychisch Erkrankte" (HPE), which was modeled on the British organization, was established in 1977. In 1978, the numerous local self-help groups for relatives in the United States joined forces in the "National Alliance for the Mentally Ill" (NAMI). After several years of local efforts, the German relatives' groups followed this example by founding a federal association for the relatives of the mentally ill in 1985. Finally, the "World Schizophrenia Fellowship" was created the same year in Brighton to serve as an umbrella organization of the national associations for the relatives of the mentally ill.

In our contribution, we wish to pursue the question as to why it came to this "relatives' movement." Furthermore, it attempts to determine the position of relatives' self-help in the efforts to cope with the many problems caused by schizophrenia. Our knowledge about the development of relatives' self-help has been gained in our work as advisors to the Viennese relatives' self-help organization HPE, in which we have been intensely involved since it was established eight years ago, not least as moderators of encounter groups for relatives.

The historical and theoretical position of relatives' self-help in psychiatry

It is no coincidence that the relatives' self-help movement in psychiatry developed only during the 1970s. We will show that this development was provoked by a certain necessity, since, beginning in the late 1950s, an increasing tendency can be observed to discharge patients from psychiatric hospitals back to the community.

191

Despite the pessimism usually ascribed to him, even KRAEPELIN ended his famous treatise of "dementia praecox" on an optimistic note: "As soon as the acute symptoms have subsided, it should be endeavored to preserve whatever has not been destroyed by the illness. In many cases, returning to the family now becomes possible and even appropriate if the circumstances are reasonably favorable. Even some problematic patients do surprisingly well at home, so that we do not need to be overly apprehensive about discharging schizophrenics" (KRAEPELIN, 1899, Volume 2, p. 213).

However, it took more than 50 years for KRAEPELIN's hypothesis to become a reality. It was primarily a change in attitude toward the mentally ill and the introduction of neuroleptics, and only in some instances also newly developed psychosocial methods of therapy, that made it possible for the psychiatric hospitals in many countries to discharge chronic patients and to shorten the duration of inpatient treatment of new cases. This is documented all over the world by the dramatic decrease in the number of psychiatric beds and the scaling down of psychiatric hospitals. In the United States, for instance, the number of psychiatric beds dropped from 559,000 in 1955 to 138,000 in 1980 (GUDEMAN & SHORE, 1984). For schizophrenic patients, whose illness typically first manifests itself during adolescence or early adulthood, these changes in treatment modalities frequently mean returning to their families.

As this "reform of psychiatry" often restricted itself to simply discharging mental patients without providing any supportive measures, the burden of caring for these chronic and mainly schizophrenic patients was placed on their families. Today, this is well documented, but it took 15 years to become common knowledge. Not until 1968 did GRAD and SAINSBURY first document this strain on the relatives, and CREER and WING published the first more detailed study on the problem only in 1974, a study that was already realized within a relatives' self-help association, the British National Schizophrenia Fellowship. For the first time, these papers revealed "another side of schizophrenia," which until then had escaped the notice of psychiatrists with their exclusively institutional background (KATSCHNIG, 1984).

The fact that the difficulties arising for families with mentally ill members living at home took so long to become apparent is connected with several factors. In our opinion, one of the most important is the isolation and stigmatization the mentally ill and their relatives are still largely subject to even today. Since they withdraw from social life and are frequently depressed, the relatives are unable to express themselves to the outside world, knowing from experience that they will probably meet with lack of understanding and indifference anyhow.

Moreover, the feelings of guilt that almost inevitably arise in the parents of schizophrenic patients are intensified by partially misinterpreting the family theories of the origins of schizophrenia, which isolates these families even further. By analyzing the case histories of a clinic with a social-psychiatric orientation, ANGERMEYER (1982) was able to show to what extent the misleading statements of family theorists and family therapists have pervaded clinical day-to-day life, where they obviously produce the effect of accusing the relatives of schizophrenic patients to varying degrees.

Together with the traditional passive role as informants, which relatives have always been expected to play in psychiatry, these are enough reasons why the suffering in many families with mentally ill relatives living at home did not penetrate to the outside world. Apparently, a period of latency of 15 or even 20 years was necessary before certain particularly articulate relatives, supported by social psychiatrists, were prepared to speak out about the great suffering caused to patients' families by a "reform of psychiatry" that was misconstrued.

However, this period of silence presumably did not end in the 1970s by pure coincidence: During this decade, self-help activities emerged in practically every area concerned with psychosocial and medical problems, expressing their founders' discontent with the services responsible for these areas (MOELLER, 1977; DAUM, 1984). This discontent mainly involved areas in which the efforts of traditional services are crowned with little success, making them unattractive for the medical profession and thus causing them to be neglected. These areas include chronic illnesses and their rehabilitation such as cardiovascular diseases, cancer, multiple sclerosis, and muscular dystrophy. In addition to that, the movement was encouraged by the considerable success such self-help activities were able to claim, a prime example being the much older "Alcoholics Anonymous." It is highly probable that this general self-help movement also prompted relatives of the mentally ill to join forces.

Aside from self-help, which is justified by a better knowledge of the real problems, the human element in mutually helping each other, the intensification of one's own initiative, and thus in general by a greater satisfaction, many self-help groups issue a challenge: They indicate gaps in the health care and welfare system and demand that these gaps be filled in by establishing adequate services. However, this connects them to another general development in the medical and social sector that marks the last decade: a trend toward increasing demand on the medical and social services with regard to all sorts of problems – demands that can be attributed to a growing concern with personal satisfaction and happiness, and an increasing knowledge about diseases and their treatability: demands which more and more often cannot be met for financial reasons (KLERMAN, 1985). Nevertheless, the reservations sometimes expressed in this context about the diminution of the potential for self-help if institutional help be overused do not apply here; the area of severe mental illness we are concerned with is characterized by a great backlog demand for services.

The self-help movement in general, and the relatives' self-help organizations founded during the past 15 years in particular, have formed a "new" type of relative who no longer displays the passivity and despondency of the "old" relative. The "new" relatives are aware of their instrumental role in solving the problems of schizophrenia, know about the implications of living with a sick person, can articulate their problems and try to find solutions together with other relatives. But they are also relatives who address the public and ask that more attention be given to the hitherto neglected difficulties of the families of the mentally ill. By describing the activities of self-help groups for the relatives of the mentally ill, we will demonstrate the variety of elements that make up this new, self-confident relative.

What does relatives' self-help consist of?

In order to understand the self-help activities of relatives of the mentally ill, it is useful to distinguish between relatives' self-help *groups* and relatives' self-help *organizations*. Most self-help groups, in which relatives establish direct and regular contact with each other, have been founded spontaneously, through chance encounters during visiting hours at the hospital. And this is indeed the most important aspect of such groups, whose main purpose keeps them small, namely, the direct personal contact with other people in similar situations and struggling with similar problems.

These contacts provide a framework within which many relatives get their first chance to reduce their information deficit, due often to the unwillingness of the specialists to inform them adequately. Thus, relatives exchange information about the origins, course, and prognosis of the illness as well as about the effects and side effects of drugs. Yet such groups also pass on valuable data about existing psychiatric and psychosocial institutions, about work and housing possibilities, and welfare benefits.

In addition to such objective information, the members share personal experiences, e.g., as to which strategies prove to be most effective in living and dealing with a chronically ill individual. After all, almost every relative is confronted with the problem of properly coping with the different symptoms of the ill member of the family. As it turns out, dealing with symptoms usually regarded as signs of "madness" by laymen – such as hallucinations and delusions – is generally felt to be easier than dealing with the so-called negative symptoms such as social withdrawal, lack of initiative, and affective flattening. A typical problem in this context is the impossibility to differentiate between inability caused by the illness and lack of willingness to cooperate on the part of the patient, for example, in doing his share of housework. In fact, this "bad/mad" problem is nearly always insoluble in the individual case, so that there cannot be a "right" response to such behavior. To find this fact confirmed by other relatives' experience is usually a great relief. Other examples for this personal sharing of experiences are discussions about the patient's need to be autonomous, and sexual needs and desires. Numerous relatives also know the feeling of helplessness if confronted with the patient's decision to discontinue the treatment or to reduce or stop taking medication. In such and similar cases, advice given by "old" relatives may be of considerable help, as they can often look back on many years' experience with a sick family member. Without a doubt, relatives accept criticism and advice with unpleasant consequences much more readily when it comes from another relative than from a specialist (cf. KATSCHNIG & KONIECZNA, 1984a).

In comparison to these cognitive factors, the emotional aspects are of still greater importance. To begin with, self-help groups give relatives an opportunity to release pent-up negative emotions, such as hate, anger, despair, and shame, without having to be afraid of being condemned or of burdening others with one's personal problems, since all relatives have the same problems. And what is more: In most cases one can count not only on being understood, but also on getting definite emotional support from the other relatives. It is this feeling of partnership and reciprocity in the relationship that distinguishes communication between relatives from communication with a professional – who frequently pushes the relative into the role of a "patient."

However, relatives' self-help groups not only help to break out of long-standing isolation, they can also form a basis for starting more intensive relationships and even friendships. These relationships often involve helping each other practically. Such immediate help may, for instance, consist in "taking on" a patient so that the relative can have an evening or a weekend to himself, or in several families organizing a joint holiday.

These face-to-face groups are an essential and indispensible component of relatives' self-help. Whenever a group becomes so big that it gradually turns into a formal organization, i.e., a relatives' self-help association, it runs the danger of these direct personal contacts taking a secondary role, except for officials. By founding a formal organization, however, relatives' self-help admittedly gains an additional new dimension, which a consistent action plan must not omit: the function of a "lobby" that attempts to influence public opinion. This public-relations work mainly consists in organizing informational events, lectures, meetings, and media appearances. Another important part of the activities of self-help organizations involves contracting competent politicians to inform them about the relatives' problems. In such organizations, an essential role is usually played by those relatives whose education, professional status, and personality structure predestine them to function as spokesmen and to safeguard the interests of the relatives. Some self-help organizations do not restrict themselves to exerting pressure on the competent institutions and authorities to establish adequate new facilities and services, but establish facilities and services of their own (as, for example, UNAFAM in France does).

Conveying information among the relatives themselves is more formalized in self-help organizations than in self-help groups. The range covers advice by phone, in writing, or from person to person; moreover, they offer seminars and lectures for relatives, often involving professionals. In addition, the social aspect is consciously emphasized, e.g., by establishing a "jour fixe" that may be linked with an informational event. However, there are also events of an exclusively social nature, such as 5 o'clock teas or excursions.

Relatives' self-help and professional help

While the afore-mentioned development took place – starting with the introduction of psychopharmacological drugs and leading to the self-help movement with the emergence of the "new" self-confident relative – some areas of the mental health care system were experiencing a reorientation process that shows certain connections to today's forms of relatives' self-help: a conceptualization of mental illness transcending the localization of the disease process in the individual and including the social network (KATSCHNIG & KONIECZNA, 1985). Family therapy can be seen as a classical, albeit controversial, example of this new network conception, which looks beyond individual psychopathology.

This new approach essentially differs from the classical psychiatric concepts – both the somatic and the psychotherapeutic – insofar as the latter are centered on the individual. These traditional approaches, which focus on the cause of the illness, are now complemented by the analysis and the therapeutic use of the social network to influence the course of mental illnesses positively. For instance, an increased interest in the concept of "social support" can be observed (BROWN & HARRIS, 1978; BEELS, 1981; SURTEES, 1984). The naive views that were originally predominating (e.g., of a purely positive effect of the social network) have recently given way to more differentiated approaches (VAUGHN & LEFF, 1984; HENDERSON, 1984; ANDERSON et al., 1984). Therapeutic activities with relatives form an integrative part of this new trend of working with the patient's social network (KATSCHNIG & KONIECZNA, 1984b).

Both these developments – the emergence of self-help among the relatives of the mentally ill and the elaboration of the network approach in the professional system – can be presented in a simplified manner in the following diagram:

Table 1: Types of supportive activities in mental illness

	Professional help	Self-help
Patient-centered approach	Psychopharmacological drugs Psychotherapy Social skills training	Self-medication Self-management
Social-network approach	Family therapy Work with relatives	Relatives' self-help

If we oppose traditional, professional help to self-help, and the traditional approach centered on the individual to the network approach, we end up with four types of supportive activities: the traditional, individual-centered, professional help utilizing psychopharmacological drugs, individual psychotherapy, including social skills training; new approaches replacing only one of the above-mentioned aspects by a new one, namely, in the form of self-help without the network aspect by self-medication and self-management of the patient; the network-approach without self-help by family therapy and the different forms of work with relatives; and finally, the form of relatives' self-help we are concerned with here, in which both new aspects, self-help and the social-network approach, are simultaneously realized.

Expert help and self-help, however, are not as sharply opposed to one another as Table 1 might suggest. Rather, they are complementary approaches, partly also pervading each other in spite of the necessity to keep them separate. On the one hand, experts can make deliberate therapeutic use of relatives' self-help in order to achieve optimal results in rehabilitation, and on the other hand, relatives can call upon experts in order to improve the yield of their self-help efforts.

The role of relatives' self-help in professional therapy

The unanimous outcome of recent studies about the social network of schizophrenics reads as follows: not only have these social networks decreased in size, they also display various qualitative changes (PATTISON et al., 1975; TOLSDORF, 1976; SOKOLOVSKY et al., 1978; PATTISON & PATTISON, 1981; cf. KATSCHNIG & KONIECZNA, 1984c). In addition to the afore-mentioned factors of stigmatization, this decrease in the size of the patient's social network certainly contributes to increasing the relatives' isolation, too. It is sufficiently well documented that such families can develop pathological emotional relationships as a consequence (VAUGHN & LEFF, 1984).

Because the "network approach" is not yet very widespread in today's psychiatry, we consider it useful to present a preliminary systematization thereof, including the social network in the rehabilitation of schizophrenic patients. Table 2 represents such a systematization.

Table 2: Social network interventions and the rehabilitation of schizophrenic patients

---

Interventions in the existing social network

- direct intervention (family therapy)
- indirect intervention (work with relatives)

Extension of the existing social network

- mobilizing "latent" relatives
- bringing relatives into contact with the relatives of other patients (self-help)
- offering the patient possibilities for contact outside the family (club, day center)

Offering an alternative social network

- temporary (half-way house)
- permanent (hostel)

This systematization has been described in detail elsewhere (KATSCHNIG & KONIECZNA, 1984c). Here, we are mainly interested in the one aspect that is directly involved in self-help and must be subsumed under the heading "extension of the existing social network." We have already pointed out the immense importance of self-help groups and organizations in combating the isolation into which the families of the mentally ill tend to fall. For this reason, we have made it our duty to draw the attention of all the relatives we meet during our clinical work in Vienna to the existing self-help association for the relatives of the mentally ill; we do this with great emphasis, distributing information sheets and leaflets from this association. We even think that professionals should, wherever possible, encourage non-organized relatives to found self-help organizations or at least to meet regularly in a group.

The role of the expert in relatives' self-help

Professionals can be of assistance to self-help organizations for the relatives of the mentally ill in various respects, and they should make themselves available to the relatives as self-help advisors (MOELLER, 1977; KATSCHNIG & SINT, 1984). A primary task of the professional advisor in relatives' self-help organizations consists of informing about the actual state of knowledge concerning diagnosis, origins, and treatability of mental illness. It also seems especially important to underline the limits of our knowledge, as relatives quite often wrongly believe psychiatrists to be withholding information. Indeed, professional advisors to self-help groups should admit their own "helplessness," i.e., the limitation of professional knowledge, which is likely to help many relatives to gain a more realistic attitude toward psychiatry in general and to develop a better relationship to the therapist of the ill family member. Another important function of professional advisors in relatives' self-help organizations charges them with providing "backing" for these associations and removing the suspicion of sectarianism, of which they are often accused. If prominent psychiatrists figure among the members of the committee of such an association, they render it trustworthy in the eyes of the public. This brings us to the expert's third function, namely, recognizing possible undesirable developments and counteracting them in good time; this may prevent a self-help organization from losing credibility because it adheres to an erroneous or even eccentric theory (such as the vitamin-deficiency theory of schizophrenia). Finally, as we know from our own experience, it is especially useful for relatives to work through concrete communication problems with mental health professionals by "role-playing" such scenes with a "model professional" in the framework of an encounter group moderated by professionals.

A final important function of professional advisors to relatives' self-help organizations consists in forming a "hinge" between the professional system on the one hand and the lay system on the other. In a certain way, they can "keep their ear to the keyhole," conveying knowledge and experience gained in everyday life with a chronic mental patient to the professional system, aspects that would normally remain hidden to traditional, hospital-centered psychiatry. In doing so, they can become spokesmen for the relatives and their concerns within the professional system.

Prospects

In treating the subject of relatives' self-help as psychiatric professionals we manifest the very dilemma immanent in the new situation: The relatives' interests should be advocated by a relative and not by a professional. However, to invite a relative to speak here was apparently not yet possible. To include relatives into our daily work does indeed introduce a "complication" into normal psychiatry. In any case, our work becomes more arduous. As psychiatrists, we have to accept that relatives want to develop a legitimate autonomy, that they sometimes criticize the existing services and professions, and that they are particularly allergic to being manipulated. Yet, the professional is also often confronted with exaggerated expectations.

In the course of our long collaboration with the relatives of schizophrenic patients, we have become aware of the fact that this ambivalent relationship between professionals and relatives simultaneously desiring autonomy and requiring help displays many similarities to the relationship between relative and patient, and can thus become a model for the complicated interaction between relative and patient. *Granting autonomy whenever autonomy is required, but at the same time being there whenever help is needed* – that is the impossible task which confront the relatives of the mentally ill and which they constantly have to solve in everyday life. To get involved in this everyday reality of families of the mentally ill is a challenge and an enrichment professionals should not renounce.

Bibliography

ANDERSON, C. M.; HOGARTY, G.; BAYER, T.; NEEDLEMAN, R.: Expressed emotions and social networks of parents of schizophrenic patients. Brit. J. Psychiat. *144,* 247–255, 1984.

ANGERMEYER, M. C.: Der theoriegraue Star im Auge des Psychiaters. Medizin Mensch Gesellschaft *7,* 55–60, 1982.

BEELS, C. C.: Social support and schizophrenia. Schizophr. Bull. *7,* 58–72, 1981.

BROWN, G. W.; HARRIS, T.: Social origins of depression. London: Tavistock Publications, 1978.

CREER, C.; WING, J. K.: Schizophrenia at home. National Schizophrenia Fellowship, 1974. German in: KATSCHNIG, H. (Hrsg.): Die andere Seite der Schizophrenie – Patienten zu Hause (2nd ed.). München, Wien, Baltimore: Urban & Schwarzenberg, 1984.

DAUM, K.-W.: Selbsthilfegruppen – Die Idee der Selbsthilfe und das Konzept von Gesprächs-Selbsthilfegruppen. Psychiatrische Praxis *11,* 157–162, 1984.

GRAD, J.; SAINSBURY, E.: The effect that patients have on their families in a community care and a control psychiatric service. A two years follow-up. Brit. J. Psychiat. *114,* 265–278, 1968.

GUDEMAN, J. E.; SHORE, M. F.: Beyond deinstitutionalization. A new class of facilities for the mentally ill. New Engl. J. Med. *311,* 832–836, 1984.

HENDERSON, A. S.: Interpreting the evidence on social support. Soc. Psychiat. *19,* 49–52, 1984.

KATSCHNIG, H. (Hrsg.): Die andere Seite der Schizophrenie (2nd ed.). München, Wien, Baltimore: Urban & Schwarzenberg, 1984.

KATSCHNIG, H.; KONIECZNA, T.: Angehörigenprobleme im Spiegel von Selbsterfahrungsgruppen. In: ANGERMEYER, M. C.; FINZEN, A. (Hrsg.): Die Angehörigengruppe – Familien mit psychisch Kranken auf dem Weg der Selbsthilfe. Stuttgart: Enke, 100–109, 1984a.

KATSCHNIG, H.; KONIECZNA, T.: Neue Formen der Angehörigenarbeit in der Psychiatrie. In: KATSCHNIG, H. (Hrsg.): Die andere Seite der Schizophrenie – Patienten zu Hause (2nd ed.). München, Wien, Baltimore: Urban & Schwarzenberg, 207–228, 1984b.

KATSCHNIG, H.; KONIECZNA, T.: Psychosoziales Netzwerk und Rehabilitation psychisch Kranker. In: ANDEL VAN, H.; PITTRICH, W. (Hrsg.): Neue Konzepte der Behandlung und Rehabilitation chronisch psychisch Kranker. Münster: Schriftenreihe des Landschaftsverbandes Westfalen-Lippe, 6–28, 1984c.

KATSCHNIG, H.; KONIECZNA, T.: Social network and long-term course of mental disorder – research needs. In: HELGASON, T. (ed.): The long-term treatment of functional psychoses: needed areas of research. Cambridge: Cambridge University Press, 163–174, 1985.

KATSCHNIG, H.; SINT, P.: Zwischen Selbsthilfe und Expertenhilfe: Die Angehörigenvereinigung "Hilfe für psychisch Erkrankte" in Wien. In: ANGERMEYER, M. C.; FINZEN, A. (Hrsg.): Angehörigenarbeit und Angehörigenselbsthilfe in der Psychiatrie. Stuttgart: Enke, 1984.

KLERMAN, G. L.: Trends in utilization of mental health services. Perspectives for health services research. Medical Care 23, 584–597, 1985.

KRAEPELIN, E.: Psychiatrie (6th ed.). Leipzig: Barth, 1899.

MOELLER, M. L.: Zur Bildung von Selbsthilfegruppen. Ein Erfahrungsbericht für Teilnehmer und Experten. Psychiat. Praxis 4, 197–212, 1977.

PATTISON, E. M.; DEFRANCISCO, D.; WOOD, P.; FRAZIER, H.; CROWDER, J.: A psychosocial kinship model of family therapy. Am. J. Psychiat. 132, 1246, 1975.

PATTISON, E. M.; PATTISON, M. L.: Analysis of a schizophrenic psychosocial network. Schizophr. Bull. 7, 135–143, 1981.

SOKOLOVSKY, J.; COHEN, J.; BERGER, D.; GEIGER, J.: Personal networks of ex-mental patients in a Manhattan SRO Hotel. Human Organization 37, 5–15, 1978.

SURTEES, P.: Kith, kin and psychiatric health: A Scottish survey. Soc. Psychiat. 19, 63–67, 1984.

TOLSDORF, C. C.: Social networks, support and coping: An exploratory study. Family Process 15, 407–417, 1976.

VAUGHN, C.; LEFF, J. P.: Umgangsstile in Familien mit schizophrenen Patienten. In: KATSCHNIG, H. (Hrsg.): Die andere Seite der Schizophrenie – Patienten zu Hause (2nd ed.). München, Wien, Baltimore: Urban & Schwarzenberg, S. 181–194, 1984.

Prospective Developments in Research and Practice

H. D. BRENNER, W. BÖKER

In schizophrenia research, restricted perspectives – be they of biomedical, psychosocial, or other provenience – have long been preventing a general understanding of the fact that the phenomenon of schizophrenia can never be adequately described by a theory that does not take into account either the interaction of biological abnormalities with the environment or the relationship between psychosocial factors and the biological matrix. The contributions to this volume of collected papers – in spite of their primarily psychosocial orientation – share the assumption that *schizophrenia must be understood as a complex biological, psychosocial, and social abnormality.* In this context, diverging opinions should be regarded as complementary rather than competitive. This is an indication not only of the substantial progress that has been made, but also of the considerable distance that still separates us from a comprehensive theory of the effects of psychosocial factors.

We therefore feel justified in concluding this book with a delineation of the theoretical and practical problems facing future research and the development of a "psychosocial management" of schizophrenia. We base our conclusions on the conviction that the different directions in schizophrenia research are best integrated in a *vulnerability-stress model.*

Until now, *vulnerability* research, which involves the aspect of risk, has placed the main emphasis on seeking individual indicators of vulnerability. However, since vulnerability itself is presumably the result of complex interactions between numerous factors, the adequacy of a one-dimensional model seems unlikely. We therefore consider a strategy of simultaneous coverage of as many different vulnerability indicators as possible to be of great importance for future vulnerability research. Which relationships exist between the different indicators? Are there systematic connections between individual indicators or indicator patterns and a particular manifestation of schizophrenia? Does the number or type of indicators play a determining role in this context, or is the manifestation of this illness primarily controlled by environmental factors? Are we dealing with a specific or with a non-specific vulnerability? These and other questions could be answered by family studies incorporating families with and without increased occurrence of schizophrenias or other mental illnesses as well as psychopathologically normal families.

Such considerations make it clear that vulnerability to schizophrenia may not simply be equated with biological or family vulnerability, as it is often done (at least implicitly). Many schizophrenics come from families without any history of this illness and thus do not belong to a group with a high-risk family background. Therefore, major predictors of a schizophrenic episode do not have to coincide with factors characteristic of high-risk groups as opposed to low-risk groups, nor with factors allowing to separate patients from non-patients within high-risk groups.

In the narrower field of experimental psychological and psychophysiological indicator research, the growing interest in process models of information processing should lead to an increased recognition of process characteristics vs. particularities of structural organization in the description of lasting dysfunctions. The re-examination of theoretical constructs out of a-priori models would then take the place of the search for ever more specific task aspects correlating as closely as possible with the occurrence of a schizophrenic disorder. This would also facilitate the establishment of connections with neuropsychological concepts, for example, by way of electrophysiological correlates of cortical activity in the case of cognitive dysfunctions. Taking this approach would offer a fascinating possibility of bridging the gap between psychopathology on the one hand and neurophysiology and neurochemistry on the other. This process is most likely to be initiated by neuropsychological models of the intra- and/or interhemispherical organization of the brain, especially since several authors have connected such models to their latest findings about disorganized information processing in schizophrenics (cf. VENABLES, 1984).

Additional interesting aspects of indicator research could derive from a more distinct differentiation between indicators displaying a nearly complete correlation and indicators showing a weaker correlation with schizophrenia. An indicator with nearly complete correlation would contribute considerably to improving the construct validity of the diagnosis schizophrenia. At present, there are no objective criteria for this (i.e., criteria not gained from interviews); this is extremely unsatisfactory in comparison to other fields of medicine. It is often erroneously supposed that the improved operational criteria of DSM-III not only increased reliability, but also construct validity. Compared to earlier reliable diagnostic criteria, however, the DSM-III criteria do not improve construct validity. The emphasis on positive symptoms possibly even decreased predictive validity, and there are almost no operational criteria for the negative symptoms, although they are more important in this context.

It is of particular interest in this respect that several simple experimental psychological parameters have displayed a surprisingly high predictive value for the prognosis of the course and treatment of schizophrenia (cf. ZAHN et al., 1981). The specific deficiencies discussed as vulnerability indicators in this field of research have hardly been studied from this viewpoint until now.

Indicators with weaker correlation in particular – a more fitting term would be "schizophrenia-associated factors" (cf. also CROMWELL, 1984) – are very likely to gain significance for future research under this aspect. If such indicators proved to possess superior predictive value for the prognosis of course and/or treatment compared to present diagnostic criteria, they could lead to an operational definition of more homogeneous diagnostic categories via a new assessment of clinical manifestations. Correlational studies connecting biomedical findings not only to relatively crude diagnostic constructs, but also to schizophrenia-associated factors in other areas of research, also seem to deserve more thorough study. Finally, factors that correlate positively with other syndrome complexes aside from schizophrenia could be useful in isolating related or even shared basic disorders.

Another important aspect of the vulnerability-stress model of schizophrenia lies in the shift of focus away from the structure of psychopathological particularities to their development, i.e., to the relationship between dysfunctions of elementary psychological or psychobiological processes and specific schizophrenic symptoms. It is therefore also necessary to study vulnerability indicators with regard to cause-and-effect relationships, which leads us to the final pathogenetic stage of schizophrenia. For instance, what is the nature of the connections between disorders in information processing considered crucial to several integrative models (cf. CIOMPI, this volume) and behavior or subjective experience? Crude analogies, as described by BROEN (1968) or SHAKOW (1979), among others, are of less interest here than specific relationships that can be predicted and tested (cf. BRENNER et al., in press).

Such relationships are extremely complex, which partly accounts for the virtually complete lack of information about them. We consider it highly improbable for them to be represented within the framework of purely cognitive models, e.g., of information processing models exclusively. Such a representation would presumably require systemic models, that, in addition to cognitive functions, integrate task characteristics, emotion, and arousal, and at present can only be studied via reductionist partial models limited to individual deficiencies. At the moment, we are thus studying how specific disturbances in attention are assimilated and coped with, by including psychophysiological (arousal) and experiential psychological (cognition and emotion) parameters.

Characteristic dysfunctions in information processing manifest themselves on the levels of overt behavior by a large number of continuous factors, via intermediate deficits. Hence, the distinction between vulnerability-associated and symptom-associated deficiencies, upon which several authors insist (cf. CROMWELL & SPAULDING, 1978; NUECHTERLEIN & DAWSON, 1984; SPAULDING, 1986), in fact might refer to different development stages of deficient processes rather than to dysfunctions differing in principle. Likewise, the particularities described as vulnerability indicators on the level of instrumental and social skills result from elementary dysfunctions and thus are not separate factors (cf. BRENNER, this volume). To put it candidly, the fact that the different factors relevant to the manifestation of schizophrenia display great variability as well as a continuous range of intensities allows us to assume that the essence of schizophrenia is to be found in processes of interaction between biology, behavior, and environment. In other words, it is a disorder that must be conceptualized in a systemic way. For this reason, we consider it inadequate to search merely for dispositional features in isolated areas of research.

However, regarding the episodic nature of the illness postulated by the vulnerability-stress model of schizophrenia, the search for relationships between existing vulnerability characteristics and behavior is also of great interest from a clinical point of view. This leads us to the question of decompensation and/or exacerbation or restabilization. Detailed studies concerning the nature of the interaction between current stress factors and pre-existing vulnerability characteristics within processes leading up to the critical overtaxation of the vulnerable personality could also contribute considerably to the recognition of early signs of an imminent first episode or recidivism, and to the development of effective crisis-intervention strategies. Such studies would, so to speak, transfer the above-mentioned systemic approach with regard to individual cognitive deficiencies onto the level of behavior. Numerous studies have shown that most cases indeed display an estimable period of decompensation during the development of schizophrenic episodes.

Bearing this in mind, HERZ (1984) attempted to differentiate between prodromal symptoms and complete relapse by means of structured and unstructured questioning of patients and their relatives. The most common prodromal symptoms he describes are nervous tension, reduced appetite, lack of concentration, memory loss, sleep problems, restlessness, depressive mood, apathy, meaningless speech, hearing of voices, delusions in relationships, etc. Using this kind of investigational approach, it seems possible to detect completely unspecific complaints on the one hand and early symptoms that can already be qualified as psychotic on the other. As helpful as this approach might be in individual cases, it seems doubtful whether it is a suitable basis for wider and more optimal crisis intervention in the early stages of decompensation.

When investigated on a phenomenological basis, subjectively experienced symptoms or symptoms observable in behavior give little insight into the processes of decompensation. This is confirmed by the finding that there are no significant relationships between objective deficiencies and subjective disorders (cf. BRENNER et al., 1987; WILLIAMS et al., 1984). WILLIAMS and his collaborators account for this by drawing attention to the difficulties involved in measuring subjective discomfort, especially where interpersonal communication is disturbed, as is the case with schizophrenics. We, however, consider it more likely that this lack of significant correlations has to be attributed to the fact that objective and subjective measurements cover different aspects of psychopathology, or in other words, to the fact that, on the level of subjective experience, primary disorders can no longer be clearly separated from coping reactions.

If, as we presume, decompensation processes are essentially of a systemic nature, the factors responsible for the emergence or avoidance of decompensation are not primarily structural components such as vulnerability threshold, stress factors, etc., or individual signals for increased tension or pathology, but rather interaction phenomena, e.g., the individual's or the environment's reaction to such signals. This should lead to new criteria for and forms of crisis intervention. On a clinical level, the simultaneous evaluation of dispositional features, specific stress factors, and behavior has to be given priority. In addition to that, the interaction processes in stressful social situations should be systematically evaluated and studied. At present, we are trying to devise an adequate methodology for such studies.

Promising approaches for further research into the process of decompensation could also be produced by biological schizophrenia research. The dopamine hypothesis, for example, can also be understood as a psychotic decompensation hypothesis, i.e., as a gradual dynamic process in which interactions with other neurotransmitter systems are probably complemented by interactions with environmental influences increasing or decreasing the susceptibility for neurochemical disturbances.

The second major concept of the vulnerability-stress model, namely *stress* also needs further research and differentiation (cf. also SPRING, 1981). While stress is mainly a trigger, specific forms of stress, particularly in psychosocial development, presumably also contribute to vulnerability. According to the model of ZUBIN and SPRING (1977), stress factors triggering an episode of schizophrenia do not modify the degree of vulnerability; rather, they allow the vulnerability of the prepsychotic personality to become manifest. We tend to adopt a less static approach here. At the moment, current situational strains, crucial life-events, and emotionally tense relationships to important people in the patient's life are discussed as triggering stress factors of particular significance.

With regard to the above-mentioned function of stress in the vulnerability-stress model of schizophrenia, a clear distinction between acutely influential stress factors (e.g., crucial life-events) and chronically effective stress factors in the sense of repetitive day-to-day pressures (e.g., "expressed emotions" [EE] or "cognitive deviance" [CD]) seems desirable. This would encourage research about possible interactions between stress factors within one category and between factors from both categories. Several factors from any one category are probably cumulative in their effect; but when stress factors from both categories coincide, chronic pressures presumably function as moderators on acute pressures.

Let us illustrate these considerations by elaborating on the concept of "expressed emotions." In spite of the popularity of this concept and its indubitable usefulness for therapeutic interventions, it still raises numerous questions in its present form, in which it is restricted to quasi-characteristics of relatives. Thus, studies about interaction processes in high-EE and low-EE families might indicate which circular processes between patients and relatives contribute to the emergence of "expressed emotions" or are conducive to their continuance. Based on our own, albeit unsystematic, observations, we have gathered the impression that in very tense emotional atmospheres, relatives *and* patients strive to control each other, and every attempt at appeasement by one side at first even kindles this striving for dominance. Conversely, our experience shows that families with a comparatively relaxed emotional climate are not only characterized by the absence of criticism and intrusive behavior, but also by numerous signs of encouragement, recognition, and of mutual solidarity. ZEMP and HUBSCHMID (in press) reported to us the results of interviews with relatives which allow comparable conclusions to be drawn. Corresponding studies would therefore have to focus increasingly on the protective potential of a favorable environment, which has been rather neglected until now.

There is also an urgent need for studying the relationship between "expressed emotions" and other chronically effective family pressures, such as the cognitively inconsistent, confusing patterns of communication ("cognitive deviance") described by DOANE et al. (1981) and GOLDSTEIN (1984). Thus, the CD-concept could be of pathogenetic relevance, but it could possibly also cover phenomena that are connected with "expressed emotions."

Finally, the undisputed significance of the EE-concept as a chronically effective psychosocial stress factor makes it only too easy to overlook the fact that most patients in danger of relapsing do not live with their families. It would therefore be important to attempt to transfer concepts developed with regard to family pressures to situations outside the family. For instance, could it be that chronic stress factors – in the sense of relentless overstrain, demoralizing or even threatening situations, peripheral, lonely, and unproductive existence, etc. – play a comparable role here? Are we dealing with particular manifestations of the social support concept, and are the effects of such chronic pressures relayed by similar psychophysiological and neurochemical processes? The findings of TARRIER et al. (1979) concerning the connection between "expressed emotions" and central nervous hyperarousal could point in this direction.

In our opinion, the danger of relapsing has been studied in too one-sided a manner up to now, focusing on florid relapses, i.e., the re-emergence of positive symptoms. In actual fact, however, the problem is also a partial aspect of chronification. ZUBIN (this volume) has demonstrated that chronification during the course of an illness only seemingly causes a dilemma for the vulnerability-stress model. Contrary to common opinion, chronic courses of illness even show much clearer relationships to psychosocial than to biological factors (cf. CIOMPI, this volume). It is thus all the more surprising that psychosocial research has not yet developed new approaches toward the understanding of chronically deficient conditions.

On the one hand, factors that are of decisive importance in the manifestation of schizophrenic episodes are likely to be partially identical with factors that determine the course of the illness, for example, in the case of the chronification process being characterized by numerous acute episodes of the illness with only short periods of remission. That would make many findings about the danger of relapsing, especially those concerning chronically stressful or protective environmental influences, applicable to the problem of chronification and useful in developing innovative intervention strategies. On the other hand, the process of chronification is not only controlled by known negative influences such as hospitalization, insufficient stimulation, labelling, etc., but certainly also by a number of other factors – particularly in the case of the so-called new long-term patients – about which we know nothing or too little up to now. Decompensation during acute episodes of the illness, often experienced as an existential threat, in many cases leads to lasting alterations of functional organization on the psychological as well as the biological level. This results in specific changes in the processes of interaction with environmental influences during the subsequent course of the illness. Again, systematic studies of system processes are necessary to determine which factors most effectively prevent or attenuate the process of chronification.

Keeping with our previous considerations, the vulnerability-stress model also makes possible a direct connection between theoretical aspects and questions of *therapeutic practice.* Many empirically tried and tested guidelines for treatment find their theoretical justification in this model. Thus, M. BLEULER was fully justified in emphasizing again and again that our general therapeutic intercourse with schizophrenics, which consists in calming the agitated patient, stimulating the patient lost in negative symptoms, and in integrating the patient into an active community, is no makeshift measure, but essential therapy. However, the knowledge we have gained about schizophrenic courses is by no means fully exhausted in practice.

For example, the speedy influencing of early psychotic symptoms by the use of neuroleptics should be realized more consistently than before. Bearing in mind the vulnerability-stress model, we also need to reconsider our established practice of treating acutely psychotic patients in hospital admission wards, in the company of other agitated or confused patients, in an environment that is usually too hectic and overstimulating. For patients with high vulnerability and correspondingly high susceptibility to disorders of fundamental attentional/perceptual functions and their feedback with arousal and emotion, it would probably be advantageous for them to be admitted to small, peaceful units, perhaps even not sexually mixed, with a small number of patients as well as limited and relatively constant personnel. This measure is likely to reduce the need for neuroleptica and restraints.

In accordance with the vulnerability-stress model of schizophrenia, effective methods of therapy reaching beyond the mere treatment of symptoms can be aimed at either (1) *directly influencing vulnerability,* (2) *avoiding or reducing acute and chronic stress factors,* (3) *improving the patient's ability to cope,* or (4) *influencing the processes of interaction between these factors.* Corresponding programs of intervention are described and discussed in individual contributions to this volume. Hence, we would like to conclude by examining only such aspects, which at present hold our own interest, too.

In the area of psychosocial treatment programs, which usually aim at avoiding or reducing chronic stress factors or at increasing the general ability to cope, the findings concerning dysfunctions in information processing should gain particular significance for the development of more effective therapeutic methods, above all in long-term treatment, especially if these dysfunctions are not only related to variations in symptomatology, but constitute persistent deficiencies. For example, ineffective social behavior is also caused, and none the least, by inexact comprehension of critical situational and social stimuli, and by only insufficient development of behavioral alternatives or by their incorrect evaluation. However, a better understanding of the role of basal cognitive dysfunctions in relevant stress situations would be a prerequisite for the systematic integration of cognitive training methods into psychosocial therapeutic programs.

Another problem in need of further clarification are the interactions between socio- and pharmacotherapy. In our experience, for instance, the normalization of cognitive functions achieved by neuroleptic medication is in many cases a prerequisite for effective interventions on a behavioral level, since the complexity of the therapeutical situation can otherwise overstrain the available information processing capacity, which not only prevents the therapy from being successful, but often also leads to the re-emergence of florid symptoms. There is no doubt that better knowledge of such synergistic effects would allow the planning of improved and differentiated comprehensive treatment strategies.

A further specific aspect concerns *self-help* or efforts at self-stabilization, an area that has hardly been utilized therapeutically until now. It would be a highly interesting research subject to study the extent to which schizophrenics recognize early disturbances in their mental functioning – e.g., the first changes in perception and the beginning of psychotic misinterpretations in a reality they experience as changed – as "symptoms" and when they first strive to keep them under control by conscious efforts to cope. Problems such as coping with "mini-episodes," the phenomenon of spontaneous remission, the dynamics of attempted reordering in the process of recovery all present themselves for further study. The analysis of auto-protective efforts doubly benefits practice. With increasing knowledge about successful self-help attempts, we can develop training programs that will complement the expert's therapeutic equipment. They should analyze restabilizing modes of behavior intuitively tested by individual patients, searching for effective invariant elements.

However, our gathering interest in efforts at self-help also strengthens the schizophrenic's weak sense of autonomy. Patients thereby no longer see themselves as objects of different forms of treatment imposed by the experts, but as partners whose own efforts to "manage schizophrenia" are taken seriously. Such a boost in self-evaluation is something these individuals are in sore need of, having mostly been oversensitive and insecure from childhood on.

Work with relatives also opens up a large potential for self-help. Although it has been neglected up to now, its importance is gradually being recognized. Hence, it should not remain restricted to interventions aiming at influencing individual factors such as "expressed emotions," no matter how effective these may prove. With regard to the planned development of a "management of schizophrenia," it gives rise to optimism to observe the relatives of schizophrenics in many countries joining forces in independent organizations, intent on helping each other, tapping new medical and social resources, preparing the path to rehabilitation, and breaking out of the ghetto to which they feel condemned by the crippling taboo associated with mental illness.

Bibliography

BRENNER, H. D.; BOEKER, W.; MUELLER, J.; SPICHTIG, L.; WUERGLER, S.: Autoprotective efforts among schizophrenics, neurotics and controls. Acta Psych. Scand. 75, 1987.

BRENNER, H. D.; KRAEMER, S.; HERMANUTZ, H.; HODEL, B.: Cognitive treatment in schizophrenia: State of the art. In: HAHLWEG, K.; STRAUBE, E. (eds.): Schizophrenia: Models and interventions. Berlin, Heidelberg, New York: Springer (in press).

BROEN, W. E.: Schizophrenia. Research and theory. New York: Academic Press, 1968.

CROMWELL, R. L.: Preemptive thinking and schizophrenia research. In: SPAULDING, W. D.; COLE, J. K. (eds.): Theories of schizophrenia and psychosis. Lincoln and London: University of Nebraska Press, 1984.

CROMWELL, R. L.; SPAULDING, W.: How schizophrenics handle information. In: FANN, W. E.; KARACAN, I.; DOKORNY, A. D.; WILLIAMS, R. L. (eds.): The phenomenology and treatment of schizophrenia. New York: Spectrum Press, 1978.

DOANE, J. A.; WEST, K.-L.; GOLDSTEIN, M. J.; RODNICK, E. H.; JONES, J. E.: Parental communication deviance and affective style: Predictors of subsequent schizophrenia – spectrum disorders in vulnerable adolescents. Arch. Gen. Psychiat. 38, 679-685, 1981.

GOLDSTEIN, M. J.: Family factors that antedate the onset of schizophrenia and related disorders: The results of a fifteen year prospective longitudinal study. Paper presented at the Regional Symposium of the World Psychiatric Association, Helsinki, Finland, 1984.

HERZ, M. I.: Recognizing and preventing relapse in patients with schizophrenia. Hospital and Community Psychiatry 35, 344-349, 1984.

NUECHTERLEIN, K. H.; DAWSON, M. E.: A heuristic vulnerability/stress model of schizophrenic episodes. Schiz. Bull. 10, 300-312, 1984.

SHAKOW, D.: Adaptation in schizophrenia: The theory of segmental set. New York: Wiley & Sons, 1979.

SPAULDING, W. A.: Assessment of adult-onset pervasive behaviour disorders. In: CIMINERO, A.; CALHOUN, K.; ADAMS, H. (eds.): Handbook of behavioral assessment (2nd ed.). New York: Wiley, 1986.

SPRING, B.: Stress and schizophrenia: Some definitional issues. Schizophr. Bull. 7, 24-33, 1981.

TARRIER, N.; VAUGHN, C.; LADER, M. H.; LEFF, J. P.: Bodily reactions to people and events in schizophrenics. Arch. Gen. Psychiat. 36, 311-315, 1979.

VENABLES, P. H.: Cerebral mechanisms, autonomic responsiveness and attention in schizophrenia. In: SPAULDING, W. D.; COLE, J. K. (eds.): Theories of schizophrenia and psychosis. Lincoln and London: University of Nebraska Press, 47-91, 1984.

WILLIAMS, R. M.; ALAGARATNAM, W.; HEMSLEY, D. R.: Relationship between subjective self-report of cognitive dysfunction and objective information-processing performance in a group of hospitalized schizophrenic patients. Eur. Arch. Psychiat. Neurol. Sci. 234, 48-53, 1984.

ZAHN, T. P.; CARPENTER, W. T.; MCGLASHAN, T. H.: Autonomic nervous system activity in acute schizophrenia II. Relationships to short term prognosis and clinical state. Arch. Gen. Psychiat. 38, 260-266, 1981.

ZEMP, M.; HUBSCHMID, T.: Interactions in high- and low- EE families (in press).

ZUBIN, J.; SPRING, B.: Vulnerability – a new view of schizophrenia. J. Abnorm. Psychol. 86, 103-126, 1977.

Subject Index

214

216

Author Index

221

Kurt A. Heller / John F. Feldhusen (Editors)

Identifying and Nurturing the Gifted

An International Perspective. 1986, 187 pages, 14 figures, 19 tables, hardcover Fr. 42.- / DM 48.- / US $ 29.00

This volume represents the latest information on the phenomena and developmental conditions of the highly gifted the world over. It is written in a comprehensible form for scientists from the fields of developmental and educational psychology, diagnostics, and the behavioral sciences as well as for the broader interested lay public.

Siegfried Frey

Analyzing Patterns of Behavior in in Dyadic Interaction

1987, approx. 250 pages, illustrations, tables, hardcover approx. Fr. 42.- / approx. DM 48.- / approx. US $ 28.50

There is proably no area of human behavior which has been subjected to more speculation and at the same time has remained so difficult to investigate empirically than the nonverbal, unspoken component of the communication process. This book traces the controversial history of nonverbal research as it developed from the early personality-oriented «physiognomic» phase through the emotion-centered period of «expression-studies» to the modern communicational views. The author shows that nonverbal phenomena are fundamentally misunderstood when considered as indicators of personality or emotion. He elaborates the view that nonverbal behavior functions not as an «informer» but as an «effector» in communication.

 Hans Huber Publishers
Toronto, Lewiston N.Y., Bern, Stuttgart